# Digital Integrated Circuits
## For Electronics
## Technicians

# Digital Integrated Circuits
## For Electronics
## Technicians

**Edward Pasahow**
**San Diego Community Colleges**
**San Diego, California**

**McGraw-Hill Book Company**
**Gregg Division**

New York   Atlanta   Dallas   St. Louis   San Francisco
Auckland   Bogotá   Düsseldorf   Johannesburg   London
Madrid   Mexico   Montreal   New Delhi   Panama   Paris
São Paulo   Singapore   Sydney   Tokyo   Toronto

*For my mother and father.*

**Library of Congress Cataloging in Publication Data**

Pasahow, Edward.
    Digital integrated circuits for electronics technicians.

    Includes index.
    1. Integrated circuits.  I. Title.
TK7874.P38        621.381'73        78-8742
ISBN 0-07-048710-3

## DIGITAL INTEGRATED CIRCUITS FOR ELECTRONICS TECHNICIANS

*Digital Integrated Circuits for Electronics Technicians* was originally published in 1979 under the title *Integrated Circuits for Electronics Technicians.*

234567890 WCWC 785432109

The editors for this book were George J. Horesta and Mark Haas, the designer was Eileen Thaxton, the art supervisor was George T. Resch, and the production supervisor was Regina R. Malone. It was set in Caledonia by Progressive Typographers.
Printed and bound by Webcrafters, Inc.

# CONTENTS

# PREFACE

This book has one main purpose, that of presenting a state-of-the-art study of integrated circuits. It was written because no existing text offered a modern approach to these devices at the level of a student working for the Associate of Arts degree. Hobbyists and engineers who want to increase their understanding of practical integrated circuit theory and applications will also find this text useful. The unique integration of theory with experiments provides not only a description of idealized devices, but also an appreciation of actual circuit operation.

Current practice in the field has guided the presentation throughout. The use of state tables to complement timing diagrams in the study of sequential circuits furnishes the student with a powerful analytical tool. The coverage of $I^2L$, Schottky TTL, SOS, bubble memories, charge-coupled devices, and microprocessors along with more traditional topics (TTL, MOS, combinatorial and sequential circuits, memories, and linear circuits) assures a complete overview of today's electronic systems.

The mathematics is limited to basic college algebra, and no previous student exposure to integrated circuits is assumed. New techniques such as Boolean algebra and number systems are fully developed in the chapters in which these subjects appear. The text material can be used in lecture and laboratory courses with several different approaches. A basic digital circuits course, a computer circuits course, or a course emphasizing integrated circuits other than those used in computers can be developed from this book. The latter is covered in my classes at San Diego Community Colleges.

A suggested one-semester sequence for the basic digital circuits course would draw from Chapters 1 through 10, omitting the optional material marked with a vertical line down the left-hand margin.

The advanced computer circuits course should be preceded by a number systems and Boolean algebra prerequisite. Coverage would include:

Chapter 1                         Chapter 6
Chapter 2 (review only)           Chapter 7
Chapter 3                         Chapter 8
Chapter 4                         Chapter 9
Chapter 5 (review only)          Chapter 12

The course emphasizing other integrated circuit applications would follow the sequence:

Chapter 1                         Chapter 6
Chapter 2 (omit optional          Chapter 7
        material)                 Chapter 9 (omit optional
Chapter 3                                 material)
Chapter 4                         Chapter 10
Chapter 5 (omit optional          Chapter 11
        material)

Proper acknowledgement for the help which so many others provided me with in writing this book can hardly be expressed. The comments and suggestions by students in my courses have been of great assistance in clarifying the presentation and correcting errors. Their review has greatly strengthened the text. But without the particular encouragement and assistance along the way from Rosemarie Pasahow this book would never have been written.

*Edward Pasahow*

# CHAPTER ONE
# INTRODUCTION TO
# INTEGRATED CIRCUITS

Numbers are all around us. Every day numerical displays confront us at work, in our homes, and even during our leisure time. Annual sales of 60 million calculators, 30 million electronic watches, and 10 million digital games prove the popularity of integrated circuit technology. Digital equipment has advanced from its original position as a minor area of specialization to a point where it occupies an estimated 80 percent of the electronics market. This emphasis on digital electronics means that anybody developing, testing, or maintaining electronic equipment must understand digital logic and control systems.

Integrated circuits are a major cause of this change from analog to digital methodology. These small packages provide simple, low-cost solutions to designing and manufacturing electronic devices. Inexpensive pocket calculators, digital clocks, and microprocessors are some results of the shift away from discrete components. In fact, these products could not exist without the integrated circuit.

Even in analog applications integrated circuits have grown in importance. The same economic factors that make integrated circuits practical for digital components also affect analog equipment manufacture. As this trend continues to grow, electronic technology will become even more committed to replacing discrete transistors, resistors, and capacitors with integrated circuitry.

**CHAPTER OBJECTIVES**   Upon completing this chapter you should be able to:

1. Discuss the advantages of integrated circuits.
2. List the processes used to manufacture integrated circuits.
3. Describe the electronic components that comprise integrated circuits.
4. Discuss crystal growth, epitaxial growth, solid-state diffusion, and ion implantation processes which introduce controlled impurities during the manufacture of semiconductors.
5. List the steps in constructing a monolithic integrated circuit.
6. Distinguish between various types of pulse signals.

**HOW TO USE THIS BOOK**   Before we start, a brief explanation of how this book is put together should help make your study time more effective. Each chapter begins with a list of objectives. These objectives concisely describe what you should have learned by the time you have completed the chapter. A review at the end of each section lets you check your understanding of the material just covered before you go on to a new section.

The chapter summaries show you how each topic fits together as a whole and how the topics satisfy the chapter objectives. Included as part of the summary is a list of key terms and concepts that help you see how well you have grasped the most important points of the subject. The problems allow you to test your knowledge of the subject and identify areas where you may need further study. Finally, the experiments relate the theoretical discussion to actual circuit applications. This opportunity to see how real integrated circuits differ from the idealized models is an especially important facet of learning about them.

**INTEGRATED CIRCUITS**   Integrated circuits are composed of transistors, diodes, resistors, and capacitors used in combination. These circuit elements are inseparable from the base material, called the *substrate*. Each circuit is produced as a microscopic network on the substrate.

A major advantage of integrated circuitry is the resulting reduction in the number of discrete electronic components. As Fig. 1-1 shows, the number of components in a single integrated circuit has risen from less than 10 to more than 100,000 in 20 years. As the circuits grew more complex, the costs began falling, as Fig. 1-2 shows, making the use of integrated circuits economically attractive. Simplified designs and modular circuits with fewer interconnections also cut costs. To these factors add small size, low power requirements, increased speed, and improved reliability—and the reasons why integrated circuits are increasingly being selected become obvious.

Even in the beginning, demand for these circuits was high. Miniature electronic systems built with resistor arrays were used during World War II. The wiring and resistors in the arrays were manufactured by screen-printing silver paste and resistive ink on a ceramic substrate. When the transistor was invented in 1947, a major obstacle to developing the integrated circuit was overcome. The first monolithic integrated circuit with a single transistor, two

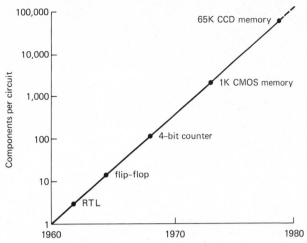

**Figure 1-1. Number of components in integrated circuits.**

resistors, and a resistor-capacitor network was demonstrated in 1958.

As the need for integrated circuits grew, several manufacturing processes for them evolved. The *monolithic* method of circuit manufacture builds the elements within or on top of the semiconductor substrate. The *multichip* circuit process requires microassembly of two or more chips on a single substrate. The substrate supplies the interconnections and isolation for the chips. *Vacuum-deposited films* are used in a third type of integrated circuit; these can be further divided into *thin* and *thick films*. The elements are formed of films deposited on the substrate. Usually only passive components such as resistors and capacitors can be fabricated by the film process. Combining monolithic and thin-film elements produces *hybrid circuits*. Each of these fabrication processes and their effects on the structure and properties of the integrated circuit will be discussed further in the following paragraphs.

**Monolithic Circuits**  Monolithic circuits are formed layer by layer in a three-dimensional network of conductors, insulators, and semiconductors. A variety of circuits can be produced during the processing sequence by changing the pattern, or *mask*, for each of the

**Figure 1-2. Cost of integrated circuits.**

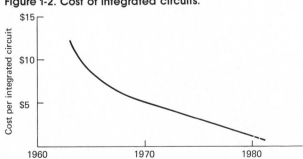

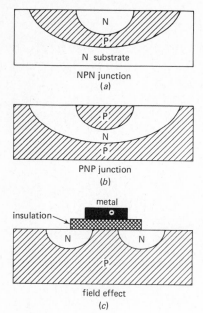

NPN junction
(a)

PNP junction
(b)

field effect
(c)

**Figure 1-3. Transistors.**

layers. The mask covers an area larger than a single circuit and repeats the same pattern across an entire semiconductor wafer. (The semiconductor is usually silicon.) So from 100 to 1000 complete circuits are produced at one time.

Structurally the electronic components of the circuit include diodes, transistors, and passive elements. Just as in discrete semiconductors, the P-type material has an excess of positive majority carriers ("holes") resulting from a precise "doping" level of impurities added to the silicon. The N-type material has an excess of negative majority carriers (electrons) also produced by the dopant. The boundary between two regions of P- and N-type materials forms the junction of a diode.

Transistors can be produced in either bipolar or field-effect form as shown in Fig. 1-3. The bipolar or junction transistor has two adjacent PN junctions; the field-effect device has separate PN junctions spaced along the surface.

Resistors can be formed from the semiconductor, which is itself a relatively poor conductor. Regions of either P- or N-type material with uniform conductivity are used. Capacitors require that a dielectric and a metal electrode layer be placed over the semiconductor, which acts as the second electrode. The insulator and the two electrodes form the capacitor.

**Film Circuits**

Elements are deposited on either glass or ceramic to produce thin-film components. Resistors are created from nickel-chromium alloys, tantalum, tantalum nitride, or metal silicides mixed with other metals and insulators (cermets). The precise amount of resistance is adjusted by vaporizing the film with a laser while monitoring the resultant resistor value. Capacitors are simply a layer of dielectric between two conductors. Thick-film circuits use special inks printed through silk-screen masks. After they have been fired in an oven, the inks become resistors, conductors, or insulators. Resistor values are adjusted by grinding away the material.

**Hybrid Circuits**

Making hybrid circuits by attaching and connecting the terminals of the semiconductor chips to films requires one of three procedures: (1) The chip may merely be soldered to a metallized pad on the substrate and fine wires are welded between the chip electrodes and the film. (2) The *inverted assembly* process uses solder-coated metal balls to join the chip to the substrate. (3) Metal fingers protruding from the chip are welded to the film in the *beam lead* method.

**Monolithic Circuit Fabrication**

A simplified example of the steps necessary to make a monolithic circuit will indicate the complexity of the modern fabrication techniques which produce such circuits as the one shown in Fig. 1-4. The process almost always starts with a single crystal of silicon that was pulled from a melt. The crystal is sliced into disks 2 inches [50 millimeters] or more in diameter and about 0.01 inch

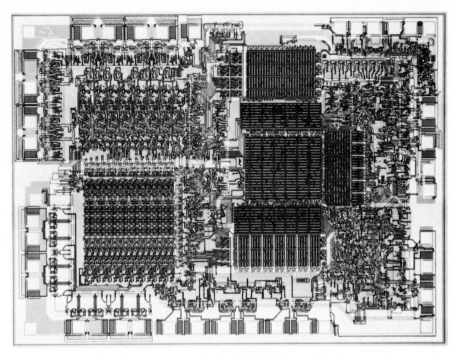

Figure 1-4. Microprocessor integrated circuit (Intel Corporation).

[0.25 millimeter] thick. After they have been lapped and polished, these wafers have a mirrorlike surface.

Impurities have to be introduced to change the silicon to either P- or N-type. Impurities can be introduced during crystal growth by adding the dopant to the melt. Alternatively, doping can be accomplished by *epitaxial growth.* That is, the wafer is heated to 1000 to 1300°C in an atmosphere consisting of a doped silicon compound. Silicon from the compound deposits on the wafer as a continuation of the single crystal lattice. *Solid-state diffusion* is yet another method of depositing impurities on the surface when it is heated to 1000 to 1300°C. The impurity atoms enter the crystal lattice and diffuse into the silicon as a shallow layer. A photoengraved mask limits the areas where impurities can enter. Finally, the *ion implantation* method accelerates impurity ions with a voltage potential (50 to 500 kilovolts) and causes them to strike the silicon. The kinetic energy of the ions causes them to penetrate the crystal. This low-temperature process makes sharp gradients between P- and N-type materials possible and provides precise doping levels.

Figure 1-5 shows the series of steps involved in processing a wafer to prepare a simple monolithic integrated circuit (IC). After the silicon substrate—here P-type material—has been prepared for processing, the surface is oxidized. Silicon dioxide is glass, which is an excellent insulator. The oxide layer is etched in some areas to form a mask with windows to limit the growth of the next layer (Fig. 1-5c). Then N-type impurities are diffused into the substrate to form the transistor base junction (Figs. 1-5d and 1-5e). An epitaxial layer is grown and a similar process is used to diffuse the

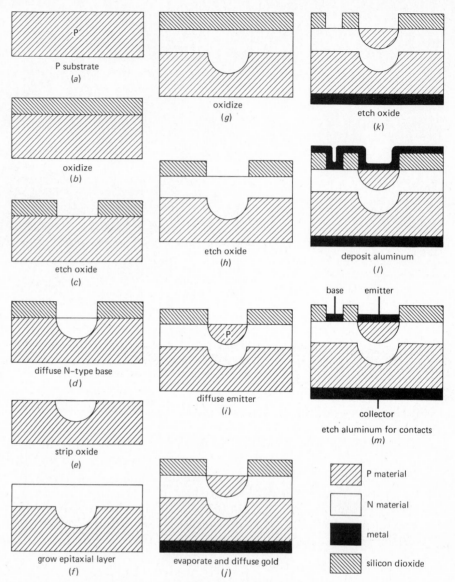

**Figure 1-5. Manufacturing a monolithic integrated circuit.**

P substrate
(a)

oxidize
(b)

etch oxide
(c)

diffuse N–type base
(d)

strip oxide
(e)

grow epitaxial layer
(f)

oxidize
(g)

etch oxide
(h)

diffuse emitter
(i)

evaporate and diffuse gold
(j)

etch oxide
(k)

deposit aluminum
(l)

etch aluminum for contacts
(m)

base    emitter

collector

P material

N material

metal

silicon dioxide

emitter (Figs. 1-5*f* through 1-5*i*). The final steps are used to provide metal contacts for the junction terminals.

**Integrated Circuit Review**

1. List the advantages of integrated circuits as compared to discrete components.
2. Describe the fabrication methods used in manufacturing integrated circuits.
3. Distinguish between field-effect and bipolar transistors.
4. Describe the various processes used to dope semiconductors with impurities.

**PULSE SIGNALS**   In your previous study of electronic circuits, you were mostly concerned with dc and ac steady-state signals. While some integrated

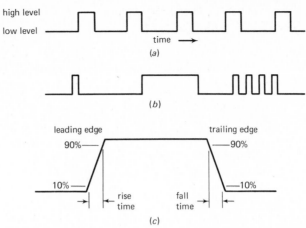

**Figure 1-6. Pulse Signals. (a) Periodic, (b) aperiodic, (c) rise and fall time.**

circuits use these types of signals, most respond to individual pulses or pulse trains. As Fig. 1-6 shows, the pulses may be spaced at regular intervals or they may arrive at random times. The regular pulses are called *periodic* (Fig. 1-6*a*), while the others are *aperiodic* (Fig. 1-6*b*).

The amplitude of the signal at any time is either at a high- or low-voltage level. Intermediate values are not allowed. The time required for the voltage to rise from 10 percent of the high level to 90 percent of that voltage on the leading pulse edge is called the *rise time*. The *fall time* is the time elapsed while the voltage drops from 90 percent to 10 percent of the high-voltage level on the trailing edge. These values are shown in Fig. 1-6*c*.

**Pulse Signal Review**

1. Distinguish between periodic and aperiodic pulse signals.
2. Define the terms *rise time* and *fall time*.

**CHAPTER SUMMARY**

1. The active and passive elements which make up an integrated circuit are inseparable from the substrate. The elimination of discrete transistors, resistors, and capacitors by integrated circuitry results in significant savings in constructing electronic equipment.
2. Advantages of integrated circuits include simplified designs, fewer interconnections, small size, increased speed, low power, and improved reliability.
3. Integrated circuits are fabricated by the monolithic, multichip, film, and hybrid-circuit processes.
4. Bipolar and field-effect transistors are used for integrated circuits. Bipolar transistors are characterized by two adjacent PN junctions.
5. Hybrid circuits require that chips be joined to the thin film by soldering them to a metallized pad or by the inverted assembly or beam lead methods.
6. Pulse signals can be classified as periodic or aperiodic. The transition time between the high and low voltages of the pulses is specified by the rise and fall times.

**KEY TERMS
AND CONCEPTS**

integrated circuit
discrete components
substrate
monolithic integrated
  circuit
multichip circuit
thin- and thick-film integrated circuits
hybrid integrated circuits
mask

doping
bipolar transistor
field-effect transistor
epitaxial growth
solid-state diffusion
ion implantation
periodic and aperiodic
  pulses
rise time
fall time

# EXPERIMENT 1 INTRODUCTION

The experiments at the end of each chapter will increase your understanding of integrated circuits more than any other section in this book. The experiments have been designed to use a minimum of equipment, yet demonstrate the most popular types of ICs commonly found in the electronic equipment of today. Every attempt has been made to include components which do not require critical values to be selected. For example, circuit operation is generally not sensitive to resistor values, so 10 percent resistors are adequate. Other resistors of approximately the same values can often be substituted without degrading circuit operation. Your instructor may suggest circuit elements equivalent to type shown in the book, or you may wish to try some on your own.

A power supply suitable for TTL operation is required in all experiments. While only low voltage is used in the experiments, 115-volt line voltage is applied to the power supply input, so all electrical safety precautions should be followed. Your instructor will probably explain the guidelines for electrical safety in the laboratory. Check with the instructor if you have any questions before proceeding with any experiment.

**TOOLS AND TEST EQUIPMENT**

Only common hand tools and a voltmeter are required for these experiments. The suggested tools and meter are:

diagonal cutters
needle-nose pliers
knife
wire stripper
small screwdriver
voltmeter (either VOM or VTVM)

**HINTS FOR WORKING WITH TTL**

1. All inputs to a TTL integrated circuit must be connected to either an input signal, the power supply, or a ground. If they are allowed to "float," the inputs will rise to a high-level input producing incorrect outputs and will also become excellent sources for introducing noise. You may also be surprised to find that TTL outputs are often much less than +5 volts. A value around 3.3 volts is chosen for real devices to get optimal performance from the design.
2. If you are not familiar with integrated circuit pin numbering, be extra careful to insert the chip with the indicating notch or dot toward the left. When the pins are pointing downward and the notch (or dot) is toward the left, pin 1 is in the left bottom corner of the IC.
3. Use solderless breadboarding systems to build your circuits. ICs and other components snap in place on the board. Remove ICs by gently prying them up with a screwdriver, so the pins are not bent. Sources for breadboarding systems are listed in most electronics periodicals.

4. A good low-impedance power supply is required for proper TTL operation. The power supply must be capable of decoupling the current spikes encountered when certain types of integrated circuits change state. The + 5-volt supply should be regulated to within 250 millivolts. The supply current should be at least 500 milliamperes.

5. Keep your wiring neat. Leads should be no longer than the minimum necessary to interconnect circuit components.

6. A complete description of the electrical and logical operation of each integrated circuit used in these experiments is included in this book. More information on these ICs, as well as many others, can be found in the manufacturers' data books which you may wish to use for reference. Sources for these references are given in Table 1-1. Any one of the books should be adequate, because standard ICs are used in the experiments.

**Table 1-1**
**Sources for TTL Data Books**

Fairchild TTL Data Book
Fairchild Semiconductor
464 Ellis Street
Mountain View, CA 94040

MTTL Data Book
Motorola Semiconductor Products, Inc.
Box 20912
Phoenix, AZ 85036

Signetics Digital-Linear-MOS
Signetics
811 E. Arques Avenue
Sunnyvale, CA 94086

The TTL Data Book
Texas Instruments, Inc.
Box 5012
Dallas, TX 75222

**HINTS FOR WORKING WITH CMOS**

1. Connect the power supply to the IC before you hook up the inputs.

2. Store ICs on conductive foam to prevent static damage. Place them on aluminum foil during experiments.

3. Detailed CMOS descriptions are listed in various manufacturers' data books. Any of the books in Table 1-2 would be good reference material.

**Table 1-2**
**Sources for CMOS Data Books**

Isoplanar CMOS Data Book
Fairchild Semiconductor
464 Ellis Street
Mountain View, CA 94042

McMOS Semiconductor Data Library #5
Motorola Semiconductor Products, Inc.
Box 20912
Phoenix, AZ 85036

RCA COSMOS Databook
RCA Solid State Division
Box 3200
Somerville, NJ 08876

Hewlett-Packard
1507 Page Mill Road
Palo Alto, CA 94304

Solid State Systems
Box 617
Columbia, MD 65201

# CHAPTER TWO
# COMBINATORIAL CIRCUITS

Little did the English mathematician, George Boole, realize how important his abstract conception of the way we think would become. An analysis of the human thought process was his objective when he wrote *Analysis of Logic* in the spring of 1847. These laws of thought were not applied to practical problems until Claude E. Shannon used Boolean algebra to design relay switching circuits. Today almost all digital circuit designers and maintainers use this technique to understand the operation of their equipment.

Boolean algebra allows us to represent complex expressions and manipulate equations of logic and switching circuits with ease. This powerful tool is as basic to understanding digital logic as the alphabet is to writing. This chapter will introduce Boolean algebra and logic gates.

A *gate* is a logic circuit with one or more input terminals and a single output terminal. The output produces the desired signal when certain combinations of input signals exist. In other words, a gate can give a true or false indication of the specified input conditions. For that reason these gates are referred to as *combinatorial circuits*.

**CHAPTER OBJECTIVES**  In this chapter you will see how gates operate, how they can be combined into more complex functions, and how they may be analyzed. After completing this chapter you should be able to:

1. Discuss logic functions and how they can be represented on Venn diagrams.
2. Interpret the American National Standard notation and symbology used to represent the basic logic functions.
3. Use truth tables of any logic function.
4. Define positive and negative logic.
5. Discuss the identities, laws, and theorems of Boolean algebra and simplify circuits using these techniques.
6. Use a Karnaugh map to simplify logic equations.
7. Analyze the operation of combinatorial circuits.

## LOGIC FUNCTIONS

We often divide any group of objects into two classes. There are those we are interested in and those of no concern. On the way to a football game, for example, we may think about the weather, the route, and the starting time, but we probably would not care about the phase of the moon. A formal mathematical description would denote things of interest as the *universal set* and the things we do not care about as the *null set*. Boolean algebra uses just such an approach. It further limits its concern to elements that can have only two possible states. For example we can examine the universal set of electronic devices. One element of the universal set would be computers. Obviously the element called computers has two states: (1) devices that are computers and (2) devices that are not computers. We see that computers have two stable states; that is, a computer does not change to a noncomputer without some external action. A sledgehammer could turn a computer into junk, but the computer cannot spontaneously become an airplane. It also cannot assume an unstable state which would sometimes be a computer and sometimes not.

A pictorial representation of the statements we have made about computers is called a *Venn diagram*. Figure 2-1a shows the universal set of electronic devices by means of the square. Everything that is drawn in the square must be an electronic device, and everything outside the square (the null set) is something else. The universal set is divided into two areas, computers and not computers. On the Venn diagram the size of the square has no meaning, so the dividing line did not have to be drawn in the center. Horizontal lines are as meaningful as vertical ones, and the division could even have been diagonal. The only requirement is that the line split the universal set into two *mutually exclusive* areas. That way no element can be in both states at one time. Next, we assign every electronic device we can think of to one area or the other.

Other classes of elements can be plotted on the same Venn diagram, as Fig. 2-1b shows. A horizontal line on the diagram divides it into electronic devices that are digital and those which are not digital. The diagram now has four areas which can be described as

1. Digital and computers
2. Digital and not computers
3. Not digital and computers
4. Not digital and not computers

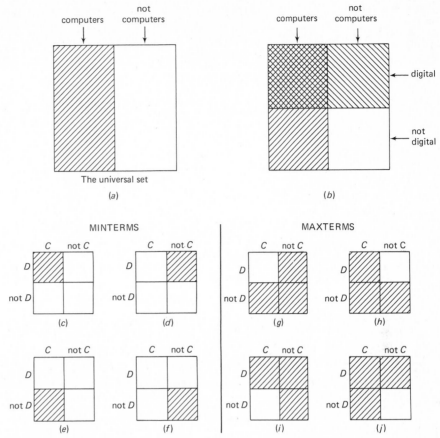

**Figure 2-1. Venn diagrams.**

These four categories can be written more compactly if we substitute the first letters of each of the elements. That is, let $C$ mean computers and $D$ represent digital. We then have

**1.** $D$ and $C$
**2.** $D$ and not $C$
**3.** not $D$ and $C$
**4.** not $D$ and not $C$

Figures 2-1$c$ through 2-1$f$ show the areas on the Venn diagram which correspond to each of these combinations of elements. The diagrams show each combination as an intersection of one column with one row, as in 2-1$c$ where the computer column and the digital row intersect. Mathematicians refer to these expressions as the *minterm form.* They are called minterms because they represent the four minimum classes of elements.

Another way to describe the areas on the Venn diagram is by means of *maxterms.* As the name indicates, maxterms are the opposite of minterms and include the four maximum classes of elements. We can find the maxterm corresponding to each minterm by a negation process. That is we collect every element that is not in the minterm to create the maxterm. Figures 2-1$g$ through 2-1$j$ show that each maxterm consists of the squares not included in the corresponding minterm.

Examination of these figures shows that the maxterm in Fig. 2-1g consists of elements that are not computers *or* are not digital. (Digital computers are excluded from the not computer column or the not digital row. Note the difference between this and the similar-sounding minterm, not digital *and* not computer.) The three other maxterms are shown also to be a union of a column with a row. The abbreviated maxterm expressions for the figures are

1. not $D$ or not $C$
2. not $D$ or $C$
3. $D$ or not $C$
4. $D$ or $C$

An obvious difference between a minterm and a maxterm is that the former relates the quantities with the word "and," while the latter uses the word "or." Later we will be discussing minterms, maxterms, and how to convert from one to the other in more detail.

Our notation would be even more compact if a symbol rather than words were used to relate the elements. The most commonly used symbols are:

$\overline{\phantom{x}}$ (bar) for **not**

$+$ for **or**

$\cdot$ for **and**

Examples of how the symbols are used and how they are read are:

$\overline{x}$ read "not $x$"

$x + y$ read "$x$ or $y$"

$x \cdot \overline{y}$ read "$x$ and not $y$"

$x + \overline{y \cdot z}$ read "$x$ or not the quantity $y$ and $z$"

**Logic Function Review**

1. Define a logic gate.
2. Distinguish between the universal set and the null set.
3. Describe how a Venn diagram can be used to relate the two elements, insulators and plastics.
4. List the differences between minterms and maxterms.
5. Rewrite the following expression using correct notation: $Q$ and not $R$ or $S$ and not the quantity $U$ and $Z$.

**TRUTH TABLES**

Carrying the study of two-state elements further, we will next examine how the values of such relationships can be expressed. Consider a perfect switching circuit, as shown in Fig. 2-2, to be a two-state device. It is either open or closed. We can arbitrarily assign the number zero (false state) to the open-switch state and the number one (true state) to the closed-switch state. This selection is arbitrary in that there is nothing requiring the open switch to be the zero state; we just chose to assign it that way. Use of the numbers zero and one to represent the states is closely related to the binary number system. Later chapters will show how two-state devices can be used for arithmetic.

Figure 2-2. Assigning Boolean values to switch states.

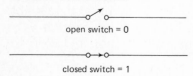

open switch = 0

closed switch = 1

## The NOT Function

**Table 2-1
NOT Truth
Table**

| $x$ | $\bar{x}$ |
|-----|-----------|
| 0   | 1         |
| 1   | 0         |

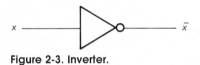

**Figure 2-3. Inverter.**

The Venn diagram showed that a variable must occupy one of two areas in a class. Letting $x$ be the element of interest, we could assign any variable to either $x$ or $\bar{x}$. If we use zero or one to indicate the state of the variable, then $x = 1$ means that $\bar{x} = 0$. Alternatively if $x = 0$, then $\bar{x} = 1$.

The relationship between $x$ and $\bar{x}$ is called the Boolean NOT function. (The Boolean relationships will be capitalized to distinguish them from the same words used in an ordinary sense.) We can also say that $x$ is the complement of $\bar{x}$ and vice versa. We can always determine $\bar{x}$ if we are given $x$. The possible values that the NOT function can take on for any value of $x$ can be listed in a truth table. Table 2-1 is such a listing.

Truth tables are often used to define Boolean functions. The output or result of any combination of inputs to the Boolean operation can be read directly from the table. The NOT function is implemented by using inverters. The inverter symbol, shown in Fig. 2-3, looks much like an amplifier, but it has a small NOT circle or bubble on the output terminal. The truth table describes the operation of the inverter for either a one or a zero input.

## The AND Function

**Table 2-2
AND Truth Table**

| $x$ | $y$ | Output |
|-----|-----|--------|
| 0   | 0   | 0      |
| 0   | 1   | 0      |
| 1   | 0   | 0      |
| 1   | 1   | 1      |

The AND function was also shown on the Venn diagram. This function is like a series circuit, as shown in Fig. 2-4a. The switches are labeled $x$ and $y$. The lamp lights when both $x$ and $y$ are closed. Both switches must be in the one state to produce a one output (lamp on). If either switch is in the open or zero state, the output is zero. Finally, if both switches are open, the result is a zero output. So the output is one only if both $x$ and $y$ are ones. Table 2-2 is the truth table for the AND function. The AND gate symbol is shown in Figs. 2-4b and 2-4c.

The center dot was previously used to indicate the AND operation. This notation is derived from AND also being considered a Boolean product. In fact, the notation is like regular multiplication and the AND operation can be written three ways.

$$x \cdot y$$
$$(x)(y)$$
$$xy$$

The most convenient and clearest method will be used to indicate the AND function in future references to it.

**Figure 2-4. AND gate.**

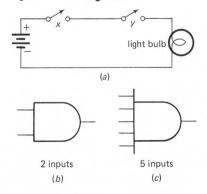

light bulb

(a)

2 inputs
(b)

5 inputs
(c)

### The OR Function

Just as we can compare the AND function with a series circuit, the OR function is like a parallel circuit. As shown in Fig. 2-5a, if either switch x or switch y [or both] are closed (in the one state), the lamp is on. The lamp is off only when both switches are open. As Table 2-3 shows, the output of an OR gate is one if either x or y is one or both inputs are ones. The circuit symbol for the OR function is shown in Figs. 2-5b and 2-5c.

**Table 2-3**
**OR Truth Table**

| x | y | Output |
|---|---|--------|
| 0 | 0 | 0 |
| 0 | 1 | 1 |
| 1 | 0 | 1 |
| 1 | 1 | 1 |

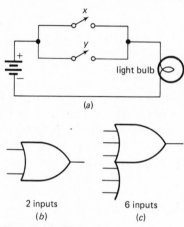

(a)

2 inputs   6 inputs
(b)        (c)

**Figure 2-5. OR gate.**

### Combinations

The three basic Boolean functions can be combined to form more logic operations. If we connect an inverter to an AND gate, as in Fig. 2-6a, we produce a new function. This function is used so often that it has been given its own name. It is called a NAND gate because it is a combination of a NOT gate with an AND gate. The symbol, shown in Fig. 2-6b, is an AND gate with an inverter bubble on the output.

The outputs produced by the AND gate in Fig. 2-6a are the same as those shown in Table 2-2, but the output is then complemented by the inverter to form the final result. The outputs of the NAND gate are listed in Table 2-4a. The outputs are the complement of those for an AND gate.

We can determine the outputs by following the signal flow from left to right on the circuit diagram. Starting with the first row of the truth table, the inputs are x = 0 and y = 0. The AND gate will have a zero output, but the inverter then complements it to a one. In the next two rows of the table, the operation is like that of the first row. In the final row, the AND gate generates a one output

**Figure 2-6. Other gates.**

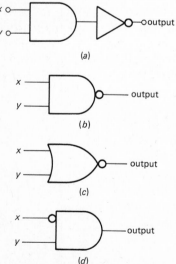

(a)

(b)

(c)

(d)

**Table 2-4a**
**NAND Truth Table**

| x | y | Output |
|---|---|--------|
| 0 | 0 | 1 |
| 0 | 1 | 1 |
| 1 | 0 | 1 |
| 1 | 1 | 0 |

**Table 2-4b**
**NOR Truth Table**

| x | y | Output |
|---|---|--------|
| 0 | 0 | 1 |
| 0 | 1 | 0 |
| 1 | 0 | 0 |
| 1 | 1 | 0 |

with $x = 1$ and $y = 1$. The one output of the AND gate is inverted, so the final NAND output will be a zero.

Joining the OR gate with an inverter also produces a new function, the NOR gate. The symbol, in Fig. 2-6c, consists of an OR with an inverter bubble on the output line. The NOR truth table, Table 2-4b, is the complement of the OR truth table. You should check the output for each combination of inputs.

Other combinations of inverters and gates can be made. Figure 2-6d shows an AND gate with an inverter on the x input. In this case, inversion takes place before the input is applied to the AND gate. If x is a one, for example, it is changed to a zero and then applied as the input to the AND gate. There is no special name for this combination of logic functions. See Problem 2-1 for other gate configurations.

At this point it may seem that ANDs, ORs, NANDs, and NORs do quite different things. We will see in this and following chapters that digital devices can be built with any of these functions or groups of functions. Computers have been constructed using only NOR gates, and some manufacturers limit their designs to only one or two basic gates for standardization. While two designs implemented using different gates may not look the same, functionally they can do the identical job. However, there may be differences in the cost, number of gates used, and speed of operation for the two pieces of equipment. As the next section will show, just the choice of the voltage level used to represent the one and zero states will change the function of a gate.

## Positive and Negative Logic

Assume that we are given a black box with two input terminals and a single output as shown in Fig. 2-7. We are asked to determine what function the box performs. To answer this question, we apply voltages of either 0 or 5 volts to the inputs and record the output voltages measured by a voltmeter. The table of voltages that each input voltage pair produces is shown in Table 2-5a.

As was stated earlier, the choice of which voltage represents a binary one and which a zero is arbitrary. Suppose we let the higher voltage, in this case 5 volts, be called the one level. The voltage table can be converted to a truth table as shown in Table 2-5b. (This may seem like a trivial step, but its importance will soon become obvious.) The first row of the voltages has inputs of zero volts, which become zeros in the truth table. The output of 5 volts means that a one is entered in the output column of that row.

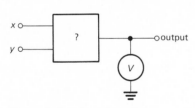

Figure 2-7. Unknown gate.

Table 2-5a
Voltage Table

| $V_x$ | $V_y$ | $V_{out}$ |
|-------|-------|-----------|
| 0 V   | 0 V   | 5 V       |
| 0     | 5     | 0         |
| 5     | 0     | 0         |
| 5     | 5     | 0         |

Table 2-5b
Positive Logic
Truth Table

| $x$ | $y$ | Output |
|-----|-----|--------|
| 0   | 0   | 1      |
| 0   | 1   | 0      |
| 1   | 0   | 0      |
| 1   | 1   | 0      |

The second row has an $x$ value of 0 volts, which is a zero; $y$ is 5 volts, a one; and the output is 0 volts, a binary zero. After completing the remainder of the table, we can compare it with the truth tables of the logic functions that we have studied so far. This examination shows that the circuit is the same as a NOR gate if we let the more positive voltage stand for a binary one.

Now let's try the opposite situation. Let the more negative voltage level, 0 volts here, be a one. The truth table then lists $x = 1$ and $y = 1$ in the first row, with an output of 0. Table 2-5c shows these values. The next line is equivalent to $x = 1$ and $y = 0$, producing an output of 1. The rest of the table is filled in the same way. Now compare this truth table with the previous one. Surprisingly enough the identical electronic circuit has a different truth table if we simply choose the other voltage level for a binary one. Which logic function does the new truth table agree with? It is a NAND, but the entries are not in the same order as Table 2-4a.

We are using *positive logic* if the more positive voltage level is to be taken as a one. If the more negative level is a one, we are using *negative logic*. There will be times when each of these types of logic will be used; in this book, unless otherwise stated, positive logic will be used. Many electronic manufacturers use only one type of logic for standardization. When you look at a technical manual, be sure to check whether the design uses positive or negative logic. It is not possible to follow the diagrams if you use the wrong one.

**Table 2-5c Negative Logic Truth Table**

| $x$ | $y$ | Output |
|-----|-----|--------|
| 1 | 1 | 0 |
| 1 | 0 | 1 |
| 0 | 1 | 1 |
| 0 | 0 | 1 |

**Truth Table Review**

1. Which logic function performs a complementing operation?
2. Define the AND function with a truth table.
3. Distinguish between the OR and NOR operations.
4. List all combination of an AND gate with one or more inverters that you can think of. (Two were shown in Fig. 2-6. There are five more.)

**BOOLEAN ALGEBRA**

Now that we understand the basic Boolean functions such as AND and OR, we can approach them from a more mathematical viewpoint. While Boolean algebra is very much like ordinary algebra, watch carefully for there are differences between the two algebras. For example, the Boolean OR symbol looks like a plus sign, but in Boolean notation

$$1 + 1 = 1 \quad \text{(not 2)}$$

That is, if we OR 1 (the universal set) with itself, we end up with the universal set again.

Because much of the design of combinatorial circuits is done with the assistance of computer programs, the designer simply describes the function to a computer and the most economical circuit is calculated automatically. With computer-aided design (CAD) and the low cost of integrated circuits, you may wonder why it is necessary to learn Boolean algebra. The major application of Boolean algebra is to help you understand how the functions of digital equipment are performed.

**Table 2-6**
**Boolean Identities**

| OR | AND | NOT |
|----|-----|-----|
| $x + 0 = x$ | $x \cdot 0 = 0$ | $\bar{\bar{x}} = x$ |
| $x + 1 = 1$ | $x \cdot 1 = x$ | |
| $x + x = x$ | $x \cdot x = x$ | |
| $x + \bar{x} = 1$ | $x \cdot \bar{x} = 0$ | |

Maintenance technicians must be able to read Boolean equations and diagrams in the technical manuals. Engineering technicians usually get their instructions in Boolean form when building equipment. Even the designer must describe the circuit in Boolean terms to the computer. So a thorough understanding of these concepts is necessary for everyone involved with digital systems.

There is a series of Boolean equations, called identities, which should be memorized. Table 2-6 lists them. Each one can be deduced from the Venn diagram. The first one tells us that if we OR $x$ with 0, the result is $x$. If $x = 1$, the result of the ORing would be 1: if $x = 0$, the result should be 0. This identity can also be verified by referring back to the truth table of the OR function. A brief comment on each of the remaining identities should make them clear.

$x + 1 = 1$    Anything ORed with 1 must be 1.

$x + x = x$    The value of $x$ must be the result.

$x + \bar{x} = 1$    Either $x = 1$ or $\bar{x} = 1$, making the equation $0 + 1$ which must equal 1.

$x \cdot 0 = 0$    ANDing 0 with any quantity produces 0.

$x \cdot 1 = x$    ANDing $x$ with 1 does not change its value.

$x \cdot x = x$    Either we have $0 \cdot 0 = 0$ or $1 \cdot 1 = 1$ depending on the value of $x$.

$x \cdot \bar{x} = 0$    Either $x$ or $\bar{x}$ must be zero.

$\bar{\bar{x}} = x$    This is the Boolean way of saying that two negatives make a positive.

There are several laws for manipulating Boolean equations. The *commutative law* tells us that the order in which we perform AND or OR operations does not matter. The law stated formally is

$$xy = yx \tag{2-1}$$
$$x + y = y + x$$

There are two versions of the law; one applies to the AND function and the other to OR. Another way to look at this law is to consider that it does not matter which terminal of a two-input OR gate we use for the $x$ input as long as we use the other one for the $y$ input. We often use this law to write the terms of an expression in alphabetical order to help keep track of the variables.

The *associative law* allows us to perform ANDing and ORing of multiple terms using the grouping we prefer.

$$(x + y) + z = x + (y + z) = x + y + z \tag{2-2}$$
$$(xy)z = x(yz) = xyz$$

Applied to gate circuits, the associative law permits us to AND $x$ with $y$ in a two-input AND gate, then AND that result with $z$. We get the same result by using a three-input AND gate performing the operation on all variables at once.

The *distributive law* is very important in simplifying Boolean equations. It allows us to distribute or collect the individual terms.

$$xy + xz = x(y + z) \qquad (2\text{-}3)$$
$$(x + y)(x + z) = xx + xz + xy + yz$$

But this last equation is not in the simplest form. By use of the identities and previous laws it can be simplified. Remembering that $xx = x$, we have

$$x + xz + xy + yz$$

Using the first form of the distributive law (Eq. 2-3) and the identity $x \cdot 1 = x$ we can write the above as

$$x(1 + z + y) + yz$$

But $1 + z$ and $1 + y$ are simply one:

$$x \cdot 1 + yz = x + yz$$

So the second form of the law can be written

$$(x + y)(x + z) = x + yz \qquad (2\text{-}4)$$

The distributive law is also called the factoring law (Eq. 2-3) and the multiplying-out law (Eq. 2-4).

DeMorgan's theorem is very useful in converting the maxterm form of an equation into the minterm form and vice versa. The theorem also allows us to clear NOT bars which include more than a single term. The two forms of the theorem are

$$\overline{u \cdot v \cdot x \cdot y \cdot z \cdots} = \bar{u} + \bar{v} + \bar{x} + \bar{y} + \bar{z} + \cdots \qquad (2\text{-}5)$$
$$\overline{u + v + x + y + z + \cdots} = \bar{u} \cdot \bar{v} \cdot \bar{x} \cdot \bar{y} \cdot \bar{z} \cdots$$

where $\cdots$ means that the expression can be of any length.

This theorem is deceptively simple looking, but it often confuses students. It seems simple because all we need to do is break up the long NOT bar into single-term bars and change every AND to an OR and every OR to an AND. The confusion comes about because the distinction between $\overline{u + v}$ and $\bar{u} + \bar{v}$ is not understood. The first expression tells us to OR $u$ with $v$ and then complement the result, while the second has us complement $u$ and $v$ first and then OR the resultant values. Letting $u = 1$ and $v = 0$, then $\overline{u + v} = 0$ while $\bar{u} + \bar{v} = 1$. Quite different results. As was pointed out earlier, another use of DeMorgan's theorem is to convert between maxterms (ORs) and minterms (ANDs) as shown in Eq. 2-5.

**The Equality Circuit**    The value of Boolean algebra can best be appreciated by applying it to logic circuit analysis. It is almost impossible to determine the function of the circuit shown in Fig. 2-8a by inspection. We must trace the signal flow from the inputs to understand the gate action.

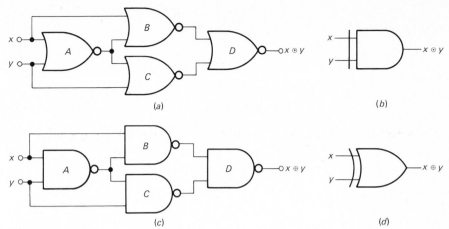

Figure 2-8. Equality and exclusive OR.

**Table 2-7
Equality Circuit
Truth Table**

| $x$ | $y$ | Output |
|---|---|---|
| 0 | 0 | 1 |
| 0 | 1 | 0 |
| 1 | 0 | 0 |
| 1 | 1 | 1 |

The output of NOR gate $A$ is $\overline{x + y}$ which is equivalent to $\overline{x}\overline{y}$ (by DeMorgan's theorem). This is input together with $x$ into gate $B$ to produce an output of $\overline{x + \overline{x}\overline{y}}$. Again using DeMorgan's theorem we can simplify this expression by removing the long NOT bar over the three terms to give $\overline{x}(x + y)$ which can be further reduced to $\overline{x}y$. The output of gate $C$ in simplest terms is $x\overline{y}$. Using these as inputs into gate $D$, we find the output to be $\overline{\overline{x}y + x\overline{y}}$. While this expression looks more complex than the previous ones, it is simplified the same way. First, the NOT bar is removed to form the expression $(x + \overline{y})(\overline{x} + y)$. Then the distributive law allows us to multiply out the terms. Use of identities eliminates the terms which equal zero, such as $x\overline{x}$, leaving us with the final output value of $xy + \overline{x}\overline{y}$.

This expression still does not make the circuit operation clear. A truth table will do that. As Table 2-7 shows, the output is 1 if $x = 0$ and $y = 0$ or if $x = 1$ and $y = 1$. Otherwise the output stays zero. In other words, this circuit will indicate when both input values are equal. This is the reason for calling it an equality circuit. Because the circuit is so useful, it has been given a special symbol, shown in Fig. 2-8$b$. Sometimes the notation $x \odot y$ is used to indicate the equality function.

**The Exclusive
OR Circuit**

**Table 2-8
Exclusive OR
Truth Table**

| $x$ | $y$ | Output |
|---|---|---|
| 0 | 0 | 0 |
| 0 | 1 | 1 |
| 1 | 0 | 1 |
| 1 | 1 | 0 |

Another frequently used combination of gates performs the exclusive OR function. One implementation of this function is shown in Fig. 2-8$c$. Again we use DeMorgan's theorem and the distributive law extensively to simplify the output of the circuit. You should check your understanding of the gate operation by finding the outputs and comparing them to the following:

gate $A$    $\overline{x} + \overline{y}$
gate $B$    $\overline{x} + y$
gate $C$    $x + \overline{y}$
gate $D$    $x\overline{y} + \overline{x}y$

Table 2-8 indicates that the output is one if $x = 1$ and $y = 0$ or if

$x = 0$ and $y = 1$. That is, the output is one if the inputs are in different states. The name exclusive OR distinguishes this circuit from an ordinary OR gate. The symbol for the exclusive OR is shown in Fig. 2-8$d$. The notation which is often used to indicate the exclusive OR is $x \oplus y$

**Boolean Algebra Review**

1. Why is the expression $\bar{a} + \bar{b} + \bar{c}$ not equal to $\overline{a + b + c}$?
2. Name the law that allows us to group multiple terms in an expression consisting of ANDing and ORing in any order we prefer.
3. Describe how Boolean equations may be factored.
4. Name the circuit that could be used to give an output of one if either of the turn signals of an automobile were on, but would give a zero output if both signals were on.

**KARNAUGH MAPS**

Simplification of complex Boolean equations is so important that many methods have been developed to make the process easier. One powerful tool is the Karnaugh map. This map is closely related to the Venn diagram that we studied in an earlier section of this chapter. While the Venn diagram was good for showing the relationship between variables, it could not be used to reduce the equation to lowest terms as the Karnaugh map can. Many variations of the mapping technique have evolved. Another that is often encountered is the Veitch diagram. Learning the Karnaugh map method will permit you to quickly read and use other types of maps.

The Karnaugh map has one characteristic in common with geographical maps of the earth; both types of maps are the projection of a sphere onto a two-dimensional surface. It is important to remember this aspect of the Karnaugh map, as it will be required later. The spherical nature of the map is shown in Fig. 2-9$a$. In this case, the sphere is divided into four areas: $xy$, $\bar{x}y$, $x\bar{y}$, and $\bar{x}\bar{y}$. If we cut the sphere either horizontally or vertically and flatten the resulting shape, we can produce many seemingly different maps. Figures 2-9$b$ through 2-9$e$ show some of the possibilities. As far as we are concerned, all of these maps are identical in function. It is only a topological property that makes the maps look different, but this property does not enter into our use of the maps. The map must just be divided into the proper number of areas, and the relative location of each does not matter.

Look at the map in Fig. 2-9$b$. Here the map is divided into four areas which allow us to associate each with one of the four minterms of the two variables. The left column is assigned to $y$ and the right column to $\bar{y}$. We label the rows to represent the two states of $x$ and $\bar{x}$. The intersection of the left column with the top row is assigned to the minterm $xy$, that of the right column with the top row to $x\bar{y}$, and so on. This means we can match an area on the map with any combination of states of $x$ and $y$. Now look at Fig. 2-9$c$. Although the locations are different, there is still only one square that can be associated with each of the four minterms. For example, $xy$ matches the labels on the square in the lower

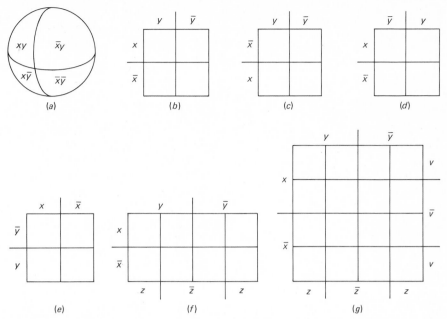

**Figure 2-9. Karnaugh maps.**

left-hand corner. Study the other variations of the labels in 2-9*d* and 2-9*e*. Decide which squares on those maps correspond with each minterm.

So far we have only discussed minterms. Because we can always convert maxterm equations to minterm form, this is not a limitation of the mapping method.

What about Boolean equations with more than two variables? For example, consider an equation consisting of terms with $x$, $y$, and $z$ in them. Figure 2-9*f* shows one possible Karnaugh map that would allow us to place each minterm in one square. The top left-hand square represents $xyz$. Remember, the map is a projection of a sphere, and, therefore, the four corners are in contact with each other. The same can be said of the top and bottom edges as well as the right and left sides. One way to imagine this is to think of a map made of rubber sheeting. Form a cylinder by gluing the top and bottom edges together. Then the ends of the cylinder must be pushed in until the sphere is reformed.

We need not stop with three variables. Figure 2-9*g* shows a map of four variables. The expression of the variables that matches the labeling on the top left-hand square is $vxyz$. Drawing Karnaugh maps with more than four variables is possible, but it is difficult to keep track of the labels on the squares of a two-dimensional map. For that reason, equations with more than four variables are usually simplified by other methods.

**Plotting Terms on the Map**

Now that we understand how to construct a map, let us look further into plotting minterms on it. Figure 2-10 shows a three-variable map. The expression that we want to plot is $A\overline{B}C + ABC$. (The squares are numbered so that we can refer to them, but after we are more acquainted with plotting, the numbers will be

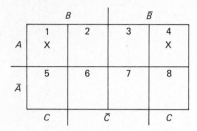

**Figure 2-10. Plotting $A\bar{B}C$ + ABC.**

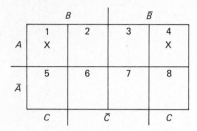

**Figure 2-11. Plotting A + B + C.**

## Simplifying the Map

omitted.) The first minterm can be plotted by seeing that the $A$ state is represented on the map by the top row. We next look for the intersection of that row with the two columns that represent the $\bar{B}$ state.

This intersection forms squares 3 and 4. Finally, locate the intersection with the columns for the $C$ state. This forms square 4 only. We show that a term occupies that square by placing an X in it. The next term is plotted by finding the intersection of the $A$ row with the $B$ and $C$ columns. This is square 1. Again an X is placed in the square to show that a minterm has been plotted. Now we have a Karnaugh map that reads the same as our original Boolean expression. We can read the value $ABC$ directly from square 1 and $A\bar{B}C$ from square 4. So the equation and the map are two ways to indicate the same information about the minterms.

So far, we have only had terms plotted in one square. Figure 2-11 shows a different situation. What would the map of the expression $A + B + C$ look like? Here each term consists of a single variable. Taking $A$ first, we see that it is in all four squares of the top row. So we place an X in each. Doing the same for $B$ requires that an X be placed in squares 1, 2, 5, and 6. But 1 and 2 already have an X in them from the $A$ term, so a new X is placed only in squares 5 and 6. The $C$ variable occupies squares 1, 5, 4, and 8. But only 8 does not already have an X, so only one X is needed to complete the map. While this map is perhaps harder to read, it, too, properly shows the Boolean expression.

Once we have all of the Boolean terms plotted on the map, we can start simplifying the expression. Figure 2-12$a$ shows the map corresponding to the expression $ABCD + AB\bar{C}D$. (The first term is plotted in square 1 and the second in square 2.) Simplification of the map consists of grouping squares with an X in them. We can gather the squares into either horizontal or vertical groups of 2, 4, 8, or 16. Remembering the spherical nature of the map, these groupings include the four corners or the edges. The two squares in Fig. 2-12$a$ can be collected into a single horizontal group of two squares. The grouping is indicated by circling the appropriate squares. The rule for grouping squares together requires that each collection of squares contain at least one square not in any other group. While the grouping rule may seem a little confusing at first, several examples should make it clear.

Once all possible groups have been made, the next step is to eliminate the unnecessary variables. In Fig. 2-12$a$, we see that the group contains only the $A$, $B$, and $D$ states, but both the $C$ (square 1) and $\bar{C}$ (square 2) are in the group. This means that the expression can be simplified by removing the $C$ variable. We have determined that

$$ABCD + AB\bar{C}D = ABD$$

The rules for eliminating variables is straightforward. If there are two squares in a group, then one variable can be dropped because it is present in both states. Four square groups allow us to delete two variables, eight squares three variables, and sixteen squares four variables.

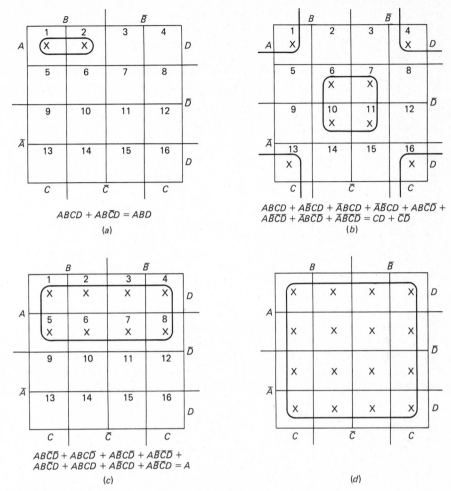

Figure 2-12. Grouping terms on a Karnaugh map.

Examples of these rules are shown in Fig. 2-12*b* through 2-12*d*. The expression plotted on Fig. 2-12*b* is shown below the map. In this case the terms occupy the four corners and the four squares in the center. We can group squares 6, 7, 10, and 11 into one collection. The four corner squares also are grouped together. Because there are four squares in each group, two variables may be removed from each.

Let's begin with the center group first. Which two variables are present in both states? We see that $A$ is in squares 6 and 7 while $\overline{A}$ is in 10 and 11, so that is one variable we can remove. $B$ is in 6 and 10 and $\overline{B}$ is in 7 and 11. This makes the $B$ variable the second one to drop. As a check, we see that only $\overline{D}$ is present in all four squares and this is also true for $\overline{C}$. Thus this group can be represented by $\overline{C}\overline{D}$.

Now consider the four corners. $A$ is in 1 and 4, but $\overline{A}$ is in 13 and 16. While $B$ is in 1 and 13, $\overline{B}$ is in 4 and 16. Only $C$ and $D$ are found in all the squares, so the result is $CD$. The entire map can be read as $CD + \overline{C}\overline{D}$.

A map containing a group of eight squares is shown in Fig. 2-12*c*. This means that three of the variables can be dropped. Only

$A$ is present in a single state in all eight squares. The pairs $B$ and $\overline{B}$, $C$ and $\overline{C}$, and $D$ and $\overline{D}$ are located in the squares. This means that all eight squares can be expressed simply as $A$.

The entire map of Fig. 2-12$d$ is filled. Because the grouping contains sixteen squares, all four variables can be eliminated and we are left with a map that equals one.

As we have seen, the simplification of a Karnaugh map requires that the terms be grouped into horizontal or vertical squares. These groups may include the four corners and the edges. The squares are grouped by twos, fours, eights, or sixteens. Depending on the number of squares in a group, we can eliminate variables.

| If a group contains this number of squares | Eliminate this number of variables |
|:---:|:---:|
| 2 | 1 |
| 4 | 2 |
| 8 | 3 |
| 16 | 4 |

### Simplification of Circuits Using the Karnaugh Map

Suppose we have the job of finding out whether or not a Boolean equation has been constructed from the minimum number of gates. The Karnaugh map can be used to accomplish this task.

The circuit shown in Fig. 2-13$a$ consists of four AND gates and one OR gate. Can the same outputs be generated from the inputs with fewer gates? The answered is approached by first writing the Boolean equation for the circuit. The necessary equation is

$$AB\overline{D} + ABD + \overline{A}B\overline{D} + \overline{A}\overline{B}\overline{D}$$

Next we plot the minterms on the map as shown in Fig. 2-13$b$.

**Figure 2-13. Avoiding the redundant term.**

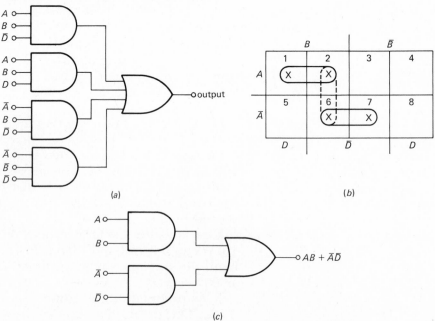

We can begin to form groups of two terms as shown in squares 1 and 2 and 6 and 7. But what about squares 2 and 6? Remember that each group of minterms must contain at least one term not already in some other group. Since square 2 is in one group and square 6 in the other, forming a collection of 2 and 6 is wrong. This is a common error and one that is easy to make. To prevent it, carefully check that each group has at least one term not in any other after all of the circles are drawn. If this error is not caught, a redundant term will be introduced.

Finally, read the resulting expression from the map. Figure 2-13c depicts the resulting logic circuit. Two fewer gates are required than in the original version.

**Review of Karnaugh Maps**

1. Why is the Karnaugh map like a map of the earth?
2. Explain how the seemingly different maps in Figs. 2-9c and 2-9e can both be used to plot an equation consisting of terms in $x$ and $y$.
3. List the number of variables that can be eliminated if a group on the four-variable Karnaugh map consists of (a) four squares in a vertical column, and (b) the eight squares on the right edge and the left edge.
4. Describe how a redundant term may be introduced when the groups are formed on a Karnaugh map.
5. Explain how to decide which variables can be dropped from the expression after the groupings have been made on a Karnaugh map.

**SIMPLIFYING CIRCUITS WITH BOOLEAN ALGEBRA**

The Karnaugh map is actually a mechanical method of applying the theorems and laws to reduce an equation to lowest terms. The same process can be carried out by directly using the laws, theorems, and identities.

The circuit in Fig. 2-14a consists of three gates, but we will see that these are still more than are necessary. The equation for the logic circuit is read from the diagram.

$$(A + B + C)(A + \overline{B} + C)$$

Using the distributive law to clear the maxterms and the commutative law to write the terms in alphabetical order, we have

$$AA + A\overline{B} + AC + AB + B\overline{B} + BC + AC + \overline{B}C + CC$$
$$①\quad②\quad③\quad④\quad⑤\quad⑥\quad⑦\quad⑧\quad⑨$$

**Figure 2-14. Circuit simplification.**

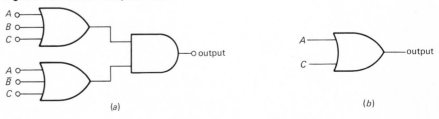

(The terms are numbered so that we can refer to them more easily.) Term one is reduced by an identity:

$$AA = A$$

Terms two and four give us

$$AB + A\overline{B} = A(B + \overline{B})$$ Distributive Law
but $$B + \overline{B} = 1$$ Identity
$$A(1) = A$$ Identity

Terms three and seven result in

$$AC + AC = AC$$ Identity

Term five

$$B\overline{B} = 0$$ Identity

Terms six and eight

$$BC + \overline{B}C = (B + \overline{B})C$$ Distributive Law
$$(B + \overline{B}) = 1$$ Identity
$$(1)C = C$$ Identity

And term nine

$$CC = C$$ Identity

Collecting terms we have

$$A + A + AC + 0 + C + C \quad \text{but}$$
$$A + A = A \quad \text{and} \quad C + C = C \quad \text{Identities}$$
$$A + AC = A$$

Leaving just $A + C$ as the result.

Figure 2-14$b$ shows the new logic diagram.

As you use Boolean algebra more, you will learn to recognize the patterns that indicate the most straightforward approach to the solution. For example, another form of the distributive law uses many of the same methods used above.

Prove:

$$(x + y)(x + z) = x + yz$$
$$(x + y)(x + z) = xx + xz + xy + yz \quad \text{Distributive Law}$$

But

$$xx = x \quad \text{Identity}$$

Substituting for $xx$:

$$(x + y)(x + z) = x + xz + xy + yz$$
$$= x(1 + z + y) + yz \quad \text{Distributive Law}$$
$$= x + yz \quad \text{Identities}$$

**OTHER FUNCTIONS**

**Introduction to Digital Comparators**

Combinatorial circuits are used in many applications that require arithmetic operations. One common operation is the comparison of two numbers to decide if they are equal or, if not, which is the larger. Simple gates can be used to perform this comparison on single-bit quantities. There are many times when the relative size of 2 bits is of interest, for example the sign bit of a number can be

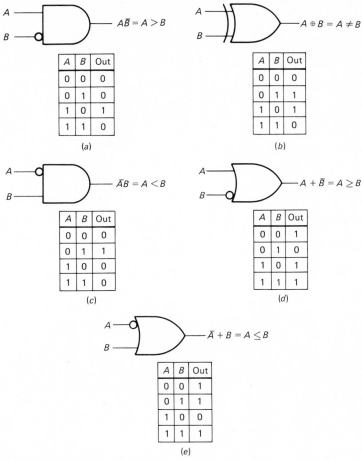

**Figure 2-15. Comparators.**

checked to determine if it is positive or negative by comparing it with another bit. Numbers with more than one digit require more complex circuits as described in Chap. 5.

The gates that can make these comparisons are called comparators. Figure 2-15 shows several logic circuits which produce a one output if the condition being tested is true. If we want to know whether $A$ is larger than $B$, the gate in Fig. 2-15a can be used. As the truth table shows, the output is 1 if $A = 1$ and $B = 0$. This is the only case for 1-bit numbers that allows $A$ to be greater than $B$. The circuit to tell us when $A$ is not equal to $B$ is the exclusive OR that we studied in an earlier section. The output is one whenever $A$ and $B$ are not in the same states. If we want to make comparisons for greater than or equal, an OR gate with an inverter on the proper input terminal can be used as shown in Figs. 2-15d and 2-15e.

**Multiplexers**     Often several signals must be routed to a common point in a digital application. If these signals are all available at the same time, we can build a switch, or multiplexer, to select the desired signal. A multiplexer constructed of combinatorial circuit elements is shown in Fig. 2-16. This circuit performs the function of

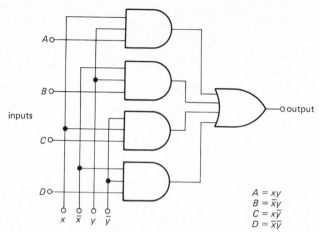

Figure 2-16. Multiplexer.

selecting only one input out of the four available to forward to the output terminal, so it is called a 1-of-4 line multiplexer. Multiplexers are also called data selectors because of their switching capability.

The selection of the input, that is $A$, $B$, $C$, or $D$, is made by setting the proper address on the select lines. Input $A$ will be selected if we set the $x$ and $y$ lines to ones. Only if these two lines are ones will the top AND gate be enabled to allow the $A$ input to flow to the OR gate. All of the other AND gates have at least one select input of zero, so those gates are disabled and will have zero outputs. The OR gate output will depend only on the value of $A$.

The selections to enable the other outputs are shown on the figure. Typically multiplexer integrated circuits have more inputs to select from than our example has. Selections of 1-of-8 or 1-of-16 lines are available. These multiplexers may also have a strobe input to each AND gate which provides faster operation.

**Demultiplexers** We can also transmit the input data out on a selected line from many output lines as well. The circuit we use is called a demultiplexer. The output line is determined by the address we place on the select lines. The circuit shown in Fig. 2-17 permits one output to be sent to any of the four destinations. This device would be called a 1-to-4 line demultiplexer.

If we want to route the input to output line number 2, the select line address must be $x = 1$ and $\bar{y} = 1$. This address enables only the third gate from the top to pass the input through. All of the other AND gates have at least one input equal to zero which will force the outputs of those gates to zero.

A typical example of the demultiplexer is the 54154 integrated circuit. This IC package has 24 pins; four are used as inputs and 16 are for the outputs. It has the capability of allowing four inputs to be forwarded to one of sixteen output lines. This 4-to-16 demultiplexer is used to convert from one number system to another.

The following chapters will provide a detailed description of how combinatorial circuits such as the multiplexer and demulti-

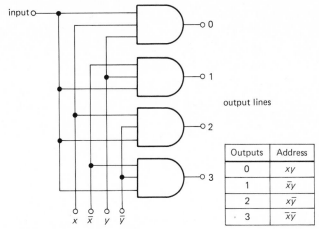

**Figure 2-17. Demultiplexer.**

| Outputs | Address |
|---------|---------|
| 0 | $xy$ |
| 1 | $\bar{x}y$ |
| 2 | $x\bar{y}$ |
| 3 | $\bar{x}\bar{y}$ |

plexer are fabricated from solid-state components. The use of these circuits in various arithmetic and logic applications will be illustrated as well.

**CHAPTER SUMMARY**

1. Combinatorial circuits consist of logic gates which have one or more inputs and a single output which depends on the input states.
2. Logic functions can be depicted on the Venn diagram which represents the universal set of items of interest. Elements in the null set are not shown on the diagram. Any element with two stable states can be plotted on a Venn diagram.
3. Boolean equations can be written in minterm or maxterm form. Minterms consist of Boolean AND terms which are ORed together, while maxterms are OR terms that are ANDed.
4. A symbolic notation is used to make written Boolean equations more compact.
5. Truth tables are used to define logic functions. They show the outputs generated by every combination of the inputs.
6. The basic Boolean relationships are AND, OR, and NOT.
7. Combinations of the basic functions produce NAND, NOR, equality, and exclusive OR gates.
8. The logic function that an electronic circuit performs depends on the voltage level selected to represent a Boolean one. If the more positive voltage is used, the logic is positive. Alternatively negative logic defines the more negative voltage to be a one.
9. The laws, identities, and theorems of Boolean algebra allow us to simplify equations and understand the performance of combinatorial devices and circuits.
10. A Karnaugh map is a method for solving Boolean equations. The map is based on the principles of Boolean algebra.
11. Digital comparators, multiplexers, and demultiplexers are examples of combinatorial circuits that are available as integrated circuits.

stable-state devices
Venn diagram
minterms and maxterms
truth tables
AND, OR, NOT, NAND, NOR
positive and negative logic
Boolean algebra

associative, commutative,
and distributive laws
DeMorgan's theorem
Karnaugh maps
comparators
multiplexers
demultiplexers

## PROBLEMS

2-1. As was mentioned earlier, the combinatorial elements used to implement a Boolean equation are not limited to a single type. Prepare truth tables for the circuits in Figs. 2-18a and 2-18b. Which functions do these circuits perform?

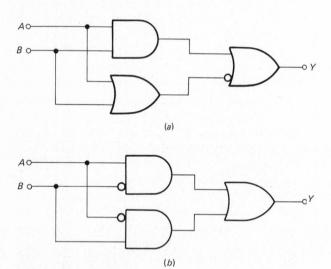

(a)

(b)

**Figure 2-18. Problem 2-1.**

2-2. Develop the truth tables for the following voltage tables. A positive and negative logic table for each is required. Draw the proper logic symbols to indicate the function performed if positive logic is used for each table.

a.

| Inputs | | Output |
|---|---|---|
| C | D | Output |
| 1 V | 1 V | 1 V |
| 1 | 0 | 0 |
| 0 | 1 | 0 |
| 0 | 0 | 0 |

b.

| Inputs | | Output |
|---|---|---|
| E | F | Output |
| 5 V | 5 V | 0 V |
| 5 | 0 | 0 |
| 0 | 5 | 5 |
| 0 | 0 | 0 |

2-3. Positive logic is to be used to determine the Boolean function performed by an electronic circuit with the following voltage table. What function does the circuit perform?

| | Inputs | | |
|---|---|---|---|
| A | B | C | Output |
| -5 V | -5 V | -5 V | -5 V |
| -5 | -5 | -7 | -7 |
| -5 | -7 | -5 | -7 |
| -5 | -7 | -7 | -7 |
| -7 | -5 | -5 | -7 |
| -7 | -5 | -7 | -7 |
| -7 | -7 | -5 | -7 |
| -7 | -7 | -7 | -7 |

2-4. Write the output of the logic circuit in Fig. 2-19 as a Boolean expression of minterms. Also show the truth table for the circuit.

**Figure 2-19. Problem 2-4.**

2-5. What positive logic function is represented by the voltage table below? What negative logic function corresponds to the same voltage table?

| Inputs | | Output |
|------|------|--------|
| A | B | |
| 0 V | 0 V | 0 V |
| 0 | −1 | 0 |
| −1 | 0 | 0 |
| −1 | −1 | −1 |

**2-6.** Use the Karnaugh map to simplify the Boolean expressions given below.

   a. $A + \bar{A}D + ABC$

   b. $ABC + A\bar{B}C + \bar{A}\bar{B}C$

   c. $(A + B)(C + D)$

   d. $ABD + AB\bar{D} + \bar{A}BCD + A\bar{B}\bar{D} + \bar{A}\bar{B}\bar{C}\bar{D}$

   e. $ACD + ABC + A\bar{C}D$

**2-7.** For a two-input NOR gate, draw the output waveform for the input square wave shown in Fig. 2-20. Assume that the signal takes no time to be propagated through the circuit.

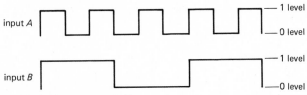

Figure 2-20. Problem 2-7.

**2-8.** Simplify the following Boolean expressions.

   a. $\overline{\bar{A} + B} + \overline{\bar{A} + \bar{B}}$

   b. $AB + AC + B\bar{C}$ (*Hint:* AND the first term on the lefthand side with $C + \bar{C} = 1$.)

   c. $\overline{AB + BC + CA}$

**2-9.** Draw the logic network corresponding with the equation

$$X = (A + \bar{B} + \bar{C})D$$

Then write the output of the circuit shown in Fig. 2-21 in terms of the inputs. Reduce the expression to minterm form.

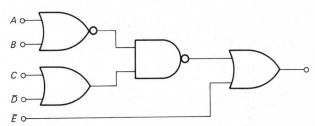

Figure 2-21. Problem 2-9.

**2-10.** Write the Boolean equation for the circuit in Fig. 2-22 in simplest form.

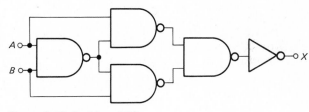

Figure 2-22. Problem 2-10.

# EXPERIMENT 2 TTL LOGIC GATES

**PURPOSE**   To investigate positive and negative logic and truth tables.

**PARTS LIST**

| Item | Quantity |
|---|---|
| 7408 | 1 |
| 7421 | 1 |
| 7427 | 1 |
| 7430 | 1 |
| LED | 1 |
| 330 Ω resistor | 1 |
| DPDT switch | 4 |

**IC DIAGRAMS**

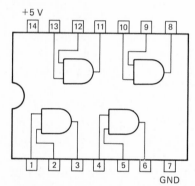

Figure 2-23. 7408.

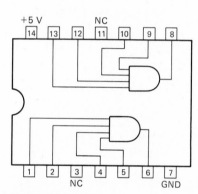

Figure 2-24. 7421.

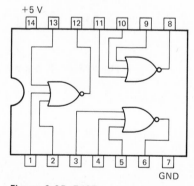

Figure 2-25. 7427.

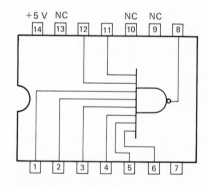

Figure 2-26. 7430.

**PROCEDURE**   Step 1.   Using the 7408 IC connect the circuit shown in Fig. 2-27. (Be sure to connect the ground and +5-volt terminals of the 7408 IC as well as the logic input and output pins.) By opening and closing the DPDT switches *A* and *B*, complete the voltage table for this circuit. (The LED state indicates the voltage level.)

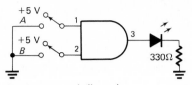

Numbers on gate indicate pins.

**Figure 2-27. AND gate experiment.**

| Inputs | | Output |
|---|---|---|
| **A** | **B** | |
| 0 V | 0 V | |
| 5 | 0 | |
| 0 | 5 | |
| 5 | 5 | |

From the voltage table, draw truth tables using positive and negative logic. What function does the gate perform using each type of logic?

**Step 2.** Using one of the AND gates of the 7421 IC, four logic switches, and the LED to indicate the output states, develop a four-input AND circuit. Then complete this voltage table.

| Inputs | | | | Output |
|---|---|---|---|---|
| **A** | **B** | **C** | **D** | |
| 0 V | 0 V | 0 V | 0 V | |
| 0 | 0 | 0 | 5 | |
| 0 | 0 | 5 | 0 | |
| 0 | 0 | 5 | 5 | |
| 0 | 5 | 0 | 0 | |
| 0 | 5 | 0 | 5 | |
| 0 | 5 | 5 | 0 | |
| 0 | 5 | 5 | 5 | |
| 5 | 0 | 0 | 0 | |
| 5 | 0 | 0 | 5 | |
| 5 | 0 | 5 | 0 | |
| 5 | 0 | 5 | 5 | |
| 5 | 5 | 0 | 0 | |
| 5 | 5 | 0 | 5 | |
| 5 | 5 | 5 | 0 | |
| 5 | 5 | 5 | 5 | |

Develop a positive logic truth table from the voltage table. What function does each truth table represent?

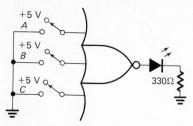

**Figure 2-28. NOR gate experiment.**

**Step 3.** Connect one gate of the 7427 as shown in Fig. 2-28. Complete the voltage table and develop positive and negative logic truth tables.

| Inputs | | | Output |
|---|---|---|---|
| *A* | *B* | *C* | |
| 0 V | 0 V | 0 V | |
| 0 | 0 | 5 | |
| 0 | 5 | 0 | |
| 0 | 5 | 5 | |
| 5 | 0 | 0 | |
| 5 | 0 | 5 | |
| 5 | 5 | 0 | |
| 5 | 5 | 5 | |

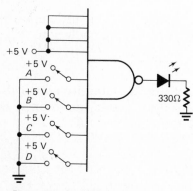

**Figure 2-29. NAND gate experiment.**

**Step 4.** Connect the 7430 IC as shown in Fig. 2-29. Complete the partial positive logic truth table after first developing your own voltage table.

| Inputs | | | | Output |
|---|---|---|---|---|
| A | B | C | D | |
| 0 | 0 | 0 | 0 | |
| 0 | 0 | 0 | 1 | |
| 0 | 0 | 1 | 0 | |
| 0 | 0 | 1 | 1 | |
| 0 | 1 | 0 | 0 | |
| 0 | 1 | 0 | 1 | |
| 0 | 1 | 1 | 0 | |
| 0 | 1 | 1 | 1 | |
| 1 | 0 | 0 | 0 | |
| 1 | 0 | 0 | 1 | |
| 1 | 0 | 1 | 0 | |
| 1 | 0 | 1 | 1 | |
| 1 | 1 | 0 | 0 | |
| 1 | 1 | 0 | 1 | |
| 1 | 1 | 1 | 0 | |
| 1 | 1 | 1 | 1 | |

# CHAPTER THREE
# INTEGRATED CIRCUIT
# FAMILIES: BIPOLAR
# INTEGRATED CIRCUITS

The growing trend toward digital devices can be attributed directly to cost reductions brought about by integrated circuits (IC). Discrete circuits built by using individual components such as resistors, capacitors, and transistors could perform the same functions, but the cost of discrete digital circuitry is high. The dramatic price drop of calculators, digital watches, and microprocessors is an economic result of improved technology. As manufacturers have reduced costs through increased yields of ICs, the reliability has risen as well.

There are two basic categories of silicon chips used to build integrated circuits: bipolar and metal oxide semiconductor (MOS). Bipolar ICs are fabricated by layering N-type and P-type materials on a single semiconductor crystal. Bipolar devices operate very much like junction transistors. With proper biasing and application of a negative base voltage (relative to the emitter) holes flow from the emitter through the base to the collector. In contrast, MOS circuits use field-effect transistors.

MOS fabrication produces a sandwich of silicon dioxide between a metal electrode and a silicon substrate. When the proper voltages are applied to the gate terminal and between the source and drain terminals, current flows. (The gate terminal of a MOS transistor should not be confused with logic gates.) Figure 3-1 shows the family tree of various IC technologies. This chapter will discuss bipolar ICs; MOS circuits will be covered in the next chapter.

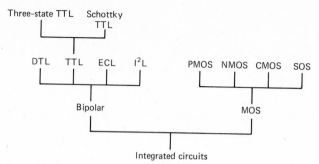

**Figure 3-1. Integrated circuit families.**

**CHAPTER OBJECTIVES**

In this chapter you will see how electronic components are used to implement logic gates and how the circuits differ from ideal Boolean functions. Because ICs cannot be repaired and are thrown away when they malfunction, the purpose of this study may not be apparent. Knowing how the circuits work provides the background necessary for learning new applications and for understanding IC limitations.

After completing this chapter you should be able to:

1. Distinguish between small-, medium-, and large-scale integration.
2. Describe the operation of various bipolar fabrication technologies.
3. Discuss the effect of propagation delay on gate operation.
4. Understand the loading effects and the limitations of gate fan-out.
5. Describe wired logic and its advantages and disadvantages.
6. Name the types of packages used for ICs.
7. Distinguish between families of ICs in terms of power dissipation, noise immunity, propagation delay, and cost.

**SCALE OF INTEGRATION**

The growth of the IC industry in the last 10 years has been caused largely by an increase in the number of gates provided on a single chip of silicon. The density of gates in the earliest circuits was 12 or less. These original ICs, with their low packing densities, are referred to as small-scale integration (SSI). Not outdated, SSI is still heavily used in modern logic designs.

As experience in building ICs was acquired, the number of gates per chip increased to about 100. This medium-scale integration (MSI) provided powerful functions in a single package. It was not until large-scale integration (LSI) that more than 100 gates could be fabricated on a chip. LSI made microprocessors, hand calculators, and digital watches practical.

**DIODE GATES**

A simple gate circuit can be constructed by using diodes. Figure 3-2 shows a schematic diagram of a diode gate. Each input is applied to one of the diodes, while the other terminals of the diodes are tied to the output. A current-limiting resistor in series with the power supply is used to protect the diodes. All voltages in the cir-

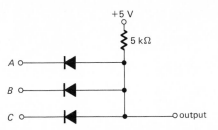

**Figure 3-2. Positive logic AND diode gate.**

cuit, as in most logic circuits, are referenced to ground. That is, the output voltage is read by using a high-impedance voltmeter connected between the output terminal and ground.

Analysis of this gate uses the rule of thumb that a forward-biased silicon diode has a 0.7-volt drop. With that introduction, the diode gate should not be difficult to understand. If the cathodes of all three diodes are grounded (0 volt input), all of the diodes will conduct. Using our rule of thumb, the anodes of each will be at 0.7 volt and current will flow out of the input terminals. The output voltage will be 0.7 volt. Table 3-1 lists these voltages in the first row.

With three input terminals there are eight different combinations of input voltages which must be examined before the voltage table is complete. The next case we want to consider is one with inputs A and B grounded and input C at +5 volts. The diodes connected to A and B will still be forward biased and drop 0.7 volt, while the diode at C will be reverse biased. The output voltage will be 0.7 volt in this situation because of the forward-biased diodes.

Obviously, if any of the diodes is forward biased, the output will be at 0.7 volt. This covers all cases except the last row of the table.

Setting all of the inputs to 5 volts will reverse bias all of the diodes. This means that no current will flow from the power supply and there will be no voltage drop across the 5-kilohm resistor. The output voltage will therefore be 5 volts.

The voltage table lists three voltage values: 0, 0.7, and 5. We

**Table 3-1**
**Diode AND Gate Voltage**

| Inputs | | | |
|---|---|---|---|
| A | B | C | Output |
| 0 V | 0 V | 0 V | 0.7 V |
| 0 | 0 | 5 | 0.7 |
| 0 | 5 | 0 | 0.7 |
| 0 | 5 | 5 | 0.7 |
| 5 | 0 | 0 | 0.7 |
| 5 | 0 | 5 | 0.7 |
| 5 | 5 | 0 | 0.7 |
| 5 | 5 | 5 | 5 |

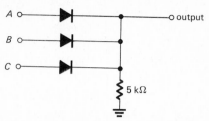

Figure 3-3. Positive logic OR diode gate.

reconcile this inconsistency with our concept of two-state devices by allowing a range of 0 to 0.7 volt for the low state. The high state is 5 volts, of course. We see that there is a 4.3-volt difference between the two states, and this is a large enough difference to make it easy for us to distinguish between an output in either state.

The amount of spread between the high and low states is a measure of the *noise immunity* of the circuit. All other things equal, a large voltage spread means that noise immunity is good, as a voltage spike of a few volts would not be sufficient to make the output erroneously appear to change state. The noise immunity of each logic family is an important characteristic that will be noted in the discussions to follow.

The type of gate we have in Fig. 3-2 depends on whether we use positive or negative logic. The voltage table is equivalent to a positive logic AND gate or a negative logic OR gate.

Another form of the diode gate is shown in Fig. 3-3. The analysis of this gate follows the same procedure as the previous one. If all inputs are grounded, the output is obviously at 0 volts. Applying 5 volts to one of the inputs, input $C$ for example, will forward bias the diode and cause 0.7 volt to be dropped in that branch of the circuit. The current flowing into the circuit will produce a voltage of 4.3 volts at the output. Applying 5 volts to one or more of the inputs will initiate the same chain of events; therefore, the output will be 4.3 volts except when the inputs are all grounded. Table 3-2 lists these voltages.

We see again that there are two voltage levels. The low state is

Table 3-2
Diode OR Gate Voltage

| Inputs | | | |
|---|---|---|---|
| $A$ | $B$ | $C$ | Output |
| 0 V | 0 V | 0 V | 0 V |
| 0 | 0 | 5 | 4.3 |
| 0 | 5 | 0 | 4.3 |
| 0 | 5 | 5 | 4.3 |
| 5 | 0 | 0 | 4.3 |
| 5 | 0 | 5 | 4.3 |
| 5 | 5 | 0 | 4.3 |
| 5 | 5 | 5 | 4.3 |

ground, but the high state ranges from 4.3 to 5 volts. The amount of noise immunity is 4.3 volts.

Converting the voltage table to a positive logic truth table shows that this circuit performs the OR function. Using negative logic we have an AND gate.

**Propagation Delay**  An important parameter in high-speed digital applications is the time it takes for a logic gate to switch states. In human terms the switching time seems rapid. Because computers can perform many operations in microseconds, the amount of time necessary to propagate the input conditions through the gate can be significant.

The amount of time a gate takes to switch from a low to a high state is usually not the same as that required to switch the opposite way. For this reason, manufacturers will often specify two propagation delay times:

$t_{PLH}$   propagation delay in switching to the high state

$t_{PHL}$   propagation delay in switching to the low state

The major source of propagation delay is the capacitance in the wiring and semiconductor junctions. Typically, this capacitance is on the order of 100 picofarads. As Fig. 3-4$a$ shows, this capacitance acts as though it were in series with the current-limiting resistor.

The propagation delay in switching to the high state, $t_{PLH}$, can be computed using standard RC (resistance-capacitance) network theory. By definition $t_{PLH}$ is equal to the time it takes for the output voltage to reach 50 percent of its maximum value, 2.5 volts in this case. The equation for the time-varying output voltage, in terms of the circuit elements, is

$$v_0 = 5 - 4.3e^{-t/RC}$$

where $RC = 5 \times 10^3 \times 100 \times 10^{-12}$
$$= 500 \text{ ns}$$

so $$v_o = 5 - 4.3e^{-t/500\times10^{-9}}$$

At the 50 percent voltage point, $v_o = 2.5$, so we can solve the equation for the time necessary for the voltage to rise to that level.

**Figure 3-4. Propagation delay in diode gates. (a) Stray capacitance, (b) dynamic performance.**

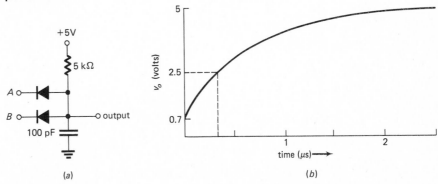

$$2.5 = 5 - 4.3e^{-t/500 \times 10^{-9}}$$
$$e^{-t/500 \times 10^{-9}} = (5 - 2.5)/4.3 = 0.58$$

Taking natural logarithms of both sides,

$$-t/500 \times 10^{-9} = \ln 0.58 = -0.54$$
$$t = (500 \times 10^{-9})(0.54)$$
$$t = 272 \text{ ns}$$

Figure 3-4$b$ is a graph of the voltage change during the propagation delay.

**Loading Effects of Diode Gates**

We have already considered one disadvantage of diode gates. The capacitance associated with the diodes makes the propagation delay long. As we will see, the loading effects of these gates is another disadvantage. From the previous chapter, we know that often many gates are chained together with the output of one gate becoming the input to another. An example is shown in Fig. 3-5$a$. The diode gate circuit, using positive logic, is shown in Fig. 3-5$b$. If the three inputs are set to the 5-volt level, the voltage at point $x$ should be about 4.3 volt, but the power supply causes the upper diode in the second gate to conduct. The two resistors form a voltage-dividing network, and the output will be approximately 2.1 volts. This is neither a high- nor a low-voltage level, so operation is not satisfactory. The output voltage does not reflect a proper relationship with the inputs.

**Diode Gate Review**

1. Describe the operation of a positive logic diode AND gate with two input terminals.
2. Define propagation delay.
3. Explain why loading effects limit the effectiveness of diode gates.

**DIODE TRANSISTOR LOGIC (DTL)**

This section will cover the first of the integrated circuits in our study of bipolar devices. DTL is named for its use of diodes and transistors in constructing gates. As Fig. 3-6$a$ shows, a DTL gate uses these two active circuit elements together with resistors.

Figure 3-5. Loading effects on diode gates.

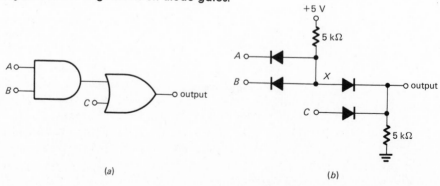

(a)

(b)

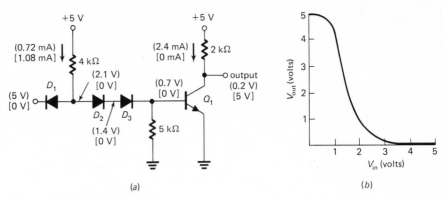

Figure 3-6. DTL inverter.

**The DTL Inverter**     Verifying that the circuit in Fig. 3-6a inverts the input voltage requires the same sort of analysis that was used on the diode gates. There is one other fact about basic transistor operation that should be recalled prior to starting the analysis: A saturated transistor has about a 0.2-volt drop between the collector and the emitter.

Assume that a 5-volt input is applied to the gate. This value is shown in parentheses on the diagram. (All of the voltages and currents that correspond with that input level are also shown in parentheses.)

This input will reverse bias $D_1$. The power supply will forward bias $D_2$ and $D_3$ (remember that this takes about 0.7 volt). Another technique used repeatedly in tracing DTL operation is simply to treat the base-emitter junction of a transistor as a diode. If we do that for $Q_1$, we see it takes another 0.7 volt to forward bias the diode. Three forward diode voltage drops or 2.1 volts are required in all. Working backward from the ground, we see this means the voltage on the base of $Q_1$ would be 0.7 volt, between $D_2$ and $D_3$ 1.4 volts, and 2.1 volts on the anode of $D_2$. Subtracting that voltage from the power-supply voltage

$$5\text{ V} - 2.1\text{ V} = 2.9\text{ V}$$

gives us the voltage drop of the 4-kilohm resistor and the current through it

$$I = 2.9/4 \times 10^3 = 0.72\text{ mA}$$

Because of the 0.7 volt on the base of $Q_1$, the transistor will be saturated, meaning that the output will be about 0.2 volt (collector-emitter drop). The current through the 2-kilohm resistor is

$$I = (5 - 0.2)/2 \times 10^3 = 2.4\text{ mA}$$

Comparing the input and output voltages, we see that inversion has occurred.

Now let's ground the input. (This time, square brackets will show voltages and currents on Fig. 3-6a.) $D_1$ is now forward biased with 0.7 volt on its anode. The current flowing through the 4-kilohm resistor is now

$$I = (5 - 0.7)/4 \times 10^3 = 1.08\text{ mA}$$

The voltage on the anode of $D_2$ is barely able to forward bias $D_2$, but does not affect $D_3$ or the base-emitter junction of $Q_1$. Because no current flows, the base of $Q_1$ is at zero and the transistor is off. This prevents current flow through the 2 kilohm resistor and produces an output voltage of 5 volts. Again inversion has occurred.

Figure 3-6$b$ is a plot of output voltage against input voltage; such a plot is sometimes called the transfer characteristics of a gate. The curve has the favorable property of a steep drop at the switching level. Another feature of DTL is its high noise immunity. The input can vary between 0 and 1 volt and still be considered a low input. A high input can range from about 2.5 to 5 volts.

The propagation delay in a DTL gate is on the order of 50 to 100 nanoseconds. While this is less than the delay in diode gates, we will see that other logic families provide even less delay.

## The DTL NAND

The simple addition of another diode changes the inverter to a positive logic NAND gate, as shown in Fig. 3-7. (The gate is also a negative logic NOR.) We can quickly follow the gate operation. If both $D_1$ and $D_2$ are grounded, their anodes will be at 0.7 volt. This will cause the base of $Q_1$ to be at 0 volt, turning it off. No current flows through the 2- kilohm resistor; thus, the output is 5 volts. If 5 volts is applied to only one of the inputs, the other grounded diode will keep the voltage on its anode at 0.7 volt. This will again produce a 5-volt output.

Applying 5 volts to both inputs will reverse bias $D_1$ and $D_2$. $D_3$, $D_4$, and the base-emitter junction of $Q_1$ will be forward biased. $Q_1$ will saturate and the output will be 0.2 volt. Table 3-3 tabulates the voltages. The table can be readily converted to a positive logic NAND truth table.

**Table 3-3**
**DTL NAND Voltages**

| Inputs | | Output |
|---|---|---|
| A | B | |
| 0 V | 0 V | 5 V |
| 0 | 5 | 5 |
| 5 | 0 | 5 |
| 5 | 5 | 0.2 |

## DTL Loading Effects

What are the limitations of attaching the output of one DTL gate to the input of another? There are many times when inputs to several different gates must be driven from the output of one gate. The limiting factor in this arrangement is the amount of current that the output transistor $Q_1$ can sink while saturated. Generally, the transistor can carry about 12 milliamperes when it is in saturation.

Let's look at the NAND gate in Fig. 3-7. When $Q_1$ was saturated,

**Figure 3-7. DTL NAND.**

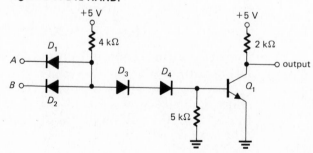

the current flowing through the 2-kilohm resistor was about 2.4 milliamperes. This means that a current of

$$12 - 2.4 = 9.6 \text{ mA}$$

is available for external use. The nominal current that would flow in from each of the following gates would be about 1.08 milliamperes. (We determined this current when we analyzed the DTL inverter.) The 9.6 milliamperes of current $Q_1$ can sink means that

$$\frac{9.6 \text{ mA}}{1.08 \text{ mA}} \quad \frac{\text{total available}}{\text{per gate}} = 8 \text{ input stages}$$

can be handled simultaneously without damaging $Q_1$. The number of following gates that can safely be connected to the output is called the gate fan-out capacity. The related term, fan-in, refers to the number of inputs provided by a gate. The gate in Fig. 3-7 has a fan-in of 2.

## Wired Logic

The current sinking ability of the output transistor can be used for the wired-logic method of connecting gates. If we want to perform an ANDing operation on the outputs of several DTL gates, as in Fig. 3-8a, we can save the cost of a gate by just wiring the outputs to a common point. The dotted symbol in Fig. 3-8b indicates this operation. Wired logic is also called wired-OR and wired-AND. The circuit may be identical in either case, but the function is determined by the use of positive or negative logic.

If the output stage of one or more of the AND gates (gates 1–4) is saturated, it will sink the current from the power supply of any output stage that is off. See Fig. 3-8c. This will pull the potential at the common point down to 0.2 volt. Only if all output stages are off will the voltage at the common point be high.

If we are using wired logic, we must take care not to exceed the output limitation of sinking 12 milliamperes, or less, in the output transistor. Because 1.08 milliamperes can flow into the circuit from the inverter, this leaves

$$12 - 1.08 = 10.92 \text{ mA}$$

of current sinking capacity. Since each output stage produces about 2.5 milliamperes, no more than four DTL gates can be safely wired together. Whenever the current capacity of a circuit is investigated, the worst-case situation must be used to ensure that current will always be within limits.

Although wired logic can save a gate, it is not without its own problems. Obviously there is no reasonable way to service the point where several open collectors are tied. The only way the outputs of gates 1 through 4 (in our example) could be measured would be to break the connection. This is a nuisance for maintenance technicians and also reduces equipment reliability if it is done repeatedly. Other disadvantages of wired logic include increased noise and a reduction in speed. Wired logic is suitable only for small, simple circuits, though many designers unwisely choose to ignore this advice.

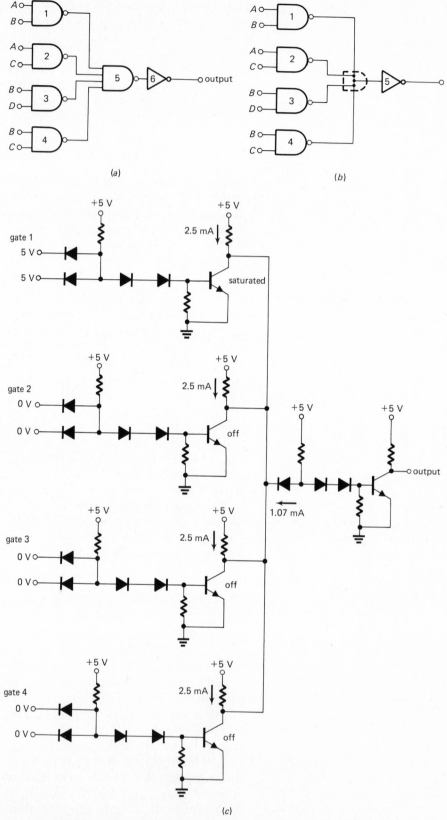

Figure 3-8. Wired logic. (a) Logic diagram, (b) wired AND, (c) Schematic.

**DTL Review**
1. List the assumptions used to calculate voltage drops in DTL integrated circuits.
2. Describe the switching voltage characteristics of DTL. Why are they considered favorable?
3. Describe how a DTL NAND gate can perform as an inverter.
4. Define the limiting factor in DTL fan-out.
5. List the disadvantages of wired logic.

## TRANSISTOR TRANSISTOR LOGIC (TTL or T²L)

The advent of TTL provided shorter propagation delays, reduced power requirements, and many more logic functions in IC packages. Several series of TTL have improved on the original speed and power parameters; designers can choose among the standard series (low-cost), low-power (and slower) TTL, high-speed (and more power) TTL, or Schottky low-power TTL which is heavily used today.

### The TTL Inverter

A standard TTL inverter is shown in Fig. 3-9. Operation of the inverter can be understood by using the techniques that we have developed. If a 5-volt input is applied, the base-emitter junction of $Q_1$ will be reverse biased. The base-collector junction of $Q_1$ also forms a diode, and the current from the power supply through the 4-kilohm resistor will forward bias this junction. The base-emitter junctions of $Q_2$ and $Q_4$ will be forward biased as well. Working backward from ground, the base of $Q_4$ must be at 0.7 volt because of the voltage dropped by the junction. By the same reasoning, the base of $Q_2$ must be 1.4 volts and that of $Q_1$ 2.1 volts. These base voltages cause all three transistors to be in saturation.

Now consider the state of $Q_3$. Its base must have approximately 0.9 volt on it (0.7 volt at the base of $Q_4$ plus the saturated transistor $Q_2$ collector-emitter drop of 0.2 volt). Is this base voltage sufficient to drive $Q_3$ into saturation? Although the answer is apparently yes, current does not flow in that branch. The base-emitter junction of $Q_3$ requires 0.7 volt, but so does $D_2$ if it is to be forward biased. The 0.9 volt is insufficient to forward bias both diode junctions, so $Q_3$ is off. The output voltage is the collector-emitter drop of $Q_4$, about 0.2 volt.

**Figure 3-9. TTL inverter.**

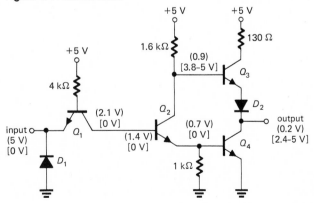

Next apply an input of 0 volt to the gate. The base-emitter junction of $Q_1$ is forward biased, and a current of 1.08 milliamperes flows out of the circuit. The 0.7 volt on the base of $Q_1$ is not enough to overcome three diode drops: therefore, no current flows, and $Q_2$ and $Q_4$ are off. Current can flow through the 1.6-kilohm resistor, the base-emitter junction of $Q_3$, and $D_2$. The voltage on the base of $Q_3$ is initially 5 volts, but it falls to about 3.8 volts. $Q_3$ is saturated, and current flows out of the circuit through the 130-ohm resistor. Output voltage will be in the range of 2.4 to 5 volts, and maximum output current will be about 38 milliamperes. This steady-state current accounts for much of the power consumed by TTL devices.

There are a few details of the TTL inverter yet to be discussed. If $Q_1$ is used only as a pair of diodes, why is a transistor better than a diode in this application? Let the input to the TTL inverter be 5 volts, then the base of $Q_2$ is at 1.4 volts. Now if the input drops to 0 volt, the base of $Q_1$ will reach 0.7 volt. At this time its collector will be reverse biased by

$$1.4 - 0.7 = 0.7 \text{ V}$$

With the collector reverse biased and the emitter forward biased, $Q_1$ is in the active region of transistor operation. Therefore, a large collector current will flow, removing the stored charge carriers from the junctions of $Q_2$ and $Q_3$. The change to the new output state will take about one-third as long as that of DTL.

The purpose of $D_1$ becomes clear if we consider the effect of a negative input. Any voltage high enough to forward bias the diode would be shorted to ground. Negative inputs can result from oscillation, or "ringing," caused by lead inductance and shunt capacitance in the circuit. The clamping diode quickly stops the ringing.

**The TTL NAND**  The TTL inverter can perform as a positive logic NAND gate with a slight change to the input transistor. Figure 3-10 shows a multiple-emitter transistor being used as the input stage, $Q_1$. $Q_1$

**Figure 3-10. TTL NAND gate.**

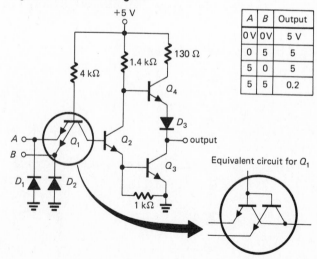

| A | B | Output |
|----|----|--------|
| 0 V | 0 V | 5 V |
| 0 | 5 | 5 |
| 5 | 0 | 5 |
| 5 | 5 | 0.2 |

can be considered to be two independent transistors which have their bases and collectors wired together.

If either input becomes zero, the base of $Q_1$ reaches 0.7 volt as the base-emitter diode conducts. If the base-emitter junctions of $Q_2$ and $Q_3$ are to be forward biased, about 2.1 volts is required; therefore, $Q_2$ and $Q_3$ must be off. The output is the voltage of the power supply, or 5 volts. If both inputs were raised to 5 volts, the emitters of $Q_1$ would be back biased and the power-supply voltage would be available at the base of $Q_1$. This is sufficient to forward bias the base-collector junctions of $Q_2$ and $Q_3$ and drive them into saturation. The output is the collector-to-emitter saturation voltage of $Q_3$ which would be about 0.2 volt. Converting the voltages to a truth table proves that the circuit is a NAND gate.

**TTL Output Stages**  So far, we have considered only a single type of output stage for TTL circuits. Figure 3-11$a$ shows the "totem-pole" output that we used in the two previous gates. The resemblance of the diagram to the carved poles gives it the name. Contrast this output stage with the open-collector output shown in Fig. 3-11$b$. The major differences are the lack of $Q_4$ and $D_1$ in the open-collector output and the requirement for an external pull-up resistor in 3-11$b$.

Principally, the more complex totem-pole output increases switching speed. At the output of the TTL gate, there is a load capacitance $C_L$, consisting of the capacitance in the diodes of the downstream gates and the stray wiring capacitance. The pull-up resistor in the open-collector output stage increases the RC time constant of the gate considerably.

The resistor on the totem-pole output stage is much smaller. Eliminating this resistor entirely would produce current spikes in the output when the gate changes state; thus, using $Q_4$ as an active pull-up with a small resistor produces fast switching without the spikes. As Fig. 3-11$a$ shows, the load capacitor can be lumped between the output terminal and the ground. When $Q_4$ saturates, the output voltage rises to the power-supply voltage with a time

**Figure 3-11. TTL output stages. (a) Totem pole, (b) open collector.**

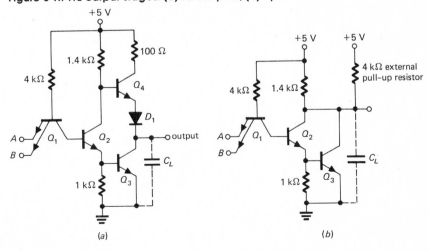

constant of

$$(100 + R_{S4} + R_D)C_L$$

where $R_{S4}$ = the saturation resistance of $Q_4$
$R_D$ = the diode forward resistance

The $R_{S4}$ and $R_D$ terms in the expression are on the order of a few ohms, so the active totem-pole output produces switching an order of magnitude faster than does the passive open-collector output.

The totem-pole output cannot be used with wired logic, however. If two totem-pole outputs were wired together and the output of one gate were high and the other low, there would be a steady-state output current of almost 40 milliamperes. This would exceed the current sinking capacity of $Q_3$ of the low-output gate. Open-collector TTL gates are available for this reason. The user of an open-collector gate sacrifices speed for the economy of using wired logic.

**Schottky TTL** | Using Schottky transistors in a TTL configuration offers several advantages. First the switching delay is cut by a factor of 2 or 3 to 1. The efficiency of the Schottky transistor is also higher because the forward-bias voltage is on the order of 0.3 volt instead of the 0.7 volt of standard TTL transistor junctions. The disadvantages of Schottky transistors include higher power requirements and the possibility of producing ringing from the faster rise time in the output transistors. Ringing is especially troublesome in printed circuit boards with connections longer than 5 inches.

Calling these devices Schottky transistors is slightly misleading. Actually, they consist of Schottky diodes used in conjunction with transistors. Figure 3-12 shows two ways in which Schottky diodes are used in TTL.

The Schottky diode has a smaller forward voltage drop because it does not have many minority carriers stored in the junction as ordinary PN-junction diodes do. In the Schottky diode, the use of a metal (usually aluminum) junction with silicon produces a surface barrier that has a rectifying characteristic similar to that of the PN-junction device. The Schottky diode is primarily a majority carrier device. These majority carriers easily cross the junction between the silicon and the metal, and no storage charge builds up near the junction.

**Figure 3-12. Schottky diodes and transistors.**

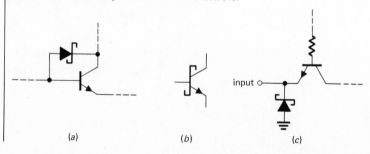

(a)          (b)          (c)

The Schottky transistor in Fig. 3-12a uses a diode to route excess base current to the collector. The symbol for the Schottky transistor is shown in Fig. 3-12b. A standard transistor is slow when switching out of saturation because excess base charge carriers must be removed before the transistor can become active. In the Schottky transistor, any charge greater than the 0.3 volt necessary to forward bias the diode is passed through to the collector, so the transistor never saturates.

Figure 3-12c uses a Schottky diode to clamp the input of a TTL gate in the manner that we have already seen. In this case only a small negative going signal (0.3 volt) would turn the diode on and clamp the input to ground.

## Three-State TTL

A three-state form of TTL has been developed which can operate as a normal gate or effectively be disconnected from the circuit. Figure 3-13a shows an example of a three-state inverter; its symbol is shown in Fig. 3-13b. A zero input on the strobe line produces normal inverter operation. After the strobe passes through the inverter on that line, the 5 volts from $\overline{\text{strobe}}$ on $Q_1$ back biases that base-emitter junction. A zero on the input forward biases its base-emitter junction on $Q_1$, causing $Q_2$ and $Q_3$ to be off. Diode $D_2$ is reverse biased because of the 5-volt $\overline{\text{strobe}}$ signal on its cathode. $Q_4$ is saturated, and the output is 5 volts. A 5-volt input causes $Q_2$ and $Q_3$ to saturate, $Q_4$ to turn off, and the output to be 0.2 volt. Table 3-4a tabulates these results.

Now the strobe is set to 5 volts. This produces a forward bias on the base-emitter junction of $Q_1$ connected to the $\overline{\text{strobe}}$ signal, causing $Q_2$ and $Q_3$ to turn off. $Q_4$ would normally be saturated, but diode $D_2$ is forward biased, preventing a voltage large enough to forward bias $Q_4$. Regardless of the input voltage, the output appears as an open circuit.

Use of three-state TTL for wired logic is shown in Fig. 3-13c. The output states of the circuit are listed in Table 3-4b. If the two forbidden states are avoided, the TTL circuit with a totem-pole

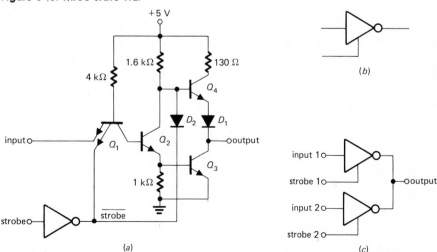

**Figure 3-13. Three-state TTL.**

(a)

(b)

(c)

**Table 3-4a**
**Three-State TTL Inverter**

| Strobe | Input | Output |
|--------|-------|--------|
| 0 V | 0 V | 5 V |
| 0 | 5 | 0.2 |
| 5 | 0 | open circuit |
| 5 | 5 | open circuit |

**Table 3-4b**
**Three-State Wired Logic**

| Strobe 1 | Strobe 2 | Input 1 | Input 2 | Output |
|----------|----------|---------|---------|--------|
| 0 V | 0 V | 0 V | 0 V | 5 V |
| 0 | 0 | 0 | 5 | * |
| 0 | 0 | 5 | 0 | * |
| 0 | 0 | 5 | 5 | 0.2 |
| 0 | 5 | 0 | 0 | 5 |
| 0 | 5 | 0 | 5 | 5 |
| 0 | 5 | 5 | 0 | 0.2 |
| 0 | 5 | 5 | 5 | 0.2 |
| 5 | 0 | 0 | 0 | 5 |
| 5 | 0 | 0 | 5 | 0.2 |
| 5 | 0 | 5 | 0 | 5 |
| 5 | 0 | 5 | 5 | 0.2 |
| 5 | 5 | 0 | 0 | open cirucit |
| 5 | 5 | 0 | 5 | open circuit |
| 5 | 5 | 5 | 0 | open circuit |
| 5 | 5 | 5 | 5 | open circuit |

* Forbidden state: produces output current of 40 mA.

output can be used in this configuration. The open-circuit condition protects the output transistors from too much current.

**The 54/74 Family of TTL**

The ease with which logic functions can be implemented by using TTL has led to the development of compatible integrated circuits. The 54/74 family is a group of such standard ICs with matched input and output characteristics. The numbers refer to the first two digits of the IC designator and the temperature range over which the circuit can operate. The 7408 circuit, Fig. 3-14a, is a package containing four 2-input AND gates and called a quad gate package. The two digits, 74, mean that this IC is in the low temperature range. That is, it can be operated safely from 0° to 70°C. A more rugged IC is the 5400 which is a quad 2-input NAND gate package. The 54 indicates high temperature use. Its temperature range is −55° to 125°C.

These ICs are available in two mechanical package configurations. Figure 3-14b is an example of the dual-inline (DIP)

**08**

QUADRUPLE 2-INPUT
POSITIVE-AND GATES

positive logic:
Y = AB

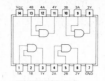

SN5408/SN7408(J, N,W)
SN54LS08/SN74LS08(J, N, W)

supply current¶

| TYPE | $I_{CCH}$ (mA) Total with outputs high | | $I_{CCL}$ (mA) Total with outputs low | | $I_{CC}$ (mA) Average per gate (50% duty cycle) |
|---|---|---|---|---|---|
| | TYP | MAX | TYP | MAX | TYP |
| '08 | 11 | 21 | 20 | 33 | 3.88 |
| 'H11 | 18 | 30 | 30 | 48 | 8 |
| 'H21 | 12 | 20 | 20 | 32 | 8 |
| 'LS08 | 2.4 | 4.8 | 4.4 | 8.8 | 0.85 |
| 'LS11 | 1.8 | 3.6 | 3.3 | 6.6 | 0.85 |
| 'LS21 | 1.2 | 2.4 | 2.2 | 4.4 | 0.85 |
| 'S08 | 18 | 32 | 32 | 57 | 6.25 |
| 'S11 | 13.5 | 24 | 24 | 42 | 6.25 |

¶ Maximum values of $I_{CC}$ are over the recommended operating ranges of $V_{CC}$ and $T_A$; typical values are at $V_{CC}$ = 5 V, $T_A$ = 25°C.

switching characteristics at $V_{CC}$ = 5 V, $T_A$ = 25°C

| TYPE | TEST CONDITIONS | $t_{PLH}$ (ns) Propagation delay time, low-to-high-level output | | | $t_{PHL}$ (ns) Propagation delay time, high-to-low-level output | | |
|---|---|---|---|---|---|---|---|
| | | MIN | TYP | MAX | MIN | TYP | MAX |
| '08 | $C_L$ = 15 pF, $R_L$ = 400 Ω | | 17.5 | 27 | | 12 | 19 |
| 'H11, 'H21 | $C_L$ = 25 pF, $R_L$ = 280 Ω | | 7.6 | 12 | | 8.8 | 12 |
| 'LS08, 'LS11 'LS21 | $C_L$ = 15 pF, $R_L$ = 2 kΩ | | 8 | 15 | | 10 | 20 |
| 'S08, 'S11 | $C_L$ = 15 pF, $R_L$ = 280 Ω | | 4.5 | 7 | | 5 | 7.5 |
| | $C_L$ = 50 pF, $R_L$ = 280 Ω | | 6 | | | 7.5 | |

schematics (each gate)

'08 CIRCUITS

'H11, 'H21 CIRCUITS

'LS08, 'LS11, 'LS21 CIRCUITS

'S08, 'S11 CIRCUITS

Resistor values shown are nominal and in ohms.

(a)

16-PIN N
DUAL-IN-LINE PACKAGE OUTLINE
(INCH & METRIC)

Package configuration of 16-pin N package (see alternative sideviews) is at the option of TI.

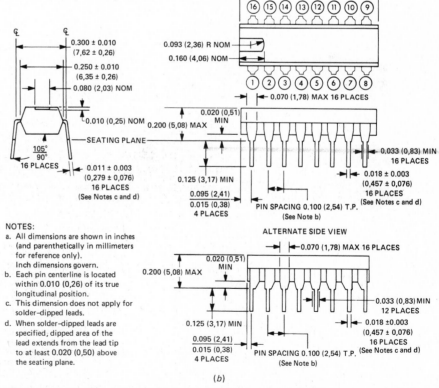

NOTES:
a. All dimensions are shown in inches (and parenthetically in millimeters for reference only). Inch dimensions govern.
b. Each pin centerline is located within 0.010 (0,26) of its true longitudinal position.
c. This dimension does not apply for solder-dipped leads.
d. When solder-dipped leads are specified, dipped area of the lead extends from the lead tip to at least 0.020 (0,50) above the seating plane.

(b)

**Figure 3-14. TTL integrated circuits. (a) 7408 quad 2-input AND gate, (b) dual-in-line package, (c) flat package (Texas Instruments Incorporated.)**

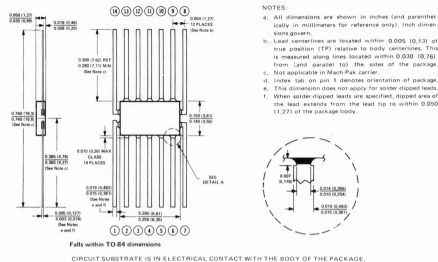

**14-PIN FLAT PACKAGE OUTLINE**

NOTES:

a. All dimensions are shown in inches (and parenthetically in millimeters for reference only). Inch dimensions govern.

b. Lead centerlines are located within 0.005 (0,13) of true position (TP) relative to body centerlines. This is measured along lines located within 0.030 (0,76) from (and parallel to) the sides of the package. Not applicable in Mach-Pak carrier.

c. Not applicable in Mach-Pak carrier.

d. Index tab on pin 1 denotes orientation of package.

e. This dimension does not apply for solder-dipped leads.

f. When solder-dipped leads are specified, dipped area of the lead extends from the lead tip to within 0.050 (1,27) of the package body.

Falls within TO-84 dimensions

CIRCUIT SUBSTRATE IS IN ELECTRICAL CONTACT WITH THE BODY OF THE PACKAGE.

(c)

**Figure 3-14.** (*Continued*)

package. It is the most common form. The flat package in Fig. 3-14c is used where space and weight are restricted.

**TTL Review**

1. Describe TTL inverter operation.
2. Explain why clamping diodes are used on the input terminals of TTL gates.
3. List the advantages and disadvantages of the two TTL output stages.
4. Distinguish between an ordinary transistor and a Schottky transistor.
5. How does the strobe input make three-state TTL appear to be an open circuit?
6. Define the difference between a 7401 and a 5401 TTL package.
7. List the packaging techniques used for TTL.

**EMITTER-COUPLED LOGIC (ECL)**

The demand for high-speed operation can often be satisfied only by the power of ECL circuits. From the circuit diagram for an ECL inverter shown in Fig. 3-15a, we see that the gate has two output terminals and requires two power supplies. The inputs to the inverter are either 3.3 volts (low) or 4.3 volts (high). The base of $Q_2$ has 4 volts on it from the power supply. If $Q_1$ has a low input on its base, then $Q_1$ must be off. We arrive at this conclusion because of the voltages required to forward bias the base-emitter junctions of $Q_1$ and $Q_2$. This means that $Q_1$ tries to make the potential at the common point approximately 2.6 volts (3.3 V − 0.7 V), while $Q_2$ tries to make the same point 3.3 volts (4V − 0.7 V). Since the point cannot be at two different voltages, the higher potential of $Q_2$ will keep $Q_1$ off.

The outputs of the circuit can be found after the current $I_E$ is determined.

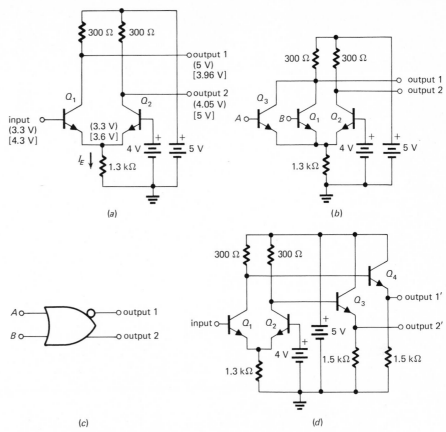

Figure 3-15. ECL Gates. (a) Inverter, (b) and (c) OR-NOR, (d) output stage.

$$I_E = 3.3/1.3 \times 10^3 \qquad \text{(If we assume } Q_2 \text{ has an } \alpha \text{ of 1.)}$$
$$= 2.5 \text{ mA}$$

Then $\qquad v_{o2} = 5 - (2.5 \times 10^{-3})(300) = 4.25 \text{ V}$

$v_{o1}$ is 5 volts, of course, because $Q_1$ is off.

Now let the input voltage be 4.3 volts. Again there is a tug-of-war for the potential at the common point, but this time $Q_1$ wins; its base-emitter drop raises the potential of that point to 3.6 volts. This prevents the base-emitter junction of $Q_2$ from being forward biased, and $Q_2$ switches off. The current through the 1.3-kilohm resistor becomes

$$I_E = 3.6/1.3 \times 10^3 = 2.8 \text{ mA}$$
$$V_{o1} = 5 - (2.8 \times 10^{-3})(300) = 4.16 \text{ V}$$

Because $Q_2$ is off, output 2 will be 5 volts. Examining the output voltages, we see that output 1 is inverting. A low input produces a high output, whereas output 2 is not inverting.

Figure 3-15b shows an ECL OR-NOR gate. The function performed is dependent upon which output terminal we select. The symbol in Fig. 3-15c shows that output 1 acts as an inverter. Any time the A or B input or both inputs are high, $Q_2$ is off; this situation results in a high on output 2 and a low on output 1. If both inputs are low, then $Q_1$ and $Q_3$ are off. This makes makes the voltage of output 1 high and that of output 2 low.

So far, the analysis of the ECL circuit assumed that the transistors were saturated when they were on, but this is only an approximation. In fact, they are in the active region. Returning to the inverter diagram, reconsider the low-input case. The base-collector voltage for $Q_2$ is

$$4 \text{ V} - 4.25 \text{ V} = -0.25 \text{ V}$$

This junction is reverse biased, so the transistor cannot be saturated. In the high-input case, the voltage between the base and collector of $Q_1$ is

$$4.3 \text{ V} - 4.16 \text{ V} = 0.14 \text{ V}$$

which is less than the 0.7 volt necessary for saturation; thus $Q_1$ is also in the active region of operation. Because neither transistor saturates, ECL switching is more rapid than TTL switching. Typical speeds are 1 to 8 nanoseconds.

There are distinct disadvantages to ECL. First, we require two different voltage levels to operate it. Second, noise immunity is low. The difference between the high and low states is only 1 volt. This permits an input margin error of only ±0.5 volt. This margin is usually adequate in a good design because ECL does not have the large current spikes characteristic of TTL.

**The ECL Output Voltage Stage**

An extra stage is required in ECL circuits to restore the output levels to those required for inputs to the next gate. This is apparent from a comparison of the input and output voltages.

| State | Input | Output 1 | Output 2 |
|-------|-------|----------|----------|
| low   | 3.3 V | 4.16 V   | 4.25 V   |
| high  | 4.3   | 5        | 5        |

The outputs are about 0.7 to 0.9 volt too high.

Two transistors added to the basic inverter, as shown in Fig. 3-15d, provide the voltage drop of one diode junction to restore voltages to their proper levels. The action of the output stage is summarized below.

| Output 1 | Output 2 | Output 1′ | Output 2′ |
|----------|----------|-----------|-----------|
| 4.16 V   | 5 V      | 3.46 V    | 4.3 V     |
| 5        | 4.25     | 4.3       | 3.55      |

ECL gates can be used in a wired-OR configuration. Figure 3.16 shows the output stages of two ECL gates tied together. The output of the upper gate is 3.46 volts and the lower has an output of 4.3 volts. The common point is at 4.3 volts, otherwise the base-emitter junction of the output stage transistor of gate 2 (corresponding to $Q_4$ of Fig. 3-15d) would have a voltage drop in excess of 0.7 volt. This is an impossible condition.

**Figure 3-16. ECL wired-OR circuit.**

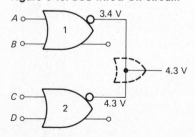

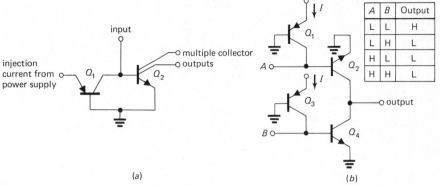

Figure 3-17. I²L circuits. (a) inverter, (b) NOR gate.

| A | B | Output |
|---|---|--------|
| L | L | H |
| L | H | L |
| H | L | L |
| H | H | L |

## INTEGRATED INJECTION LOGIC (I²L)

Offering low power dissipation and small size, I²L technology uses two types of transistors in each gate. The I²L inverter is shown in Fig. 3-17a. It is fabricated from both PNP and NPN transistors. Because heat-producing resistors are not needed in this logic, the chips can be smaller than in TTL. Typically, the density of I²L is 100 times that of TTL.

The PNP transistor in the circuit provides the current source and the load, while the NPN transistor performs the inversion. A multiple-collector transistor can be used to provide more than one output. With no input, $Q_2$ is biased on by the current injection from $Q_1$, therefore, the output is low.

If a low input (less than 0.7 volt) is applied, the injection current is diverted from the base of $Q_2$, which turns off. The transistor switching produces a high impedance or open circuit output. A high input allows the injector current to hold $Q_2$ on and the output is low.

A positive logic NOR gate is shown in Fig. 3-17b. If either input, A or B, or both are high, then $Q_2$, $Q_4$, or both will be on and the output will be low. Low inputs on both A and B cause $Q_2$ and $Q_4$ to switch off and result in a high output.

## ECL and I²L Review

1. Define the relationship between the two output terminals of an ECL gate.
2. Explain why the transistors in an ECL gate are never saturated.
3. Describe the voltage restoration stage of an ECL gate.
4. Why is the density of I²L much greater than that of TTL?
5. Distinguish between the types of transistors used in I²L for current injection and for inversion.

## CHAPTER SUMMARY

1. There are two basic groups of integrated circuits: bipolar and MOS.
2. Depending on the number of gates per chip, the scale of integration in the fabrication of ICs may be small, medium, or large.
3. Diode gates are simple examples of techniques used by more complex integrated circuits.
4. The switching time of a gate determines the propagation

delay. This time can be varied with the type of circuit and the power dissipated per gate.

5. DTL gates have good noise immunity because of the relatively large voltage difference between the high and low states.

6. The fan-out of DTL gates is limited by the amount of current the output transistor can sink. This is usually about 12 milliamperes.

7. Wired logic can be used in simple circuits to save gates. Its disadvantages include difficulty in servicing, increased noise, and reduced speed.

8. TTL gates provide the designer with a large number of modules that can be used to construct complex logic functions. TTL with a totem-pole output is used where speed is important, while open-collector TTL can be used with wired logic.

9. Schottky TTL gains a speed advantage by using diodes with transistors to prevent saturation.

10. Three-state TTL provides the normal high and low outputs as well as an open-circuit condition.

11. The 54/74 family of TTL is a standard set of functional ICs that can operate over one of two temperature ranges.

12. ICs are packaged in DIP and flat-pack configurations.

13. The transistors used in ECL never saturate, so ECL can provide very high speeds with associated high-power operation.

14. Using a transistor for the load in $I^2L$ produces very dense circuits with low power requirements. A PNP transistor acts as the current source and load for an NPN inverting transistor.

15. There is a wide range of capabilities available in bipolar devices. Table 3-5 provides a comparison and summary of the major types of bipolar logic circuits.

**Table 3-5**
**Bipolar Logic Summary**

| Parameter | Family | | | |
|---|---|---|---|---|
| | DTL | TTL | ECL | $I^2L$ |
| Basic positive logic gate | NAND | NAND | OR-NOR | NOR |
| Fan-out | 8 | 10 | 15 | 1 |
| Supply voltage, V | 5 ± 10% | 5 ± 10% | −5.2 + 20% − 10% | 1 to 15 |
| Power dissipation per gate, mW | 8–12 | 12–22 | 40–50 | 0.070 |
| Noise immunity | good | very good | fair | fair |
| Propagation delay per gate, ns | 30 | 12 | 4 | 25 to 250 |
| Cost | low | low | medium | medium to high |

**KEY TERMS AND CONCEPTS**

bipolar integrated circuits
MOS integrated circuits
SSI, MSI, LSI
diode gates
propagation delay
DTL
noise immunity
fan-out
fan-in
wired logic (wired-AND,
  wired-OR)
TTL(T²L)

input clamping diodes
multiple-emitter transistor
totem-pole output
open-collector output
Schottky TTL
three-state TTL
54/74 TTL
DIP
flat pack
ECL
I²L

## PROBLEMS

3-1. The circuit shown in Fig. 3-18 obtains its inputs, $A$ and $B$, from a gate identical to itself. What are the voltage levels for logic zero and logic one? Show that the circuit performs the NAND function. (Prepare a voltage table for all combinations of the two input levels.)

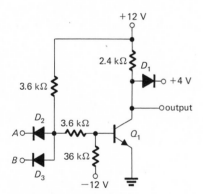

Figure 3-18. Problem 3-1.

3-2. Ignoring the problems of loading, what would the noise immunity voltage be for a circuit consisting of three diode AND gates (Fig. 3-2) each connected to one of the inputs of the diode OR gate (Fig. 3-3)?

3-3. The AND gate and the OR gate of Fig. 3-5a are interchanged. What adverse loading effects develop?

3-4. Four DTL gates are connected as shown in Fig. 3-19. What amount of current does the output transistor of gate 3 sink?

(The inputs are indicated as H—high, or L—low.)

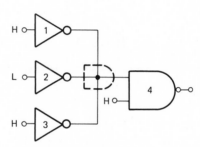

Figure 3-19. Problem 3-4.

3-5. Prepare a voltage table for Fig. 3-20. What positive logic function does the gate perform?

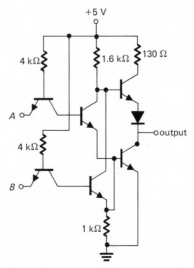

Figure 3-20. Problem 3-5.

3-6. What outputs (voltage levels) result from the possible combinations of inputs A, B, and C (if a low is 0 volt and a high is 12 volts) in Fig. 3-21? How is the voltage at point $x$ related to the C input? What Boolean function or combination of functions does the circuit perform? What is the proper symbol for the circuit?

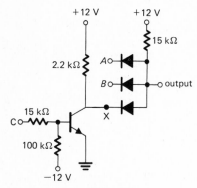

**Figure 3-21. Problem 3-6.**

3-7. Complete the voltage table for the ECL gate shown in Fig. 3-22.

| A | B | X | Y |
|---|---|---|---|
| −0.7 V | −0.7 V | | |
| −0.7 | −1.6 | | |
| −1.6 | −0.7 | | |
| −1.6 | −1.6 | | |

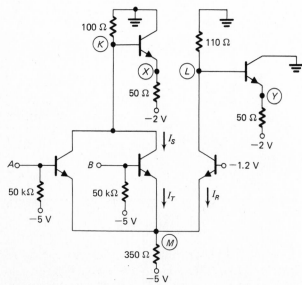

**Figure 3-22. Problem 3-7.**

What logic function(s) does the gate perform? What are the voltages or currents at the indicated points of the circuit when input $A = -1.6$ volts and input $B = -0.7$ volt?

| Voltages at points | Current at points |
|---|---|
| K_____ | R_____ |
| L_____ | S_____ |
| M_____ | T_____ |

3-8. If the capacitance of the diode gate shown in Fig. 3-4a is 150 picofarads when the gate switches to the high state, what is $t_{PLH}$?

3-9. The gate shown in Fig. 3-23 receives inputs from other gates identical to itself. What are the voltages at points A and B for high and low inputs?

| Both inputs high | Both inputs low |
|---|---|
| A_____ | A_____ |
| B_____ | B_____ |

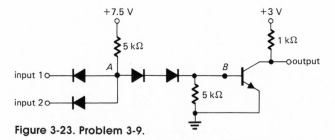

**Figure 3-23. Problem 3-9.**

Prepare a truth table for the circuit. What Boolean function does the circuit perform?

3-10. Complete the voltage table for the circuit shown in Fig. 3-24. A logic 0 is 0 volts and a logic 1 is 25 volts. The supply voltage, $V_{DD}$, is 20 volts. What are the currents through the diodes corresponding to each row in the voltage table?

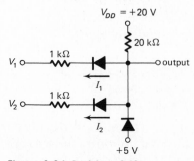

**Figure 3-24. Problem 3-10.**

# EXPERIMENT 3 TTL OUTPUTS

**PURPOSE** To investigate totem-pole and open-collector output stages and wired logic.

**PARTS LIST**

| Item | Quantity |
|------|----------|
| 7408 | 1 |
| 7409 | 1 |
| DPDT switch | 4 |
| 4-kΩ resistor | 1 |
| 330-Ω resistor | 1 |
| LED | 1 |
| voltmeter | 1 |

**IC DIAGRAMS**

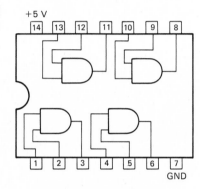

7408 has totem-pole output.
7409 has open-collector outputs.

**Figure 3-25. 7408 and 7409.**

**PROCEDURE** **Step 1.** Connect the circuit shown in Fig. 3-26. Note that the ground lead of the voltmeter goes to pin 7 of the 7409.

**Step 2.** Complete the voltage table below for the various switch conditions. Also record whether the LED is on or off for each case.

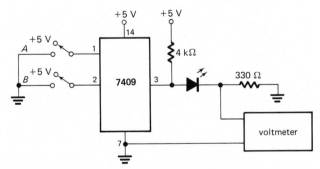

Figure 3-26. Open-collector experiment.

| Input | | Output Voltage | LED Condition |
|-------|---|----------------|---------------|
| **A** | **B** | | |
| 0 V | 0 V | | |
| 0 | 5 | | |
| 5 | 0 | | |
| 5 | 5 | | |

**Step 3.** Now remove the 4-kilohm resistor from the anode of the LED and repeat the experiment. Why is the resistor necessary?

**Step 4.**  Using the configuration of step 3, replace the 7409 with the 7408 IC. Repeat the measurements and tabulate your results. Why are the tables in steps 3 and 4 different?

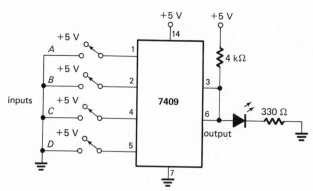

**Figure 3-27. Wired-logic experiment.**

**Step 5.**  Connect the circuit shown in Fig. 3-27. Opening and closing the switches, complete the positive logic state table. Draw the equivalent logic diagram for this circuit.

**CAUTION: Do not use the 7408
in this circuit configuration.**

| Gate 1 | | Gate 2 | | |
|---|---|---|---|---|
| A | B | C | D | Output |
| 0 | 0 | 0 | 0 | |
| 0 | 0 | 0 | 1 | |
| 0 | 0 | 1 | 0 | |
| 0 | 0 | 1 | 1 | |
| 0 | 1 | 0 | 0 | |
| 0 | 1 | 0 | 1 | |
| 0 | 1 | 1 | 0 | |
| 0 | 1 | 1 | 1 | |
| 1 | 0 | 0 | 0 | |
| 1 | 0 | 0 | 1 | |
| 1 | 0 | 1 | 0 | |
| 1 | 0 | 1 | 1 | |
| 1 | 1 | 0 | 0 | |
| 1 | 1 | 0 | 1 | |
| 1 | 1 | 1 | 0 | |
| 1 | 1 | 1 | 1 | |

# CHAPTER FOUR
# INTEGRATED
# CIRCUIT FAMILIES:
# MOS INTEGRATED CIRCUITS

Metal oxide semiconductor (MOS) transistors have become an important facet of the IC technology, industry. The MOS transistors use an electric field, rather than the base current of bipolar transistors, for control. That is the reason they are called MOS field-effect transistors (MOSFETs). Another major difference between the two types of transistors is that MOS devices, unlike junction transistors, use only majority carrier current. In spite of the distinctions, both types of transistors can be used in logic circuits. This chapter will explain how MOS ICs operate and what unique characteristics they have.

**CHAPTER OBJECTIVES**   After completing this chapter, you should be able to:

1. Distinguish between P-channel and N-channel MOS transistors.
2. Define the terms *enhancement* and *depletion* MOS and list the advantages and disadvantages of each.
3. Explain how MOS gates perform Boolean functions.
4. Describe how a complementary MOS is formed using P- and N-channel transistors.
5. Discuss typical MOS IC packages and the practical requirements for handling MOS circuits.
6. Indicate the differences between static and dynamic MOS.
7. Describe the related silicon on sapphire (SOS) fabrication technique.

**P-CHANNEL MOS (PMOS)**

The PMOS transistor is best understood by examining a cross section of the silicon chip. The area of the chip shown in Fig. 4-1 is about 5 mils$^2$ (152.4 $\mu$m$^2$). The transistor is fabricated on a lightly doped N-type substrate. Two highly doped P regions are then added and covered with an insulating layer of silicon dioxide. Contact areas are etched in the insulating layer to provide connection points for the source and drain terminals. These terminals, and the gate which overlies the insulating layer, are usually made of aluminum.

The MOS transistor, consisting of an insulator between the aluminum and semiconductor substrate, forms a parallel-plate capacitor. The insulating silicon dioxide also gives the transistor a high input impedance ($10^{10}$ to $10^{15}$ ohms).

The transistor shown in Fig. 4-1 is an *enhancement* type of MOSFET. If we were to ground the substrate and apply a negative voltage to the gate, an electric field would be established. The negative charge on the gate repels electrons from the top of the silicon dioxide layer. The bottom of the insulator then would have an excess of electrons and a negative charge. This charge, in turn, attracts (induces) positive charge carriers (holes) in the N-type material. Because holes are minority carriers in an N-type semiconductor, an inversion layer called the induced P-channel forms.

If we make the drain negative relative to the source, current can flow from the source to the drain. The amount of voltage applied to the gate controls the thickness of the induced P-channel and the amount of current flow. That is, the drain current is enhanced by gate voltage.

A typical PMOS characteristic curve is shown in Fig. 4-2. The voltage characteristics of this transistor indicate the same perform-

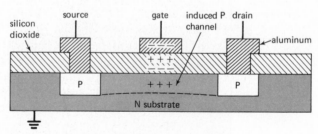

Figure 4-1. Enhancement P-channel MOSFET.

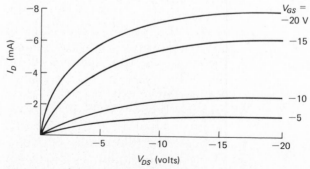

Figure 4-2. PMOS characteristic curve.

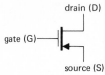

**Figure 4-3. PMOS symbol.**

ance that the MOS chip led us to expect. We see that when the drain-to-source voltage is held constant, drain current increases with increasingly negative gate voltages.

The symbol for a P-channel MOSFET is shown in Fig. 4-3. Because of the capacitor-like nature of the MOSFET, the symbol is derived from a combination of the transistor and capacitor symbols. The arrow on the source terminal points in the direction of conventional (positive carrier) current flow. The substrate is also connected to the source, but the symbol does not show this contact explicitly.

## The PMOS Inverter

As Fig. 4-4 shows, the MOS inverter consists entirely of FETs. No resistors, diodes, or capacitors are used. We will see that this condition holds for all other MOS digital circuits.

The inverter is composed of two transistors. The driver $Q_1$ provides inversion, whereas $Q_2$ acts as a load. Because the gate of $Q_2$ is tied to the power supply, that transistor is always on. The load resistance provided by $Q_2$ is not linear, but circuit operation is satisfactory in spite of the nonlinearity.

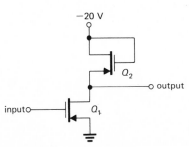

**Figure 4-4. PMOS inverter.**

If the input is $-20$ volts, $Q_1$ conducts and the output is equal to the source-to-drain voltage drop of $Q_1$; that is, about $-2$ volts. If the input terminal is then grounded, the output is the power-supply voltage. Because there is no current flowing, there is no drop across $Q_2$. Output voltage is $-20$ volts.

Is the slight difference in the low input and output voltage levels significant? Figure 4-2 can be inspected to decide that an input of $-2$ volts on the gate provides hardly any more drain current than a grounded gate. So a low-input range of 0 to $-2$ volts is acceptable.

## The PMOS NAND

PMOS operates with negative voltage on the gate, so it is appropriate to use negative logic with these circuits. A PMOS NAND gate is shown in Fig. 4-5. Each input controls one MOSFET. A third transistor, $Q_3$, acts as the load for the logic gate.

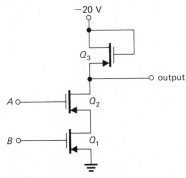

**Figure 4-5. PMOS NAND gate.**

If inputs $A$ and $B$ are 0 volts, no current flows through $Q_1$ or $Q_2$. Although the gate of $Q_3$ is heavily biased negative, no current path exists to ground. The output voltage is, therefore, $-20$ volts. If one input is changed to $-20$ volts, the output level remains the same. Either $Q_1$ or $Q_2$ is off, preventing current flow in the circuit. The output is still $-20$ volts.

Applying $-20$ volts to both inputs causes $Q_1$ and $Q_2$ to conduct.

**Table 4-1**
**PMOS NAND Voltages**

| A | B | Output |
|---|---|---|
| 0 V | 0 V | $-20$ V |
| 0 | $-20$ | $-20$ |
| $-20$ | 0 | $-20$ |
| $-20$ | $-20$ | $-3$ |

$Q_3$ is also on, so the output is low. The output is equal to the voltage drop of three transistors which is a few volts. The output will be around $-3$ volts.

Table 4-1 summarizes the NAND gate operation. Using negative logic to change the voltages to a truth table proves that the circuit is equivalent to a Boolean NAND gate.

**PMOS Review**

1. Describe the fabrication of an enhancement P-channel MOSFET.
2. What properties of the PMOS transistor make it similar to a capacitor?
3. List the correct polarities between the drain and source and between the gate and source terminals for normal PMOS operation.
4. What component serves as the load for a PMOS inverter?
5. Why is negative logic used with PMOS circuits?

**N-CHANNEL MOS (NMOS)**

The N-channel enhancement MOSFET differs from the previous example in that its majority carriers are electrons instead of holes. In contrast to the cross section of Fig. 4-1, a P-type substrate is used for the NMOS transistor and N-type material forms the source and drain regions. The polarities of the terminals are also reversed in a NMOS. That is both the gate and drain are positive with respect to the source. As the gate becomes more positive, the induced N-channel grows deeper. The symbol for NMOS is the same as that for PMOS, except that the direction of the arrow is reversed, as Fig. 4-6 indicates.

Figure 4-6. NMOS symbol.

NMOS is inherently faster than PMOS. The reason for the speed difference is the majority carriers used. Electrons can move through the semiconductor lattice more easily than holes. The main disadvantage of NMOS is the extreme purity of the materials required for its manufacture. The processing steps necessary to achieve such purity make NMOS more expensive than PMOS.

**Depletion MOS**

So far our discussion of MOSFETs has been based on the enhancement structure. MOSFETs can also be produced in another form. An example of NMOS in this configuration is shown in Fig. 4-7. The change from enhancement MOS is that the source and drain regions are joined by a thin layer of N-doped semiconductor.

If a negative voltage is applied to the gate, it will cause positive

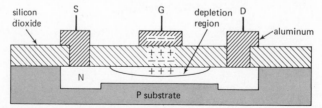

Figure 4-7. Depletion N-channel MOSFET.

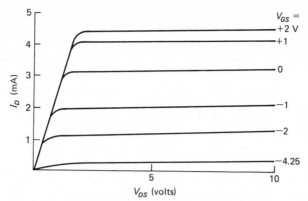

**Figure 4-8. Depletion NMOS characteristic curve.**

charge carriers to move toward the top of the silicon dioxide layer. This leaves the bottom of the insulating layer with a net negative charge. The negative charge in the insulator repels the majority carriers, the electrons, in the N-type material and attracts the holes in the material. As the gate voltage is increased, the N-type material will become depleted of majority charge carriers, so very little current can flow between the source and drain. Eventually, the depletion region can become deep enough to entirely "pinch off" the current.

Figure 4-8 shows the characteristic curve for an NMOS *depletion* type of transistor. The figure also illustrates one of the distinguishing features of depletion MOSFETs. A depletion MOSFET will conduct drain current with a grounded gate, but the enhancement type will not.

**NMOS Review**
1. List the differences between PMOS and NMOS transistors.
2. Distinguish between enhancement and depletion MOSFETs.
3. How can drain current flow in a depletion MOSFET when no voltage is applied to the gate?

**EXAMPLES OF MOS INTEGRATED CIRCUITS**
MOS gates are available in IC packages that are similar to those used for TTL circuits. A type 4000 dual 3-input NOR gate plus inverter is shown in Fig. 4-9a. The output of a NOR gate may be

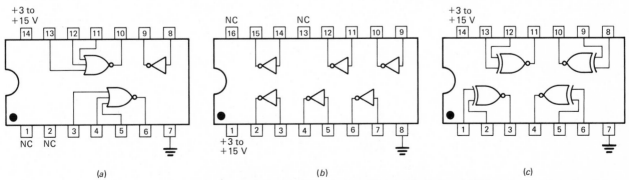

**Figure 4-9. MOS integrated circuits. (a) Dual 3-input NOR gate plus inverter, (b) hex inverter, (c) quad exclusive NOR gate.**

**Table 4-2
Using an Exclusive NOR as a
Controllable Inverter**

| Control Input | Data Input | Output |
|---------------|------------|--------|
| 0 | 0 | 1 |
| 0 | 1 | 0 |
| 1 | 0 | 0 |
| 1 | 1 | 1 |

connected to the inverter in the package to form an OR gate. Propagation delay for the 4000 IC ranges from 60 nanoseconds with a 5-volt power supply to 25 nanoseconds with a 10-volt supply.

The 4049 in Fig. 4-9*b* contains six inverters, so it is called a hex inverter IC. The inverters can also be used as voltage-level shifters or as drivers to interface with TTL or other logic. Using a +5-volt power supply produces a standard TTL compatible output with a fan-out of two gates.

The quad exclusive NOR 4077 in Fig. 4-9*c* can be used as four independent comparators. Another function that the exclusive NOR can provide is that of controllable inversion. Using one input for a control signal, the data on the other input will be inverted if the control input is low and will be passed through unchanged if the control is high. Table 4-2 summarizes this operation.

## COMPLEMENTARY METAL OXIDE SEMICONDUCTOR (CMOS)

CMOS gates use paired transistor configurations. Each CMOS gate employs a PMOS and an NMOS enhancement transistor in a set. The pairing of transistors gives CMOS its name. Because two types of transistors are used, power consumption in CMOS is lower than in other types of MOS. The low power dissipation results from one transistor being off whenever the other is conducting.

Figure 4-10 shows a CMOS inverter. A typical supply voltage of 15 volts is used in this circuit. The noise immunity for CMOS logic is dependent on the supply voltage. A nominal noise immunity of 45 percent of that voltage is characteristic of CMOS.

Returning to the inverter diagram, let the input be +15 volts. This input makes the gates of both transistors positive. A P-channel MOSFET will be turned off by a positive gate while the N-channel transistor will be turned on. So the gate voltage will turn $Q_1$ off and $Q_2$ on. The output will be at ground potential because no current flows from the power supply.

Now the input is changed to zero. Grounding the gate on $Q_2$ turns it off. Although the gate on $Q_1$ is also grounded, the large source-to-drain potential from the power supply causes that transistor to conduct. Because current cannot flow to ground through $Q_2$, the output is 15 volts.

Notice that in either state only one of the two transistors was on. This mode of operation produces low power consumption in both states.

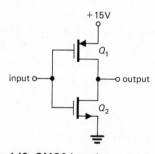

Figure 4-10. CMOS inverter.

## CMOS Clamping Diodes

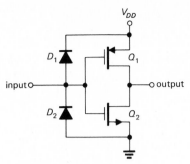

Figure 4-11. CMOS clamping diodes.

The high-input impedance resulting from the silicon dioxide layer can cause problems in CMOS transistors. Stray charges from static electricity can damage the ICs when they are not in their sockets or on properly grounded materials. This susceptibility to static electricity necessitates special handling procedures for CMOS. Otherwise, the built-up charge could exceed the insulation capacity and cause failures in the oxide. Clamping diodes are built on the chip to help prevent silicon dioxide failure.

The clamping diodes on a CMOS inverter are shown in Fig. 4-11. When the input voltage is between $V_{DD}$ and ground, both diodes will be reverse biased. But if the input exceeds $V_{DD}$, $D_1$ will conduct. A negative input will turn $D_2$ on and, in either case when the input levels exceed the range of zero to $V_{DD}$, the transistors are protected from excess voltage.

## The CMOS NOR

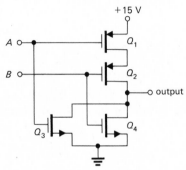

Figure 4-12. CMOS NOR gate.

A CMOS NOR gate, consisting of 2 P-channel and 2 N-channel MOSFETs, is shown in Fig. 4-12. The PMOS transistors are in series, while the NMOS transistors are in parallel.

If either input or both inputs are high, $Q_1$, $Q_2$, or both must be off because the gate will be positive with a high input. Either $Q_3$ or $Q_4$, or both, will be on with a positive gate voltage which ties the output to ground. Zeros on both inputs will turn $Q_3$ and $Q_4$ off. The power-supply potential causes $Q_1$ and $Q_2$ to conduct, so the output is 15 volts.

Gates such as the one in Fig. 4-12 have a large fan-out capacity. Up to 50 inputs may be driven from a single CMOS output. Increasing fan-out does have its price, though. While the nominal propagation delay of a CMOS NOR gate is about 30 nanoseconds, the delay increases by about 3 nanoseconds for each input driven.

## CMOS Transmission Gates

CMOS has a low-output impedance in either output state. The low impedance makes CMOS unsuitable for wired logic. A three-state form of CMOS is available which uses a transmission gate, or bilateral switch, consisting of a complementary set of transistors. The switch is bilateral in that its input and output terminals may be interchanged, and the switch will still operate in a normal manner. A strobe line is attached to the switch to allow for three-state operation. See Problem 4-8 for an example of the transmission gate.

## CMOS Review

1. Define the "complementary" feature of CMOS.
2. Describe CMOS inverter operation.
3. What accounts for the low power consumption of the CMOS inverter?
4. Explain the function of the clamping diodes used with CMOS gates.
5. Distinguish which transistors are conducting and which are off in the 2-input CMOS NOR gate for each input voltage combination.
6. Name the gate used for three-state CMOS.

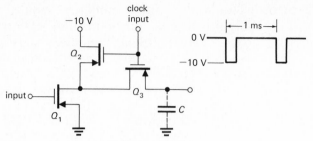

**Figure 4-13. Dynamic PMOS inverter.**

## STATIC AND DYNAMIC MOS

All of the MOS circuits we have studied so far required that the power supply constantly provide voltage to the appropriate terminals. These were examples of *static* MOS circuits. By making use of the parasitic capacitance between the gate and the substrate of a MOSFET, charge can be temporarily stored and the power supply disconnected. A clocking pulse train is used to alternately connect and disconnect the power supply in a *dynamic* MOS circuit. The time constant of the MOSFET is on the order of 1 millisecond, so a clock frequency—also called the refresh rate—of about 1 kHz is satisfactory.

An example of a dynamic PMOS inverter is shown in Fig. 4-13. When the clock signal is at 0 volts, the grounded gate causes $Q_2$ and $Q_3$ to turn off, so the power supply is not delivering any power. During the $-10$-volt clock interval, a negative gate voltage makes $Q_2$ and $Q_3$ conduct and allows $Q_1$ to perform inversion.

As long as $Q_2$ and $Q_3$ are clocked on, a $-10$-volt input causes $Q_1$ to produce a 0-volt output when it conducts. The output grounds the capacitor. A 0-volt input turns $Q_1$ off and changes the output to $-10$ volts. The capacitor charges to the new output level, so the $-10$-volt level is available as an input to downstream gates. Even when the clock is at 0 volts, the capacitor holds the charge for some time. Before the capacitor can lose a significant amount of the charge, the next negative clock pulse occurs. The clock pulse recharges the capacitor to the $-10$-volt level.

## The Dynamic MOS NAND Gate

Dynamic techniques can be used for other logic gates, as Fig. 4-14 illustrates. This gate operates in a manner similar to the inverter. During the negative clock interval, the gate operation is like that of the NAND gate in Fig. 4-5. The only difference is that the output is passed through to the capacitor, either grounding it or charging it to $-10$ volts. When the clock returns to 0 volts, the output level is maintained by the capacitor.

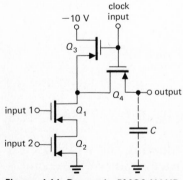

**Figure 4-14. Dynamic PMOS gate.**

**Table 4-3**
**Two-Phase Inverter**

| Input | $Q_2$ State | $Q_3$ State | Output | Capacitor |
|---|---|---|---|---|
| $-10$ V | on | on | 0 V | discharged |
| 0 | on | off | $-10$ | charged |

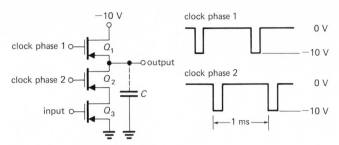

**Figure 4-15. Two-phase PMOS inverter.**

## Two-Phase Dynamic MOS

The power dissipation in the dynamic MOS can be further reduced if a two-phase clock is used. Low power consumption results because all transistors are off, except during switching. Figure 4-15 is a two-phase dynamic inverter. During the $-10$-volt clock interval of phase 1, the capacitor is charged to $-10$ volts. (Clock phase 1 is called the precharge clock.) Inversion takes place when clock phase 2 is at $-10$ volts.

Table 4-3 shows the states of the transistors, output levels, and capacitor response for either a 0- or $-10$-volt input. A $-10$-volt input grounds the capacitor through $Q_3$, and the output drops to zero. Grounding the gate of $Q_3$ turns that transistor off, maintaining the charge on $C$ at $-10$ volts.

## Dynamic MOS Review

1. Distinguish between static and dynamic MOS gates.
2. What determines the refresh rate of a dynamic MOS circuit?
3. Describe the charging and discharging of the capacitor of the dynamic inverter with an input that is originally 0 volts and changes to $-10$ volts.
4. Define the purpose of the recharge clock in the two-phase dynamic MOS.

## SILICON ON SAPPHIRE (SOS)

SOS is a form of CMOS which uses sapphire ($Al_2O_3$) as the substrate. While SOS has primarily been used in military and high-reliability applications, it is now expanding into the large-volume commercial market. As experience is gained in substrate cleaning and handling, the price of SOS should become more competitive with that of CMOS.

Figure 4-16 shows a comparison of CMOS and SOS fabrication

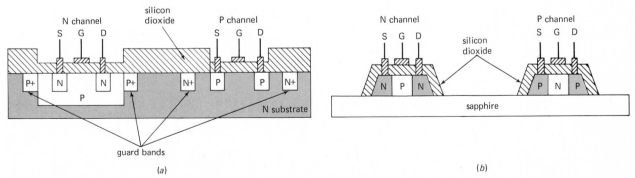

**Figure 4-16. CMOS and SOS fabrication.**

techniques. The packing density of SOS is higher than that of CMOS because the guard bands necessary to isolate the CMOS transistors are not required in SOS. Another advantage of SOS is the dielectric isolation provided by the sapphire insulator. This isolation eliminates parasitic capacitance from the substrate, increases speed, and reduces power consumption as compared to CMOS. Other favorable features of SOS are the fewer processing steps required in its manufacture and its radiation-hardened structure, which makes it suitable for use in space.

**CHAPTER SUMMARY**

1. MOS ICs use field-effect transistors instead of the junction transistors used in bipolar circuits.
2. P-channel MOS relies on holes for majority carriers. The hole current flows when proper gate voltage and source-to-drain biasing is applied.
3. One transistor acts as the load for another inverting transistor in the PMOS inverter. A similar arrangement is used in other PMOS gates.
4. N-channel MOS has electrons for majority carriers which provide faster operating speed than the holes in PMOS can.
5. There are two basic MOSFET structures: enhancement MOS induces a majority carrier channel in the crystal, while depletion MOS has a semiconductor channel between the source and drain. A grounded gate allows drain current flow in the depletion MOS, but not in the enhancement MOS.
6. MOS ICs and bipolar circuits are packaged in similar ways. With proper interfacing, MOS and TTL can be used compatibly in one circuit.
7. CMOS uses paired PMOS and NMOS transistors to provide low-power operation.
8. The susceptibility of MOS ICs to stray charges may require special handling techniques to prevent damage.
9. Transmission gates can be used for three-state CMOS operation.
10. The dynamic MOS uses a clock pulse to reduce power consumption, but unlike static MOS circuits, dynamic circuits must be periodically refreshed.

**Table 4-4**
**Comparison of PMOS and CMOS**

| Parameter | PMOS | CMOS |
|---|---|---|
| Basic positive logic gate | NAND | NOR or NAND |
| Fan-out | 20 | 50 |
| Supply voltage, V | $-10$ to $-27$ | 4.5 to 16 |
| Power dissipation per gate, mW | 0.2 to 10 | 0.01 |
| Noise immunity | fair | very good |
| Propagation delay per gate, ns | 300 | 70 |
| Cost | medium to high | medium to high |

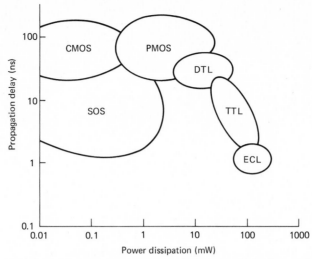

**Figure 4-17. Power and speed comparison of bipolar and MOS gates.**

11. SOS uses a sapphire substrate to fabricate CMOS transistors with higher packing density and lower power dissipation.
12. Table 4-4 compares major parameters of PMOS and CMOS ICs. The relative performance of bipolar and MOS gates in terms of power dissipation and speed is illustrated in Fig. 4-17. Generally the faster gates also require more power, and vice versa.

**KEY TERMS AND CONCEPTS**

MOSFET
PMOS
source, gate, and drain
   terminals
NMOS
enhancement MOS
depletion MOS
drivers
interface between MOS
   and TTL

CMOS
CMOS clamping diodes
transmission gates
static and dynamic MOS
single-phase and two-
   phase dynamic MOS
SOS
guard bands

**PROBLEMS**

4-1. The PMOS gate in Fig. 4-5 performs a negative logic NAND function. Write the positive logic Boolean expression, in terms of the inputs, for the same gate.

4-2. Find the voltage table for the CMOS gate in Fig. 4-18. What positive logic function does the gate provide?

4-3. What is the noise immunity of the CMOS circuit in Fig. 4-18?

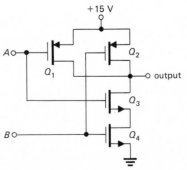

**Figure 4-18. Problem 4-2.**

4-4. What is the propagation delay for the gate in Fig. 4-12 if it has a fan-out of 37?

4-5. Draw the schematic diagram for the PMOS form of the logic gate shown in Fig. 4-19.

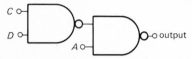

**Figure 4-19. Problem 4-5.**

4-6. A three-input NOR gate is shown in Fig. 4-20. Make a voltage table showing all possible input states. For the circuit, $V_{DD} = +12$ volts and input levels are 0 to $+2$ volts (low) and $+8$ to $+12$ volts (high).

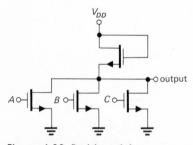

**Figure 4-20. Problem 4-6.**

4-7. Draw a logic diagram for the schematic shown in Fig. 4-21.

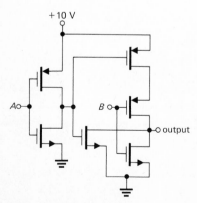

**Figure 4-21. Problem 4-7.**

4-8. The three-state CMOS gate in Fig. 4-22 uses a transmission gate on the output. A low input to terminal 1 and a high input to terminal 2 turn the gate on, allowing the signal to pass through. Reversing the inputs to the transmission gate causes it to have a resistance of more than $10^3$ megohms. Complete the state table below for the CMOS gate.

| Strobe | Input | Output |
|--------|-------|--------|
| 0 | 0 | |
| 0 | 1 | |
| 1 | 0 | |
| 1 | 1 | |

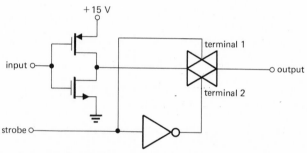

**Figure 4-22. Problem 4-8.**

4-9. A PMOS gate is shown in Fig. 4-23. Prepare a negative logic truth table for the gate.

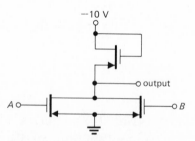

**Figure 4-23. Problem 4-9.**

4-10. Draw the schematic diagram for a two-phase dynamic PMOS NAND gate. Include a sketch of the proper time relationships between the two clock phases.

# EXPERIMENT 4 INTERFACING CMOS WITH TTL

**PURPOSE**  To investigate the method of using both TTL and CMOS devices in one circuit.

**PARTS LIST**

| Item | Quantity |
|---|---|
| 4000 | 1 |
| 7409 | 1 |
| LED | 1 |
| 330-Ω resistor | 1 |
| 2-kΩ resistor | 1 |
| DPDT switch | 4 |

**IC DIAGRAMS**

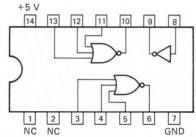

Figure 4-24. 4000.

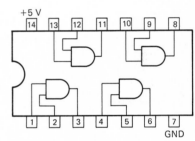

Figure 4-25. 7409.

**PROCEDURE**  **Step 1.**  Connect the ICs as shown in Fig. 4-26. Keep the 4000 on its conductive foam until you are ready to place it on the breadboard. Then hook up the ground and power supply pins (in that order) before connecting any inputs. After the circuit is completed, alternately ground and connect the switches to +5 volts to complete the voltage table below. Note that when the LED lights, the output is low.

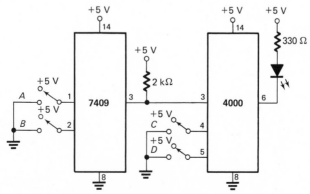

Figure 4-26. TTL-to-CMOS interface circuit.

| Switch | | | | LED |
|---|---|---|---|---|
| A | B | C | D | |
| 0 V | 0 V | 0 V | 0 V | |
| 0 | 0 | 0 | 5 | |
| 0 | 0 | 5 | 0 | |
| 0 | 0 | 5 | 5 | |
| 0 | 5 | 0 | 0 | |
| 0 | 5 | 0 | 5 | |
| 0 | 5 | 5 | 0 | |
| 0 | 5 | 5 | 5 | |
| 5 | 0 | 0 | 0 | |
| 5 | 0 | 0 | 5 | |
| 5 | 0 | 5 | 0 | |
| 5 | 0 | 5 | 5 | |
| 5 | 5 | 0 | 0 | |
| 5 | 5 | 0 | 5 | |
| 5 | 5 | 5 | 0 | |
| 5 | 5 | 5 | 5 | |

**Step 2.** Using Boolean equations prove that your results from step 1 are correct.

**Step 3.** Remove the 2-kΩ resistor and repeat step 1. What causes the results to change?

# CHAPTER FIVE
# NUMBER SYSTEMS
# AND CODES

All digital systems use numbers for counting items, representing quantities, and storing information. We have used the binary system repeatedly in the circuits covered in previous chapters. Understanding more complex integrated circuits requires that you be capable of using several number systems for counting and doing arithmetic. The number systems provide the tools for analyzing the operation of such pulse circuits as counters, calculators, converters, and computers.

**CHAPTER OBJECTIVES**

After completing this chapter, you should be able to:

1. Define the requirements for any positional number system.
2. Count in the binary, octal, and hexadecimal number systems.
3. Convert numbers from one base to another.
4. Perform arithmetic operations in binary, octal, and hexadecimal.
5. Distinguish between the two complement systems commonly used in digital equipment.
6. Describe the techniques used to code data for digital systems.

**BASIC CONCEPTS OF POSITIONAL NUMBER SYSTEMS**

Ancient civilizations probably relied on their fingers for the earliest counting methods. While fingers are not the most effective counting device ever invented, they do offer the advantages of

**Table 5-1
Number System Digits**

| System | Base | Digits |
|--------|------|--------|
| Binary | 2 | 0, 1 |
| Octal | 8 | 0, 1, 2, 3, 4, 5, 6, 7 |
| Decimal | 10 | 0, 1, 2, 3, 4, 5, 6, 7, 8, 9 |
| Hexadecimal (also called hex) | 16 | 0, 1, 2, 3, 4, 5, 6, 7, 8, 9, A, B, C, D, E, F |

portability and availability. Today the decimal number system is the one most widely used, a tribute to our ancestors' use of their 10 fingers. Unfortunately, decimal numbers are not the easiest or most economical to use in digital devices. Therefore, other number systems are used instead.

Every positional number system uses a set of symbols called digits. The quantity of digits in each system is equal to the base of that system. Table 5-1 lists the digits for the number systems of interest to us. Note that the hexadecimal number system uses the first five letters of the alphabet as digits equivalent to the numbers 10 through 15 respectively. The largest admissible digit is always one less than the base, for example the largest octal digit is

$$\text{Base} - 1 = 8 - 1 = 7$$

Another term that is used interchangeably for the word base is *radix*. In the binary system, the radix, or base, is 2. A period, called the *radix point*, is used to separate the fractional part of a number from the integer part. In the base 10 number system, we call the radix point a decimal point.

All of the positional number systems we will use assign a weighted position value to each digit. In the decimal system the count goes from 0 to 9, then the count returns to 0 and a 1 is "carried" into the next column to the left. We can represent each column of a decimal number with its value or weight. Each column is weighted by 10, the base, raised to an appropriate power.

| Decimal number | 1 | 2 | 5. | 4 | 1 |
|----------------|-----|-----|-----|------|------|
| Column value | $10^2$ | $10^1$ | $10^0$ | $10^{-1}$ | $10^{-2}$ |

The same holds true for other bases. Examples are

| Binary number | 1 | 0 | 1. | 0 | 1 | 1 |
|---------------|-----|-----|-----|------|------|------|
| Column value | $2^2$ | $2^1$ | $2^0$ | $2^{-1}$ | $2^{-2}$ | $2^{-3}$ |

| Octal number | 1 | 3 | 7. | 6 | 2 |
|--------------|-----|-----|-----|------|------|
| Column value | $8^2$ | $8^1$ | $8^0$ | $8^{-1}$ | $8^{-2}$ |

| Hexadecimal number | 2 | A | 6. | B | 4 |
|---|---|---|---|---|---|
| Column value | $16^2$ | $16^1$ | $16^0$ | $16^{-1}$ | $16^{-2}$ |

To enable us to determine the base of a number, the radix is indicated by a subscript. Without the subscript, it is impossible to distinguish the value of numbers with the same digits in two bases; the base 8 and base 2 numbers below are examples

$$101.1_2 \quad \text{binary}$$
$$101.1_8 \quad \text{octal}$$

**Concepts of Number Systems Review**

1. Define the terms base and radix as used in referring to number systems.
2. List the digits in the octal system.
3. What is the largest admissible digit in the binary system? The hexadecimal system?
4. Describe how the base of a number is indicated by a subscript.

**BASE CONVERSION METHODS**

The most convenient number system for us to use is decimal, of course. Digital circuits make use of binary arithmetic, and many times numbers must be converted from binary into decimal. The octal and hexadecimal bases are used to express binary numbers in a compact form; and so, conversion between these bases and decimal is often necessary.

**Polynomial Expansion**

The value of each digit in a number is determined by three factors:

1. The digit itself.
2. The number system base.
3. The position of the digit in the number.

The number $217.4_{10}$ can be expressed as

$$2 \times 10^2 + 1 \times 10^1 + 7 \times 10^0 + 4 \times 10^{-1}$$

Writing the digits of a number in this way is called *polynomial expansion*. The same means of expression can be used for any base.

Polynomial expansion is the basis for converting from one number system to another. Later in this chapter more efficient methods will be presented, but an understanding of polynomial expansion will provide an insight into the conversion process.

The number $100.11_2$ can be converted to a decimal number by a series of multiplications and additions.

$$100.11_2 = 1 \times 2^2 + 0 \times 2^1 + 0 \times 2^0 + 1 \times 2^{-1} + 1 \times 2^{-2}$$
$$= 4 + 0 + 0 + 0.5 + 0.25$$
$$= 4.75_{10}$$

All of the arithmetic on the right side of the equation is carried out in decimal. Because the original base of the number was 2, the multiplication involved was powers of 2.

By using the same approach, but changing the multiplication terms to powers of the appropriate bases, octal and hexadecimal numbers can also be converted to decimal numbers.

$$253.71_8 = 2 \times 8^2 + 5 \times 8^1 + 3 \times 8^0 + 7 \times 8^{-1} + 1 \times 8^{-2}$$
$$= 128 + 40 + 3 + 0.875 + 0.015$$
$$= 171.890_{10}$$

$$FCD.3_{16} = 15 \times 16^2 + 12 \times 16^1 + 13 \times 16^0 + 3 \times 16^{-1}$$
$$= 3840 + 192 + 13 + 0.1875$$
$$= 4045.1875_{10}$$

With hexadecimal numbers, it may be necessary to convert digits (those larger than 9) to their decimal equivalents.

**Conversion by Grouping**    The ease of converting binary numbers to either octal or hexadecimal is the reason that the latter two bases are so widely used. The larger bases are a convenient shorthand way of writing long binary numbers. For example:

$$101\ 001\ 110\ 101\ 011\ 000\ 111_2 = 5{,}165{,}307_8$$

It is much easier to write octal digits than long strings of ones and zeros. Simple mistakes such as inserting or deleting a digit can also be avoided by using the base 8 or base 16 number system.

A binary number can be converted to another base that is a power of two by counting off the bits from the right and left of the radix point in groups of the proper size.

To convert to octal, the binary number is arranged in groups of three digits.

$$1 \mid 100 \mid 111 \mid 011 \mid 010 \mid 101 \mid 111 \mid 011. \mid 101 \mid 11_2$$
$$= 001\ 100\ 111\ 011\ 010\ 101\ 111\ 011.\ 101\ 110$$

Note that leading and trailing zeros were added to obtain groupings of exactly three digits. Next, the digits in each group are converted to their octal equivalents; that is, $001_2 = 1_8$ for the most significant digit, and so on to the end. In this way, the number above converts to $14{,}732{,}573.56_8$.

Converting to hexadecimal is equally easy, but the groups must each contain four digits:

$$01 \mid 1111 \mid 0010 \mid 1011. \mid 0110 \mid 10_2$$

Grouping and inserting the leading and trailing zeros, we get:

$$0001\ 1111\ 0010\ 1011.\ 0110\ 1000 \quad \text{or} \quad 1F2B.68_{16}$$

Obviously, the process can be reversed. It is possible to convert octal and hexadecimal numbers to binary numbers by converting each digit in the higher base number to its direct binary equivalent.

$$65231.4_8 = 110\ 101\ 010\ 011\ 001.\ 100_2$$

$$C01.A_{16} = 1100\ 0000\ 0001.\ 1010_2$$

A little practice will make it possible for you to perform conversion by grouping in your head.

Whether you use the octal or hexadecimal system really does not matter. Any binary number can be represented in each system. Many equipment manufacturers use one system or the other in their documentation. Thus you may find that you will change from one to another to allow you to use the equipment on which you are working. For this reason, you should have knowledge of both the octal and hexadecimal systems.

**Conversion by Grouping Review**

1. Explain why the octal and hexadecimal number systems are used in digital electronics documentation.
2. Describe the grouping process for converting from binary to octal; from hexadecimal to binary.
3. What do you do if the groups are not exactly evenly divisible into groups of three digits when you are converting from binary to octal?

**Conversion by Explosion**

Whenever we want to convert to the decimal system from another base, an efficient method called explosion can be used. Mathematical descriptions of such processes are called *algorithms*. Strictly speaking, a mathematical algorithm consists of the precise rules for transforming specified inputs into specified outputs in a finite number of steps. So we are concerned with the explosion algorithm. An example will be used to illustrate this conversion method.

**Integer Conversion.** If we want to convert the number $277.356_8$ to a decimal number, we must first split it into integer and fractional components. This split is necessary because the explosion algorithm requires different processes for integers and for fractions.

The first step in the algorithm is to express the old base (octal) as a new base (decimal) number. This would be $8_{10}$. Next, the old base is multiplied by the most significant digit (MSD) of the number to be converted. That product is then added to the next digit to the right. The multiplication and adding is repeated as many times as there are digits. The final sum is the answer.

The integer portion of our octal number is converted to decimal below. The digits are spread across the page (exploded) to allow room for the arithmetic.

$$
\begin{array}{ccc}
\text{MSD} & & \\
2 & 7 & 7 \\
\times 8 & \rightarrow +16 & \rightarrow +184 \\
\hline
16 & \overline{23} & \overline{191} \\
& \times 8 & \\
& \overline{184} & \\
\end{array}
$$

$$277_8 = 191_{10}$$

Explosion also works with hexadecimal. To convert $ABC_{16}$ to decimal, the multiplier is 16.

$$
\begin{array}{ccc}
A = 10 & B = 11 & C = 12 \\
\times 16 & +160 & +2736 \\
\hline
160 & \overline{171} & \overline{2748} \\
& \times 16 \\
& \overline{2736}
\end{array}
$$

$$ABC_{16} = 2748_{10}$$

Because the hexadecimal digits were greater than 9, we had to convert them first to their decimal values.

**Fractional Conversion.** Now let's convert the fractional component of the octal number in our example ($277.356_8$). Instead of multiplying by the old base, we divide. First the least significant digit (LSD) of the fraction is divided by the original base (8). The quotient is added to the next digit to the left, and the process is repeated as many times as there are digits. The final quotient is the answer. Converting $0.356_8$ to decimal:

$$LSD \rightarrow 6/8 = 0.75$$
$$(5 + 0.75)/8 = 0.718$$
$$(3 + 0.718)/8 = 0.464$$
$$0.356_8 = 0.464_{10}$$

The mixed octal number is now converted to its decimal equivalent by adding the integer, found previously, to the fraction just converted:

$$277.356_8 = 191_{10} + 0.464_{10}$$
$$= 191.464_{10}$$

Hexadecimal fractions can be converted with the same algorithm, but the divisor must be $16_{10}$. Converting $0.A72_{16}$ to the decimal system,

$$2/16 = 0.125$$
$$(7 + 0.125)/16 = 0.445$$

Before the next step, convert $A_{16}$ to $10_{10}$

$$(10 + 0.445)/16 = 0.653$$
$$0.A72_{16} = 0.653_{10}$$

The accuracy of the answer depends on the number of places to the right of the decimal point in each quotient.

**Conversion by Explosion Summary**

The explosion algorithm for converting from any base to decimal is summarized below.

1. Separate integers and fractions.
2. Integer conversion.
   a. Express the original base as a decimal number.
   b. Multiply the most significant digit by the original base.
   c. Add the product to the next digit to the right.
   d. Multiply the sum by the original base. Repeat steps c and d

as many times as there are digits. The final sum is the answer.

**3.** Fractional conversion.
   *a.* Express the original base as a decimal number.
   *b.* Divide the least significant digit by the original base.
   *c.* Add the quotient to the next digit on the left.
   *d.* Divide the sum by the original base. Repeat steps *c* and *d* as many times as there are digits. The final quotient is the result.

**Conversion by Digit-by-Digit**

The digit-by-digit conversion algorithm is used in going from decimal to other bases. Again, mixed numbers must be separated into integer and fractional portions. Conversion of the integer will be discussed first.

**Integer conversion.** Integer conversion using the digit-by-digit algorithm requires that the number to be converted be divided by the new base. The remainder is saved and the residual quotient is again divided. The process repeats until the quotient is zero. The most significant digit of the number is the last remainder generated.

Find the octal equivalent of $99_{10}$:

$$
\begin{array}{ccc}
 & & \text{Remainder} \\
8)\overline{99} & \phantom{xx} & 3 \quad \text{LSD} \\
 & & \\
8)\overline{12} & & 4 \\
 & & \\
8)\overline{1} & & 1 \quad \text{MSD}
\end{array}
$$

$$99_{10} = 143_8$$

Convert $62_{10}$ to a hexadecimal number:

$$
\begin{array}{ccc}
 & & \text{Remainder} \\
16)\overline{62} & \phantom{xx} & 14 = \text{E} \\
 & & \\
16)\overline{3} & & 3
\end{array}
$$

$$62_{10} = 3\text{E}_{16}$$

**Fractional conversion.** Fractional conversion with the digit-by-digit method starts with the new base expressed as a decimal number. The number to be converted is multiplied by the new base and the integer generated is removed and saved. The process is repeated with the residual product until the desired number of significant digits has been generated. The first generated digit is the most significant.

Convert $0.969_{10}$ to an octal number two places past the radix point.

$$0.969$$
$$\times 8$$

Integer generated

MSD 7 ⟵ $\boxed{7}.\boxed{752}$

$$0.752$$
$$\times 8$$

6 ⟵ $\boxed{6}.\boxed{016}$

$$0.016$$
$$\times 8$$

LSD 0 ⟵ $\boxed{0}.128$

Rounding to two places:

$$0.969_{10} = 0.76_8$$

To convert $0.29_{10}$ to a hexadecimal number, we proceed in the same manner, except that the multiplier is 16.

$$0.29$$
$$\times 16$$

4 ⟵ $\boxed{4}.\boxed{64}$

$$0.64$$
$$\times 16$$

10 = A ⟵ $\boxed{10}.\boxed{24}$

$$0.24$$
$$\times 16$$

3 ⟵ $\boxed{3}.84$

Rounding to two places:

$$0.29_{10} = 0.4A_{16}$$

**Conversion by Digit-by-Digit Summary**

The digit-by-digit algorithm used to convert from decimal to any other base is summarized below.

1. Separate integers and fractions.
2. Integer conversion.
   a. Express the new base as a decimal number.
   b. Divide the number to be converted by the new base.
   c. Collect the remainder.
   d. Divide the remaining quotient by the new base. Repeat steps c and d until the quotient is zero. Collect the remainders in reverse generated order to find the number.
3. Fractional conversion.
   a. Express the new base as a decimal number.
   b. Multiply the number to be converted by the new base.
   c. Collect the integer portion of the product and multiply the residue by the base. Repeat this step until the desired number of significant digits is obtained.

**ARITHMETIC IN DIFFERENT BASES**

Most often the quickest way to verify the result of an arithmetic operation performed by an electronic device, a computer for example, is to convert the numbers to decimal equivalents and then use everyday arithmetic. When this is awkward, it becomes necessary to perform arithmetic in other bases.

**Addition**

Rules for addition and multiplication in bases 2, 8, and 16 are shown in Figs. 5-1 through 5-3. These rules are like those tables we memorized when we were learning how to add and multiply in the decimal system. Remember that carrying is performed in these bases as well as in decimal, but the value carried into the next column is equal to the base. Examples of these addition rules are provided below.

$$
\begin{array}{ccc}
 & \text{carries} & 1\ 1 \\
01_2 & & 0\ 1 \\
+11_2 & & +\ 1\ 1 \\
\hline
100_2 & & 1\ 0\ 0 \\
\end{array}
$$

$$
\begin{array}{ccc}
 & \text{carries} & 1\ 1 \\
37_8 & & 3\ 7 \\
+46_8 & & +\ 4\ 6 \\
\hline
105_8 & & 1\ 0\ 5 \\
\end{array}
$$

$$
\begin{array}{ccc}
 & \text{carries} & 1 \\
2A_{16} & & 2\ A \\
+F_{16} & & +\ \ \ F \\
\hline
39_{16} & & 3\ 9 \\
\end{array}
$$

Figure 5-1. Binary arithmetic rules.

**Addition**

|   | 0 | 1 |
|---|---|----|
| 0 | 0 | 1  |
| 1 | 1 | 10 |

**Multiplication**

|   | 0 | 1 |
|---|---|---|
| 0 | 0 | 0 |
| 1 | 0 | 1 |

Figure 5-2. Octal arithmetic rules.

**Addition**

|   | 0 | 1 | 2 | 3 | 4 | 5 | 6 | 7 |
|---|---|---|---|---|---|---|---|---|
| 0 | 0 | 1 | 2 | 3 | 4 | 5 | 6 | 7 |
| 1 | 1 | 2 | 3 | 4 | 5 | 6 | 7 | 10 |
| 2 | 2 | 3 | 4 | 5 | 6 | 7 | 10 | 11 |
| 3 | 3 | 4 | 5 | 6 | 7 | 10 | 11 | 12 |
| 4 | 4 | 5 | 6 | 7 | 10 | 11 | 12 | 13 |
| 5 | 5 | 6 | 7 | 10 | 11 | 12 | 13 | 14 |
| 6 | 6 | 7 | 10 | 11 | 12 | 13 | 14 | 15 |
| 7 | 7 | 10 | 11 | 12 | 13 | 14 | 15 | 16 |

## Multiplication

|   | 0 | 1 | 2 | 3 | 4 | 5 | 6 | 7 |
|---|---|---|---|---|---|---|---|---|
| 0 | 0 | 0 | 0 | 0 | 0 | 0 | 0 | 0 |
| 1 | 0 | 1 | 2 | 3 | 4 | 5 | 6 | 7 |
| 2 | 0 | 2 | 4 | 6 | 10 | 12 | 14 | 16 |
| 3 | 0 | 3 | 6 | 11 | 14 | 17 | 22 | 25 |
| 4 | 0 | 4 | 10 | 14 | 20 | 24 | 30 | 34 |
| 5 | 0 | 5 | 12 | 17 | 24 | 31 | 36 | 43 |
| 6 | 0 | 6 | 14 | 22 | 30 | 36 | 44 | 52 |
| 7 | 0 | 7 | 16 | 25 | 34 | 43 | 52 | 61 |

Figure 5-2. (*Continued*)

Figure 5-3. Hexadecimal arithmetic rules.

## Addition

|   | 0 | 1 | 2 | 3 | 4 | 5 | 6 | 7 | 8 | 9 | A | B | C | D | E | F |
|---|---|---|---|---|---|---|---|---|---|---|---|---|---|---|---|---|
| 0 | 0 | 1 | 2 | 3 | 4 | 5 | 6 | 7 | 8 | 9 | A | B | C | D | E | F |
| 1 | 1 | 2 | 3 | 4 | 5 | 6 | 7 | 8 | 9 | A | B | C | D | E | F | 10 |
| 2 | 2 | 3 | 4 | 5 | 6 | 7 | 8 | 9 | A | B | C | D | E | F | 10 | 11 |
| 3 | 3 | 4 | 5 | 6 | 7 | 8 | 9 | A | B | C | D | E | F | 10 | 11 | 12 |
| 4 | 4 | 5 | 6 | 7 | 8 | 9 | A | B | C | D | E | F | 10 | 11 | 12 | 13 |
| 5 | 5 | 6 | 7 | 8 | 9 | A | B | C | D | E | F | 10 | 11 | 12 | 13 | 14 |
| 6 | 6 | 7 | 8 | 9 | A | B | C | D | E | F | 10 | 11 | 12 | 13 | 14 | 15 |
| 7 | 7 | 8 | 9 | A | B | C | D | E | F | 10 | 11 | 12 | 13 | 14 | 15 | 16 |
| 8 | 8 | 9 | A | B | C | D | E | F | 10 | 11 | 12 | 13 | 14 | 15 | 16 | 17 |
| 9 | 9 | A | B | C | D | E | F | 10 | 11 | 12 | 13 | 14 | 15 | 16 | 17 | 18 |
| A | A | B | C | D | E | F | 10 | 11 | 12 | 13 | 14 | 15 | 16 | 17 | 18 | 19 |
| B | B | C | D | E | F | 10 | 11 | 12 | 13 | 14 | 15 | 16 | 17 | 18 | 19 | 1A |
| C | C | D | E | F | 10 | 11 | 12 | 13 | 14 | 15 | 16 | 17 | 18 | 19 | 1A | 1B |
| D | D | E | F | 10 | 11 | 12 | 13 | 14 | 15 | 16 | 17 | 18 | 19 | 1A | 1B | 1C |
| E | E | F | 10 | 11 | 12 | 13 | 14 | 15 | 16 | 17 | 18 | 19 | 1A | 1B | 1C | 1D |
| F | F | 10 | 11 | 12 | 13 | 14 | 15 | 16 | 17 | 18 | 19 | 1A | 1B | 1C | 1D | 1E |

## Multiplication

|   | 0 | 1 | 2 | 3 | 4 | 5 | 6 | 7 | 8 | 9 | A | B | C | D | E | F |
|---|---|---|---|---|---|---|---|---|---|---|---|---|---|---|---|---|
| 0 | 0 | 0 | 0 | 0 | 0 | 0 | 0 | 0 | 0 | 0 | 0 | 0 | 0 | 0 | 0 | 0 |
| 1 | 0 | 1 | 2 | 3 | 4 | 5 | 6 | 7 | 8 | 9 | A | B | C | D | E | F |
| 2 | 0 | 2 | 4 | 6 | 8 | A | C | E | 10 | 12 | 14 | 16 | 18 | 1A | 1C | 1E |
| 3 | 0 | 3 | 6 | 9 | C | F | 12 | 15 | 18 | 1B | 1E | 21 | 24 | 27 | 2A | 2D |
| 4 | 0 | 4 | 8 | C | 10 | 14 | 18 | 1C | 20 | 24 | 28 | 2C | 30 | 34 | 38 | 3C |
| 5 | 0 | 5 | A | F | 14 | 19 | 1E | 23 | 28 | 2D | 32 | 37 | 3C | 41 | 46 | 4B |
| 6 | 0 | 6 | C | 12 | 18 | 1E | 24 | 2A | 30 | 36 | 3C | 42 | 48 | 4E | 54 | 5A |
| 7 | 0 | 7 | E | 15 | 1C | 23 | 2A | 31 | 38 | 3F | 46 | 4D | 54 | 5B | 62 | 69 |
| 8 | 0 | 8 | 10 | 18 | 20 | 28 | 30 | 38 | 40 | 48 | 50 | 58 | 60 | 68 | 70 | 78 |
| 9 | 0 | 9 | 12 | 1B | 24 | 2D | 36 | 3F | 48 | 51 | 5A | 63 | 6C | 75 | 7E | 87 |
| A | 0 | A | 14 | 1E | 28 | 32 | 3C | 46 | 50 | 5A | 64 | 6E | 78 | 82 | 8C | 96 |
| B | 0 | B | 16 | 21 | 2C | 37 | 42 | 4D | 58 | 63 | 6E | 79 | 84 | 8F | 9A | A5 |
| C | 0 | C | 18 | 24 | 30 | 3C | 48 | 54 | 60 | 6C | 78 | 84 | 90 | 9C | A8 | B4 |
| D | 0 | D | 1A | 27 | 34 | 41 | 4E | 5B | 68 | 75 | 82 | 8F | 9C | A9 | B6 | C3 |
| E | 0 | E | 1C | 2A | 38 | 46 | 54 | 62 | 70 | 7E | 8C | 9A | A8 | B6 | C4 | D2 |
| F | 0 | F | 1E | 2D | 3C | 4B | 5A | 69 | 78 | 87 | 96 | A5 | B4 | C3 | D2 | E1 |

Starting with the far right column in the binary addition, we have $1 + 1 + 10_2$ (from Fig. 5-1). So we put down 0 in the first column and carry a 1. In the next column we have $1 + 0 + 1 = 10_2$, so again we put down 0 and carry. Finally, the last column has only a 1 in it, so we put down 1.

The octal and hexadecimal additions also rely on the tables. In the rightmost column of the hexadecimal example we have $A + F = 19$, so we write the 9 in that column and carry 1. We next have $1 + 2 = 3$. That sum is put down in the second column.

## Subtraction

As in addition, we start with the two number vertically aligned on the radix point. After the numbers are properly aligned, the operation of addition or subtraction ignores the radix point. Direct subtraction is performed column by column in any base. First the minuend is found in the body of the addition table in the same row as the subtrahend. The difference will be found directly above the minuend, in the same, column.

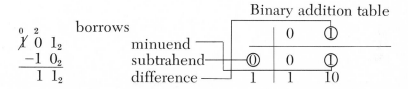

We must borrow from the next column to the left, if the digit in the minuend is smaller than the subtrahend. Remember in binary we are borrowing 2 from the next column. In octal a borrow is 8 and in hexadecimal, of course, 16.

If the subtrahend is a larger number than the minuend, we simply invert the order of the subtraction. Then we put a minus sign on the difference to indicate a negative number.

$$
\begin{array}{r}
14_8 \\
-21_8 \\
\hline
-5_8
\end{array}
\qquad
\begin{array}{cc}
\overset{1}{} & \overset{8}{} \\
\cancel{2} & 1 \\
-1 & 4 \\
\hline
& -5_8
\end{array}
\quad \text{borrows}
$$

Put minus sign on difference to indicate a negative quantity.

In hexadecimal subtraction, the same procedure holds:

$$
\begin{array}{r}
\overset{0\ \ 16}{\cancel{1}}.\, C_{16} \\
-0.\, F_{16} \\
\hline
0.D_{16}
\end{array}
\quad \text{borrows}
$$

## Multiplication

The multiplication tables in Fig. 5-1 through 5-3 provide the requirements for this operation. Multiplication in other bases uses the procedures of decimal. That is, each digit of the multiplier is multiplied by the multiplicand, then the partial products are added. The position of the radix point in the product is found by adding the numbers of places in the multiplier and the multiplicand. An example of binary multiplication is

$$
\begin{array}{r}
110\ 101_2 \quad \text{multiplicand} \\
\times 1\ 101_2 \quad \text{multiplier} \\
\hline
110\ 101 \\
0\ 000\ 00 \quad \text{partial products} \\
11\ 010\ 1 \quad \text{(move over one place for each row)} \\
110\ 101 \\
\hline
1\ 010\ 110\ 001_2 \quad \text{product}
\end{array}
$$

In octal:

$$
\begin{array}{r}
6.5_8 \\
\times 1.5_8 \\
\hline
411 \\
65 \\
\hline
12.61_8
\end{array}
\quad \text{2 radix places}
$$

Similarly, in hexadecimal:

$$
\begin{array}{r}
1C_{16} \\
\times 7_{16} \\
\hline
C4_{16}
\end{array}
$$

**Division**

Division in other bases can be quite difficult without the use of a multiplication table constructed for the problem. An octal example using such a table and illustrating the general rules of division is given below. The easiest way of developing the multiplication table is by over-and-over addition. Instead of multiplying $12_8$ by 8, simply add $12_8$ to the product above for each row of the table. As a check, the last addition should be the original number ($12_8$) with a zero on the right ($120_8$).

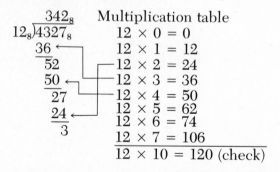

$$
\begin{array}{r}
342_8 \\
12_8 \overline{)4327_8} \\
36 \\
\hline
52 \\
50 \\
\hline
27 \\
24 \\
\hline
3
\end{array}
\qquad
\begin{array}{l}
\text{Multiplication table} \\
12 \times 0 = 0 \\
12 \times 1 = 12 \\
12 \times 2 = 24 \\
12 \times 3 = 36 \\
12 \times 4 = 50 \\
12 \times 5 = 62 \\
12 \times 6 = 74 \\
12 \times 7 = 106 \\
\hline
12 \times 10 = 120 \ \text{(check)}
\end{array}
$$

Binary division is so simple that a multiplication table is unnecessary. Note the handling of the radix points in the divisor and dividend.

$$
\begin{array}{r}
1101.0_2 \\
10.01_2 \overline{)11101.010_2} \\
1001 \\
\hline
1011 \\
1001 \\
\hline
100 \\
000 \\
\hline
1001 \\
1001 \\
\hline
0000
\end{array}
$$

But hexadecimal division does require a multiplication table.

$$\begin{array}{r} 24_{16} \\ D_{16}\overline{)1DF_{16}} \\ 1A \\ \hline 3F \\ 34 \\ \hline B \end{array}$$

Multiplication table

| | |
|---|---|
| $D \times 0 = 0$ | $D \times 8 = 68$ |
| $D \times 1 = D$ | $D \times 9 = 75$ |
| $D \times 2 = 1A$ | $D \times A = 82$ |
| $D \times 3 = 27$ | $D \times B = 8F$ |
| $D \times 4 = 34$ | $D \times C = 9C$ |
| $D \times 5 = 41$ | $D \times D = A9$ |
| $D \times 6 = 4E$ | $D \times E = B6$ |
| $D \times 7 = 5B$ | $D \times F = C3$ |
| | $D \times 10 = DO$   (check) |

**The 4-Bit Magnitude Comparator**

In our discussion of magnitude comparators in Chap. 2, we noted that only single-bit quantities could be used with those circuits. A 4-bit magnitude comparator can accept hexadecimal, decimal, or octal numbers as inputs and determine which of any two is the larger.

The 7485 IC shown in Fig. 5-4 provides the 4-bit comparison

**Figure 5-4. 7485 4-bit magnitude comparator.**

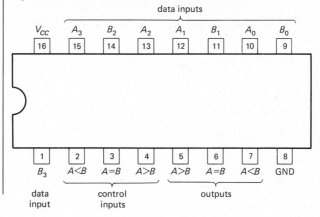

**Figure 5-4.** (*Continued*)

| Data Inputs | | | | Control Inputs | | | Outputs | | |
|---|---|---|---|---|---|---|---|---|---|
| $A_3,B_3$ | $A_2,B_2$ | $A_1,B_1$ | $A_0,B_0$ | $A > B$ | $A < B$ | $A = B$ | $A > B$ | $A < B$ | $A = B$ |
| $A_3 > B_3$ | X | X | X | X | X | X | H | L | L |
| $A_3 < B_3$ | X | X | X | X | X | X | L | H | L |
| $A_3 = B_3$ | $A_2 > B_2$ | X | X | X | X | X | H | L | L |
| $A_3 = B_3$ | $A_2 < B_2$ | X | X | X | X | X | L | H | L |
| $A_3 = B_3$ | $A_2 = B_2$ | $A_1 > B_1$ | X | X | X | X | H | L | L |
| $A_3 = B_3$ | $A_2 = B_2$ | $A_1 < B_1$ | X | X | X | X | L | H | L |
| $A_3 = B_3$ | $A_2 = B_2$ | $A_1 = B_1$ | $A_0 > B_0$ | X | X | X | H | L | L |
| $A_3 = B_3$ | $A_2 = B_2$ | $A_1 = B_1$ | $A_0 < B_0$ | X | X | X | L | H | L |
| $A_3 = B_3$ | $A_2 = B_2$ | $A_1 = B_1$ | $A_0 = B_0$ | H | L | L | H | L | L |
| $A_3 = B_3$ | $A_2 = B_2$ | $A_1 = B_1$ | $A_0 = B_0$ | L | H | L | L | H | L |
| $A_3 = B_3$ | $A_2 = B_2$ | $A_1 = B_1$ | $A_0 = B_0$ | L | L | H | L | L | H |

X = don't care

capability. In addition, the IC can be cascaded with others identical with itself for comparing larger numbers. Then the circuit can be tailored to the lengths of the numbers being used in a particular application.

The 7485 has three control inputs which are used to choose the comparison functions to be performed. The function table in the figure shows how the control inputs influence the outputs. For example, regardless of the control input settings, if $A_3$ is larger than $B_3$, the $A > B$ output becomes high. (The 4 bits of each data input are numbered. $A_0$ is the least significant bit of input $A$, and $A_3$ is the most significant. Input $B$ has its bits denoted the same way.) The flexibility of the 7495 and equivalent ICs makes them suitable for a wide variety of uses.

## Arithmetic Review

1. Describe the steps necessary for addition in any positional number system.
2. How is an addition table used to perform subtraction in different bases?
3. List the rules for multiplication in the octal number system.
4. Describe the purpose of the multiplication table constructed for division of hexadecimal numbers.
5. What simple check can be made to ensure that the multiplication table is correct before carrying out the division.

## COMPLEMENT SYSTEMS

When we are using digital circuits to perform arithmetic, it is necessary to represent both positive and negative quantities. Because the circuits do not provide an easy method of indicating the plus and minus signs that we use when we write numbers, another way must be used instead. Commonly the most significant bit in a group of bits is used to indicate the sign of a binary number.

A fixed number of bits which represent a unit of data, that is, a number, and which occupy a single storage location is called a word. The number of bits in the word establishes the word length. The sign bit is then the upper bit in a word.

Table 5-2 shows the range of hexadecimal numbers that can be contained in an 8-bit word. A zero in the most significant bit position indicates a positive number and a sign bit of one is a negative quantity. In the table, the positive numbers go from $00_{16}$ ($0000\ 0000_2$) to $7F_{16}$ ($0111\ 1111_2$). Negative numbers run from $80_{16}$ ($1000\ 0000_2$) through $FF_{16}$ ($1111\ 1111_2$). We can distinguish a positive number from a negative one by examining its sign bit.

**Table 5-2**
**A Hexadecimal 8-Bit Complement System**

| Negative Numbers | Positive Numbers |
|---|---|
| 80 81 . . . FD FE FF | 00 01 02 . . . 79 7A 7B 7C 7D 7E 7F |

**One's Complement**

Although they are not immediately apparent, there are two ways of assigning negative numbers to the quantities listed in the table. With either method, we are using a complement number for negative values. One way that the negative numbers can be assigned is to convert each positive number to its negative equivalent by using binary and subtracting each digit from one. Expressing the 8-bit number $-3A_{16}$ in this way,

$$3A_{16} = 0011\ 1010_2$$

Subtract each digit from 1:

$$
\begin{array}{cccc\;cccc}
1 & 1 & 1 & 1 & 1 & 1 & 1 & 1 \\
-0 & -0 & -1 & -1 & -1 & -0 & -1 & -0 \\
\hline
1 & 1 & 0 & 0 & 0 & 1 & 0 & 1
\end{array} = 1100\ 0101_2
$$

$$1100\ 0101_2 = C5_{16} \qquad C5_{16} = -3A_{16}$$

Note that it is necessary to specify the word length prior to converting the number to its negative equivalent.

This conversion process is called the *one's complement* or the *radix minus one complement*. Its properties are shown in Table 5-3. The table shows that all positive numbers are not changed in value, but negative numbers must be converted by subtracting each digit from 1 in binary form. (The conversion can also be carried out in hexadecimal by subtracting each digit from $F_{16}$.)

The one's complement system has the unusual property of using both a positive and negative representation for zero. Both $00_{16}$ and $FF_{16}$ are the same quantity. Proof of their equivalence is straightforward. The conversion will be performed in hexadecimal this time. Converting $FF_{16}$ to its positive equivalent, we subtract each digit from $F_{16}$.

$$
\begin{array}{cc}
F & F \\
-F & -F \\
\hline
0 & 0
\end{array}
$$

So the complement is

$$FF_{16} = -00_{16}$$

Of course $-0$ is the same as $+0$.

The negative zero in the one's complement system makes counting clumsy. However, there are equal quantities of positive and negative numbers in the one's complement system. That is, we can make a one-for-one match of positives and negatives.

**Table 5-3**
**Hexadecimal 8-Bit One's Complements**

|  | Negative Numbers | | | | | | Positive Numbers | | | | | |
|---|---|---|---|---|---|---|---|---|---|---|---|---|
| Number | −7F | −7E | ... | −02 | −01 | −00 | +00 | +01 | +02 | ... | +7D | +7E +7F |
| Representation | 80 | 81 | ... | FD | FE | FF | 00 | 01 | 02 | ... | 7D | 7E 7F |

$$
\begin{array}{cc}
\textit{Positive} & \textit{Negative} \\
7F \longleftrightarrow 80 \\
7E \longleftrightarrow 81 \\
7D \longleftrightarrow 82 \\
\cdot \\
\cdot \\
\cdot \\
02 \longleftrightarrow FD \\
01 \longleftrightarrow FE \\
00 \longleftrightarrow FF
\end{array}
$$

## Two's Complement

Another complement system that can be used starts with the one's complement and then adds the number one to it. Again using 8-bit words, the two's complement of $-3A_{16}$ is found by first determining the one's complement, which we found earlier to be $C5_{16}$. Now add one.

$$
\begin{array}{r}
C5 \\
+1 \\
\hline
C6
\end{array}
$$

So $C6_{16} = -3A_{16}$ in the two's complement system.

Let's see how this number system works. Table 5-4 shows that there are two major differences between the one's and two's complements. First there is only a single representation for zero in the two's complement. Thus, the counting properties of the two's complement are better. Second, the two's complement system has more negative numbers than positive numbers. The value of $-80_{16}$ is included in the table, but there is no corresponding positive value for this number.

## Subtraction Using Complements

A major use of complements in arithmetic circuits is to perform subtraction by means of addition. This means that the same circuitry can be used in a calculator or a computer for both operations.

**Subtraction by One's Complement.** If we want to subtract by one's complement, the minuend of the problem is not changed, but the subtrahend is converted to its one's complement. We then add the two numbers. If any carry is generated from the last column, it is "ended around" and added to find the correct difference.

**Table 5-4**
**Hexadecimal 8-Bit Two's Complements**

|  | Negative Numbers | | | | | | Positive Numbers | | | | | |
|---|---|---|---|---|---|---|---|---|---|---|---|---|
| Number | $-80$ | $-7F$ | $-7E$ ... | $-03$ | $-02$ | $-01$ | $+00$ | $+01$ | $+02$ ... | $+7D$ | $+7E$ | $+7F$ |
| Representation | 80 | 81 | 82 ... | FD | FE | FF | 00 | 01 | 02 ... | 7D | 7E | 7F |

Using an 8-bit word, subtract $03_{16}$ from $42_{16}$.

| Direct subtraction | One's complement |
|---|---|

$$\begin{array}{r} 42_{16} \\ -03_{16} \end{array} \xrightarrow{\text{one's complement}} \begin{array}{r} 42_{16} \\ +FC_{16} \end{array}$$

$$3F_{16} \qquad\qquad \text{end around} \quad \textcircled{1}3E$$
$$\xrightarrow{\hookrightarrow +1}$$
$$\text{same result} \xrightarrow{\qquad\qquad} 3F_{16}$$

**Subtraction by Two's Complement.** The same process can be carried out in the two's complement system. The subtrahend is converted to its two's complement and the numbers are added. In this case, any carry generated from the last column is just discarded.

| Direct subtraction | Two's complement |
|---|---|

$$\begin{array}{r} 42_{16} \\ -03_{16} \end{array} \xrightarrow{\text{two's complement}} \begin{array}{r} 42_{16} \\ +FD_{16} \end{array}$$

$$3F_{16} \qquad\qquad \text{discard} \longrightarrow \textcircled{1}3F_{16}$$
$$\xrightarrow{\text{same result}}$$

## Complement Review

1. Distinguish between the one's and two's complement systems.
2. List all possible octal digits of a 3-bit word. Split the list into positive and negative numbers and assign values to the numbers using first the one's complement system and then the two's complement system.
3. Describe how the one's complement of a 4-bit number can be found.
4. Describe how subtraction can be performed using addition in each complement system.

## CODES

Numbers are not the only type of information stored in an electronic circuit. Other types of information such as text characters, shaft angles, and control signals are required as well. Because digital equipment is limited to ones and zeros, many codes have been developed to translate other forms of data into binary numbers.

## Binary-Coded Decimal (BCD)

A code in very common use is binary-coded decimal. Everyone who has used a pocket calculator has used this code. As the key for each decimal digit is pressed, the data are converted into the coded form shown in Table 5-5.

As you can see, BCD is the 4-bit equivalent for each decimal digit. The 74147 encoder circuit shown in Fig. 5-5 is an example of an IC that converts each decimal digit to its BCD code. The ready availability of such circuits makes this code popular with designers.

If all inputs to the 74147 are high, the outputs will also be high. This output is a zero in negative logic. If one input, number 8 for

**Table 5-5**
**Binary-Coded Decimal Code**

| Decimal Digit | BCD Code |
|:---:|:---:|
| 0 | 0000 |
| 1 | 0001 |
| 2 | 0010 |
| 3 | 0011 |
| 4 | 0100 |
| 5 | 0101 |
| 6 | 0110 |
| 7 | 0111 |
| 8 | 1000 |
| 9 | 1001 |

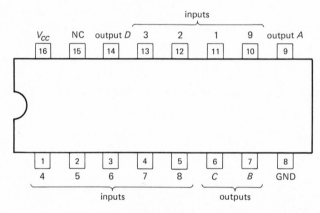

| | | | Inputs | | | | | | Outputs | | | |
|:---:|:---:|:---:|:---:|:---:|:---:|:---:|:---:|:---:|:---:|:---:|:---:|:---:|
| **1** | **2** | **3** | **4** | **5** | **6** | **7** | **8** | **9** | **D** | **C** | **B** | **A** |
| H | H | H | H | H | H | H | H | H | H | H | H | H |
| X | X | X | X | X | X | X | X | L | L | H | H | L |
| X | X | X | X | X | X | X | L | H | L | H | H | H |
| X | X | X | X | X | X | L | H | H | H | L | L | L |
| X | X | X | X | X | L | H | H | H | H | L | L | H |
| X | X | X | X | L | H | H | H | H | H | L | H | L |
| X | X | X | L | H | H | H | H | H | H | L | H | H |
| X | X | L | H | H | H | H | H | H | H | H | L | L |
| X | L | H | H | H | H | H | H | H | H | H | L | H |
| L | H | H | H | H | H | H | H | H | H | H | H | L |

X = don't care

**Figure 5-5. 74147 decimal-to-BCD encoder.**

example, goes low, then the output will provide the BCD code for that digit. For this case, the output pattern will be LHHH which can be read in binary as $1000_2$ (which is $8_{10}$).

**The Gray Code** Transmission of shaft angle data in rotating machinery often uses the Gray code listed in Table 5-6. The Gray code is well suited for rotational data because only a single bit changes state between two successive digits. With a change from 7 to 8 the code goes from 0100 to 1100. Only the most significant bit is altered.

This feature results in, at most, a one-unit error should the pickup recording the shaft position read the data as a 7 instead of an 8. Usually, a single-unit error of this type can be tolerated. There are ICs which convert between Gray code and hexadecimal, much like the one described above for BCD.

## The American Standard Code for Information Interchange (ASCII)

The ASCII code is widely used in digital communications systems and computers. The code, shown in Table 5-7, is a 7-bit code. Bit 1 is the least significant bit and bit 7 is most significant.

The code can be divided into subsets if the application does not require all 128 characters. There are 64 of the characters used for upper-case letters, numbers, common punctuation marks, and the blank space (SP). Another 32 characters specify lower-case letters and less commonly used punctuation marks; these are rarely used. The final 32 characters specify machine commands such as line-feed (LF), carriage return (CR), and ring the bell (BEL). They do not appear in a message or in print, but control the communications equipment from both ends of the channel.

In practice an eighth bit may be added for error detection or may be left zero. The 8 bits of the complete code may be sent either serially, 1 bit at a time, or in parallel, all 8 bits at once.

**Table 5-6**
**Gray Code**

| Hexadecimal | Gray Code |
|---|---|
| 0 | 0000 |
| 1 | 0001 |
| 2 | 0011 |
| 3 | 0010 |
| 4 | 0110 |
| 5 | 0111 |
| 6 | 0101 |
| 7 | 0100 |
| 8 | 1100 |
| 9 | 1101 |
| A | 1111 |
| B | 1110 |
| C | 1010 |
| D | 1011 |
| E | 1001 |
| F | 1000 |

**Table 5-7**
**American Standard Code for Information Interchange**

| Bit Numbers 7654321 | 000 | 001 | 010 | 011 | 100 | 101 | 110 | 111 |
|---|---|---|---|---|---|---|---|---|
| 0000 | NUL | DLE | SP | 0 | @ | P | ` | p |
| 0001 | SHO | DC1 | ! | 1 | A | Q | a | q |
| 0010 | STX | DC2 | " | 2 | B | R | b | r |
| 0011 | ETX | DC3 | # | 3 | C | S | c | s |
| 0100 | EOT | DC4 | $ | 4 | D | T | d | t |
| 0101 | ENQ | NAK | % | 5 | E | U | e | u |
| 0110 | ACK | SYN | & | 6 | F | V | f | v |
| 0111 | BEL | ETB | ' | 7 | G | W | g | w |
| 1000 | BS | CAN | ( | 8 | H | X | h | x |
| 1001 | HT | EM | ) | 9 | I | Y | i | y |
| 1010 | LF | SUB | * | : | J | Z | j | z |
| 1011 | VT | ESC | + | ; | K | [ | k | { |
| 1100 | FF | FS | , | < | L | \ | l | \| |
| 1101 | CR | GS | - | = | M | ] | m | } |
| 1110 | SO | RS | . | > | N | ∧ | n | ~ |
| 1111 | SI | US | / | ? | O | — | o | DEL |

**Code Review**
1. List the reasons codes are required in digital systems.
2. Distinguish between the uses of the BCD and Gray codes.
3. If the inputs to pins 5 and 10 of the 74147 IC are low and all other inputs high, what is the output?
4. List the ASCII codes for the following characters: T, ?, $, and 7.

**CHAPTER SUMMARY**
1. Every positional number system uses a set of symbols called digits. The number of digits is equal to the base of that system. The largest digit is equal to the base minus one.
2. The base of a number system can also be called the radix. A radix point is used to separate the integer from the fraction.
3. The columns in a number are weighted. Starting with the position immediately left of the radix point, the weight is the base raised to the zero power. Moving to the left, each column is weighted by the base raised to successively higher powers. To the right of the radix point, the columns are weighted by the base raised to successive negative powers.
4. A subscript on a number indicates its base.
5. Conversion from one base to another is derived from polynomial expansion. Converting between binary and bases that are powers of 2 is accomplished by grouping. Any base can readily be converted to decimal by the explosion method; going from decimal to other bases uses the digit-by-digit procedure.
6. Arithmetic operations can be performed in any base by using appropriate addition and multiplication tables.
7. When complement number systems are used, subtraction can be accomplished by addition.
8. Codes allow us to translate various kinds of information into a binary format for storage and processing in digital circuits. Many versions of integrated circuits are available to provide the encoding and decoding.

**KEY TERMS AND CONCEPTS**

| | |
|---|---|
| number systems | algorithms |
| octal number system | conversion by explosion |
| hexadecimal number system | conversion by digit-by-digit |
| base | complement |
| digit | one's complement |
| radix | two's complement |
| radix point | binary coded decimal (BCD) |
| polynomial expansion | Gray code |
| conversion by grouping | ASCII code |

## PROBLEMS

5-1. Show the polynomial expansion for the following numbers.

a. $3401_8$
b. $110\ 101_2$
c. $A63_{16}$

5-2. Convert the following numbers to decimal. Compute all fractions to two places past the radix point.

a. $23_8$　　c. $1\ 110\ 101_2$
b. $B7_{16}$　　d. $725.12_8$

5-3. Convert the following numbers from decimal to octal. Compute all fractional values to two places past the radix point.

a. $8000_{10}$
b. $249_{10}$
c. $0.14_{10}$
d. $14.691_{10}$

5-4. Convert the following numbers from decimal to hexadecimal. Compute all fractional values to two places past the radix point.

a. $18_{10}$
b. $21896_{10}$
c. $391.69_{10}$
d. $4.76_{10}$

5-5. Perform the indicated arithmetic operations using the binary number system.

a.
$$\begin{array}{r} 100\ 101\ 111_2 \\ +\ 1\ 001\ 111_2 \end{array}$$

c.
$$\begin{array}{r} 100\ 111_2 \\ \times\ 1\ 011_2 \end{array}$$

b.
$$\begin{array}{r} 001\ 111_2 \\ -\ 100\ 011_2 \end{array}$$

d. $111\ 101\ 110_2 / 1\ 001_2$

5-6. Perform the indicated arithmetic operations using the octal number system.

a.
$$\begin{array}{r} 26_8 \\ +\ 17_8 \end{array}$$

c. $345.2_8 \times 1.7_8$

b.
$$\begin{array}{r} 321_8 \\ -\ 175_8 \end{array}$$

d. $12633_8 / 25_8$

5-7. Perform the indicated arithmetic operation using the hexadecimal number system.

a.
$$\begin{array}{r} A62_{16} \\ +\ 1BC_{16} \end{array}$$

c. $2.16_{16} \times 4.5_{16}$

b.
$$\begin{array}{r} F21_{16} \\ -\ E71_{16} \end{array}$$

d. $302.E_{16} / 4.73_{16}$

5-8. Convert the binary numbers below to their octal and hexadecimal equivalents by grouping.

a. $110\ 011\ 101_2$
b. $1\ 100\ 001\ 100_2$
c. $11\ 101\ 111.\ 100_2$
d. $10\ 110.\ 11_2$

5-9. Convert the octal and hexadecimal numbers below to their binary equivalents.

a. $4013_8$
b. $AE12_{16}$
c. $105.426_8$
d. $127.C2_{16}$

5-10. The 7485 IC of Fig. 5-4 has the following inputs.

| Data Inputs | Control Inputs |
|---|---|
| $A = C_{16}$ | pin 2 high |
| $B = E_{16}$ | pin 3 high |
| | pin 4 low |

What are the voltage levels at the output terminals?

# EXPERIMENT 5 CODE CONVERTERS

**PURPOSE**  To investigate code converters.

**PARTS LIST**

| Item | Quantity |
|------|----------|
| 7442 | 1 |
| 7447 | 1 |
| DPDT switch | 4 |
| LED | 4 |
| 330-Ω resistor | 7 |
| IEE 1712 LED display | 1 |

**IC DIAGRAMS**

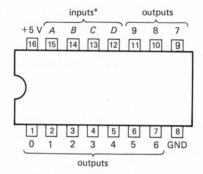

*Bit A is the least significant bit
 and bit D the most significant bit.
**Figure 5-6. 7442.**

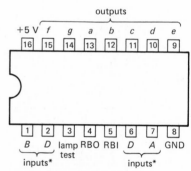

*Bit A is the least significant bit
 and bit D the most significant bit.
**Figure 5-7. 7447.**

**PROCEDURE**  **Step 1.**  Connect the 7442 to four LED indicators as shown in Fig. 5-8. By changing the input switch positions, record the state of each LED (on or off) in the table below. Explain your results.

| Switch | | | LED | | | |
|---|---|---|---|---|---|---|
| C | B | A | 1 | 2 | 3 | 4 |
| 5 V | 0 V | 0 V | | | | |
| 0 | 0 | 5 | | | | |
| 0 | 5 | 0 | | | | |
| 0 | 5 | 5 | | | | |

**Figure 5-8. BCD-to-Decimal decoder experiment.**

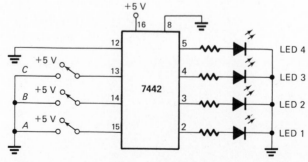

All resistors are 330 Ω.

**Step 2.** Now construct the circuit shown in Fig. 5-9 using the 7447 with the IEE 1712 display. Record the digit displayed for each of the switch settings listed below.

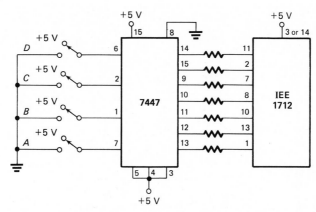

**Figure 5-9. BCD-to-seven-segment decoder/driver experiment.**

| Switch | | | | |
|---|---|---|---|---|
| **D** | **C** | **B** | **A** | **Display** |
| 0 V | 0 V | 0 V | 0 V | |
| 0 | 0 | 0 | 5 | |
| 0 | 0 | 5 | 0 | |
| 0 | 0 | 5 | 5 | |
| 0 | 5 | 0 | 0 | |
| 0 | 5 | 0 | 5 | |
| 0 | 5 | 5 | 0 | |
| 0 | 5 | 5 | 5 | |
| 5 | 0 | 0 | 0 | |
| 5 | 0 | 0 | 5 | |
| 5 | 0 | 5 | 0 | |
| 5 | 0 | 5 | 5 | |
| 5 | 5 | 0 | 0 | |
| 5 | 5 | 0 | 5 | |
| 5 | 5 | 5 | 0 | |
| 5 | 5 | 5 | 5 | |

Explain the results in the first 10 rows. Why is the operation of the display in the last 6 rows acceptable?

# CHAPTER SIX
# SEQUENTIAL
# CIRCUITS:
# FLIP-FLOPS

This chapter begins our study of circuits that operate in synchronism with pulse trains. Called *sequential* circuits, they are similar to combinatorial circuits in that they have two stable output states and the transitions of the outputs result from the inputs. Sequential circuits are unique because the outputs are functions not only of the inputs but also of time. Another way of saying this is that the circuits have a memory and can remember what the previous conditions were. We will see that feedback is another distinguishing characteristic of these circuits and that it results in a delayed output. The most important types of sequential circuits are flip-flops (described in this chapter) and registers and counters (covered in Chap. 7).

**CHAPTER OBJECTIVES**
In this chapter you will see how flip-flops are fashioned from combinatorial circuit elements. You will also see how the output signals can be determined if the inputs are known. After completing this chapter, you should be able to:

1. Analyze flip-flops and determine the output states that any set of inputs produces.
2. Distinguish between the various types of flip-flops and explain their principles of operation.
3. Understand the difference between synchronous and asynchronous circuits.
4. Describe typical flip-flop triggering methods.

## R-S FLIP-FLOP

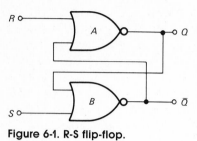

**Figure 6-1. R-S flip-flop.**

R-S flip-flops can be built from basic logic gates. Figure 6-1 shows an R-S flip-flop constructed of NOR gates. This is not the only possible implementation, and these flip-flops are frequently fabricated from AND gates. Before we analyze the circuit action, examine the schematic drawing of the flip-flop. There are two NOR gates, each of which have two inputs. Gate $A$ has an input labeled $R$ and a feedback loop from the $\overline{Q}$ output, and gate $B$ has an $S$ input and the $Q$ output feedback loop. This arrangement tells us that the present output states, used as inputs, will affect the next output state.

Since the state of $Q$ and $\overline{Q}$ change with time, a subscript is used to indicate which value of the outputs we mean. $Q_n$ is read "the present state of the output $Q$" and $Q_{n+1}$ as "the next state of the output $Q$." We use the same convention with $\overline{Q}$. The inputs do not have to be subscripted, because they must not change during the time that the outputs are developing. We will discuss this timing relationship between inputs and outputs in more detail later.

The analysis of a flip-flop, or any sequential circuit, can most easily be accomplished by using an expanded state table. This table lists every possible combination of the inputs and the present output states, so the next state of the outputs can be determined. Looking at Table 6-1, we see that all possible combinations of $R$, $S$, $Q_n$, and $\overline{Q}_n$ are listed in rows $a$ and $h$. (We have not shown that if $Q_n$ is a zero, then $\overline{Q}_n$ must be a one and vice versa. That is true, although there may be a momentary possibility of both being the same. We ignore that possibility in constructing the table.) Columns are provided to record the output parameters $Q_{n+1}$ and $\overline{Q}_{n+1}$.

Now look at row $a$. The $R$ input is set to one and $S$ is zero, while $Q_n$ is in the zero state and $\overline{Q}_n$ is one. Follow the circuit action on the figure. The inputs to NOR gate $A$ are both ones. Recalling the operation of the NOR gate, we determine that the output of this gate will be a zero. This results in $Q_{n+1}$ being equal to zero, but $Q_n$ was already zero, so there is no change. Gate $B$ has two zeros for inputs which will develop a one output, so $\overline{Q}_{n+1}$ is a one. Its previous state $\overline{Q}_n$ was already a one, so again there is no change in the output state. Notice that the $Q_{n+1}$ and $\overline{Q}_{n+1}$ columns show these values.

## Table 6-1
## R-S Flip-Flop Expanded State Table

| Rows | Inputs | | | | Outputs | |
|------|--------|--------|--------|-----------------|-----------|-----------------------|
|      | $R$    | $S$    | $Q_n$  | $\overline{Q}_n$ | $Q_{n+1}$ | $\overline{Q}_{n+1}$ |
| $a$  | 1 | 0 | 0 | 1 | 0 | 1 |
| $b$  | 1 | 0 | 1 | 0 | 0 | 1 |
| $c$  | 0 | 1 | 0 | 1 | 1 | 0 |
| $d$  | 0 | 1 | 1 | 0 | 1 | 0 |
| $e$  | 0 | 0 | 0 | 1 | 0 | 1 |
| $f$  | 0 | 0 | 1 | 0 | 1 | 0 |
| $g$  | 1 | 1 | 0 | 1 | 0 | 0 |
| $h$  | 1 | 1 | 1 | 0 | 0 | 0 |

A different situation occurs in row $b$. The $R$ and $S$ inputs are the same as they were previously, but the present states of the outputs are not. $Q_n$ is a one and $\overline{Q}_n$ is a zero. The inputs to NOR gate $A$ are one and zero, producing an output of zero. Now we have a chain reaction. The $S$ input to gate $B$ has remained a zero, but the $Q$ input has changed from a one to a zero. This forces the output of gate $B$ to change. Until the $Q$ output changed, the $\overline{Q}$ output was a zero, but because of the two zero inputs to gate $B$, $\overline{Q}$ becomes a one. As row $b$ of the table shows, the final value of $Q_{n+1}$ is a zero, and $\overline{Q}_{n+1}$ is a one. The two outputs have reversed states. $Q$ went from a one (the $Q_n$ column of the table shows this) to a zero (shown under the $Q_{n+1}$ column). And $\overline{Q}$ went from $\overline{Q}_n = 0$ to $\overline{Q}_{n+1} = 1$.

Rows $c$ and $d$ of the table are determined similarly except that, in both cases, the $Q_{n+1}$ output becomes a one and $\overline{Q}_{n+1}$ a zero. You should follow the circuit operation and convince yourself that these are the correct resultant states.

What happens if we drop both inputs to zero? This case is shown in row $e$ of the table. If $\overline{Q}_n$ is a zero, gate $A$ will retain its zero output, and $Q_n$ (being zero already) does not change the output of gate $B$. So $Q_{n+1} = Q_n$ and $\overline{Q}_{n+1} = \overline{Q}_n$. We could also say that the output is unchanged. Row $f$ covers the case where the present states of the outputs are the reverse of those in the row above. Again no change in the outputs is produced. This is a desirable feature of the R-S flip-flop. It stores the previous inputs after they are removed. This storage capability of the R-S flip-flop is the reason it is also called a latch. We cannot predict the next state of the device if zeros are applied to the $R$ and $S$ inputs, unless we know the present output states. Why is this true?

Next look at row $g$. This time both $R$ and $S$ are ones. The output of NOR gate $A$ will be forced to zero ($R = 1$ and $\overline{Q}_n = 1$). But $Q$ was already zero, so feeding it back to gate $B$ does not change the inputs to that gate. $\overline{Q}_{n+1}$ is also forced to zero. Both outputs are in the same state, and a flip-flop is supposed to be a two-state device. What went wrong? Nothing is actually wrong. This is simply a case where the electronic circuit cannot perform exactly as theory indicates it should. So we have a situation that makes no sense in Boolean algebra. Because we do not want this condition to occur in a real circuit, we must make sure that both $R$ and $S$ inputs are never allowed to become one simultaneously. This is called a forbidden, or invalid, input condition. When one of the inputs is dropped to zero—for example, if $R$ goes to zero—we change to the states of rows $c$ and $d$. This means that eventually the outputs do return to complementary states.

Once we have analyzed the circuit action by using an expanded state table, this information can be summarized in a more compact form. In rows $a$ and $b$ of the table, $R$ is one and $S$ is zero. Furthermore, $Q_{n+1}$ is zero and $\overline{Q}_{n+1}$ is a one. Then if we delete the columns for the present states of the outputs, we can write the same information in a single row. The first row of Table 6-2 shows exactly that. The name of the table indicates we are compressing the data, but the space savings has a price. We no longer know the present output states at the time the inputs are applied. So compressed state tables are useful to summarize flip-flop action, but they cannot be used to analyze it.

**Table 6-2**
**R-S Flip-Flop Compressed State Table**

| $R$ | $S$ | $Q_{n+1}$ | $\overline{Q}_{n+1}$ |
|---|---|---|---|
| 1 | 0 | 0 | 1 |
| 0 | 1 | 1 | 0 |
| 0 | 0 | $Q_n$ | $\overline{Q}_n$ |
| 1 | 1 | 0 | 0 |

The rest of the compressed state table is derived similarly. The third row requires some comment, however. Because $Q_n$ and $\overline{Q}_n$ are not included, there is no way of determining the next output states. Instead, we use $Q_n$ and $\overline{Q}_n$ in this column to indicate that the output is unchanged if we set both $R$ and $S$ equal to zero.

Another fact that becomes apparent in the compressed table is that if the $R$ input is a one, then $Q_{n+1}$ becomes zero, and $S$ being equal to one results in $Q_{n+1}$ becoming one. This is the reason the $S$ input is often called the *set* or *preset* input and $R$ the *reset* or *clear* input.

## Timing and Propagation Delay

Remembering the discussion on propagation delays for logic families, we should expect the same delay in the gates and in the feedback paths of the R-S flip-flops. This is particularly important if the next state of the output is the complement of the present state. Then the signals fed back to the cross-connected gates will change during the time the inputs are applied. (Perhaps you wish to review that case, shown in row *b* of Table 6-1.)

Obviously, the input signals must be applied long enough for all of the output-state changes to stabilize, but how long is long enough? We do not want to delay circuit operation longer than necessary because high speed is an important requirement in many kinds of digital equipment.

The tool often used to analyze propagation delay is a timing diagram. The timing diagram shows the dynamic action of the circuit better than a table can. Figure 6-2 illustrates the input and output conditions for row *b* of Table 6-1. The horizontal time scale is divided into intervals equal to the propagation delay, $t_{pd}$, for each of the NOR gates. We are assuming that all gates have the same propagation delay, which is not usually the case. Any collection of integrated circuit gates will have unequal delays, but the manufacturer specifies a maximum delay. The delays shown in our diagram could be interpreted as that maximum delay. The vertical scale shows the one and zero levels for the $R$, $S$, $Q$, and $\overline{Q}$ signals.

The initial conditions are that $Q$ is one and all of the other signals are zero. During the first propagation delay period, the $R$

**Figure 6-2. Timing diagram for the R-S flip-flop.**

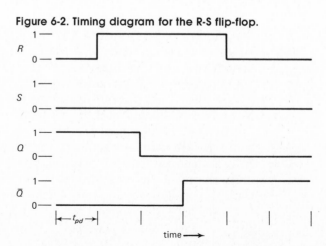

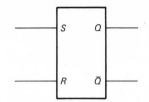

**Figure 6-3. The symbol for an R-S flip-flop.**

input goes high. The effect of this input is not sensed until the signal propagates through that gate (gate A in Fig. 6-1); this requires a time period $t_{pd}$. Then the Q output drops to zero as a result. Next the Q = 0 output is fed back to gate B. Again we must wait for the delay before the output of gate B develops; in this case $\overline{Q}$ becomes one. Next we can remove the R input and the latch stores the information.

How the R-S flip-flop performs as a function of time is now revealed. We must apply the R or S input long enough for all gate actions, including the changing feedback signals resulting from the input conditions, to be propagated through the circuit. You should plot time diagrams for the other rows of the table to be sure you understand the timing relationships. What happens if the inputs are not applied long enough for the flip-flop to latch? (See Problem 6-1.)

In schematic diagrams, flip-flops are indicated by rectangles. You can tell that the symbol is an R-S flip-flop by the labels on the input terminals, as shown in Fig. 6-3.

## Clocked R-S Flip-Flop

In the timing analysis of the R-S flip-flop, we discovered that the inputs had to be held constant long enough for a stable output to develop. There is no fixed time for maintaining the inputs; the designer must decide what duration is appropriate.

If we desire to eliminate this vague duration, we can use *synchronous circuits*. This simply means that the circuit uses a clock to determine when the inputs can change state. (If the circuit does not use a clock, then we call it an *asynchronous circuit*.) Figure 6-4 illustrates a typical clock pulse train. The positive portion of the signal $(T_1)$ is the time that the clock is on. This is often simply called the clock pulse. It has a pulse width (PW) measured in units of time. The time when the clock is off $(T_2)$ is the period when the circuit is inactive. Changing the input states during this time has no effect on the outputs. The time from any point on the pulse train until that equivalent point is reached in the next cycle is called the period (T) of the clock. There is a simple reciprocal relationship between the clock frequency (f) and the period

$$f = 1/T \tag{6-1}$$

Frequency is measured in hertz, the number of pulses per second.

A clock can be added to the R-S flip-flop as is shown in Fig. 6-5. This flip-flop is built from NAND gates, and the clock input signal is indicated by the abbreviation Ck. The flip-flop consists of two stages and a total of four gates.

Looking at the first-stage gates, we see that the clock signal is NANDed with either the S or R inputs. If the clock is one, the gate

**Figure 6-4. Clock pulses.**

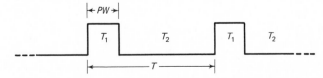

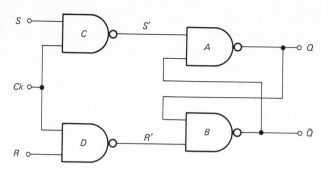

**Figure 6-5. Clocked R-S flip-flop.**

output depends only on the second input. For example, if $S$ is a one and $R$ a zero, gate $C$ will have a zero output and gate $D$ a one. If the clock changes to zero, the output of gates $C$ and $D$ both become one. As our analysis will show, this is just what we want.

Table 6-3 is an expanded state table, when the clock is one. Follow the operation for each row. The table has been adapted to reflect the change in circuit configuration. Since the $R$ and $S$ inputs are indirectly applied, intermediate values of $R'$ and $S'$ are listed. We work from left to right in following the signals through each gate. The intermediate-value column gives us a place to write the values of the inputs to gates $A$ and $B$. In addition to preventing mistakes, this technique helps us gain an insight into circuit operation.

We see that any time the $R'$ or $S'$ inputs are zero, the output of the appropriate gate becomes a one. This inverted action corrects for the NAND in the first stage. Because gates $C$ and $D$ guide the action during valid clock times, they are called steering gates. Gates $A$ and $B$ form a latch which stores the inputs. What happens when the clock pulse goes to zero? We have previously shown that the outputs of the first gates are one any time the clock is zero, and this will result in an unchanged output.

We can compress the table, just as we did before, to make the information easier to remember. (See Table 6-4.) Keep in mind that this table does not show all of the operations. The schematic diagram symbol of the clocked R-S flip-flop is shown in Fig. 6-6.

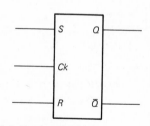

**Figure 6-6. The symbol for a clocked R-S flip-flop.**

**Table 6-4**
**Clocked R-S Flip-Flop Compressed State Table**

| $R$ | $S$ | $Q_{n+1}$ | $\overline{Q}_{n+1}$ |
|---|---|---|---|
| 0 | 1 | 1 | 0 |
| 1 | 0 | 0 | 1 |
| 0 | 0 | $Q_n$ | $\overline{Q}_n$ |
| 1 | 1 | 1 | 1 |

**Table 6-3**
**Clocked R-S Flip-Flop Expanded State Table**

| Inputs | | Intermediate inputs | | | | Outputs | |
|---|---|---|---|---|---|---|---|
| $R$ | $S$ | $R'$ | $S'$ | $Q_n$ | $\overline{Q}_n$ | $Q_{n+1}$ | $\overline{Q}_{n+1}$ |
| 0 | 1 | 1 | 0 | 0 | 1 | 1 | 0 |
| 0 | 1 | 1 | 0 | 1 | 0 | 1 | 0 |
| 1 | 0 | 0 | 1 | 0 | 1 | 0 | 1 |
| 1 | 0 | 0 | 1 | 1 | 0 | 0 | 1 |
| 0 | 0 | 1 | 1 | 0 | 1 | 0 | 1 |
| 0 | 0 | 1 | 1 | 1 | 0 | 1 | 0 |
| 1 | 1 | 0 | 0 | 0 | 1 | 1 | 1 |
| 1 | 1 | 0 | 0 | 1 | 0 | 1 | 1 |

**R-S Flip-Flop Review**

1. Name the characteristics of sequential circuits.
2. Describe the components of an R-S flip-flop.
3. Explain how the output states of an R-S flip-flop remain unchanged after the inputs are removed.
4. Distinguish between the contents of the expanded and compressed state tables. When is each used?
5. Explain what is meant by invalid or forbidden inputs.
6. Describe the purpose of a timing diagram.
7. Distinguish between synchronous and asynchronous circuits.
8. Define clock pulse width, period, and frequency.

## J-K FLIP-FLOP

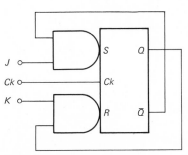

Figure 6-7. J-K flip-flop.

Using the R-S flip-flop as a building block, we can construct more sophisticated circuit elements. Figure 6-7 shows a J-K flip-flop consisting of two AND gates and an R-S flip-flop. We can see that this is a synchronous flip-flop because it has a clock input. As in the R-S flip-flop, the $Q$ and $\overline{Q}$ outputs are fed back to the input gates.

Analysis of the J-K flip-flop is straightforward. Before we start filling in the table, we must determine the input values for the R-S flip-flop in the circuit. The AND gates combine the inputs as follows

$$S = J\overline{Q}_n \qquad (6\text{-}2)$$
$$R = KQ_n$$

Knowing these equations, the intermediate inputs columns of Table 6-5 can be computed from the inputs.

Just as before, all possible states of the inputs (in this case $J$, $K$, $Q_n$, and $\overline{Q}_n$) are listed. Then we work across each row. In the first row, $S$ is found to be zero because of the ANDing of $J$ with $\overline{Q}_n$. $R$ is also zero from $KQ_n$. Referring back to Table 6-2, we see that those inputs to an R-S flip-flop produce no change at the outputs. The remainder of the table is completed in the same way.

Before we leave this table, notice what happens in the last two rows. In the seventh row, the $Q$ output is changing from a zero to a

**Table 6-5
J-K Flip-Flop Expanded State Table**

| Inputs | | | | Inter-mediate Inputs | | Outputs | |
|---|---|---|---|---|---|---|---|
| $J$ | $K$ | $Q_n$ | $\overline{Q}_n$ | $S$ | $R$ | $Q_{n+1}$ | $\overline{Q}_{n+1}$ |
| 0 | 0 | 0 | 1 | 0 | 0 | $Q_n$ | $\overline{Q}_n$ |
| 0 | 0 | 1 | 0 | 0 | 0 | $Q_n$ | $\overline{Q}_n$ |
| 1 | 0 | 0 | 1 | 1 | 0 | 1 | 0 |
| 1 | 0 | 1 | 0 | 0 | 0 | $Q_n$ | $\overline{Q}_n$ |
| 0 | 1 | 0 | 1 | 0 | 0 | $Q_n$ | $\overline{Q}_n$ |
| 0 | 1 | 1 | 0 | 0 | 1 | 0 | 1 |
| 1 | 1 | 0 | 1 | 1 | 0 | 1 | 0 |
| 1 | 1 | 1 | 0 | 0 | 1 | 0 | 1 |

**Table 6-6
J-K Flip-Flop Compressed
State Table**

| $J$ | $K$ | $Q_{n+1}$ | $\overline{Q}_{n+1}$ |
|---|---|---|---|
| 0 | 0 | $Q_n$ | $\overline{Q}_n$ |
| 1 | 0 | 1 | 0 |
| 0 | 1 | 0 | 1 |
| 1 | 1 | $\overline{Q}_n$ | $Q_n$ |

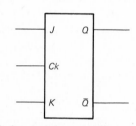

**Figure 6-8. Symbol for a J-K flip-flop.**

one. The $\overline{Q}$ output does the opposite. In the eighth row the reverse occurs. This means that, until the clock pulse is removed, the flip-flop will continuously change states between rows 7 and 8. We have no way of knowing which state will be the final one at the end of the clock pulse. When we cannot be sure which of two signals determines the output, we call it a *race condition*. Obviously the $J = 1$ and $K = 1$ situation is an invalid input.

Next we want to summarize the states in a compressed table. The first two rows can be combined as shown in Table 6-6. But what about the third and fourth rows of the extended table? At first it looks as if they cannot be compressed, but closer examination shows that $Q_n$ in row 4 is one and $\overline{Q}_n$ is zero. These are also the values found in row 3, so we have the same outputs for each row. We can place a one in the $Q_{n+1}$ column and a zero in the $\overline{Q}_{n+1}$ column. We repeat this in the third row of the compressed table, but reverse the values of $Q_{n+1}$ and $\overline{Q}_{n+1}$. The last two rows of Table 6-5 call for another technique to compress them. If we look back at the present states of the outputs ($Q_n$ and $\overline{Q}_n$), we see that the next state of each output is the complement of the present state. That is, $Q_{n+1}$ becomes $\overline{Q}_n$ and $\overline{Q}_{n+1}$ becomes $Q_n$. This fact allows us to complete the table.

The race condition is hidden in the compressed state table. This is a consequence of the more compact form, which cannot present all of the information given in the expanded table.

The J-K flip-flop symbol is a rectangle, and it is shown in Fig. 6-8. The input terminals identify the type.

## Asynchronous Inputs

Many times we will want to initialize circuits in a known state. This usually means that all flip-flops are cleared to zero or preset to one. Special asynchronous input terminals are used to select the initial settings. As the name indicates, these inputs must only be used when the clock pulse is off; if they were used during clock on time, they would disrupt the operation. Although the terminology is confusing, only synchronous circuits can have asynchronous inputs. Why is this so? These terminals are also called direct inputs.

Figure 6-9 shows another form of the J-K flip-flop which has asynchronous inputs. You should develop the state tables to con-

**Figure 6-9. J-K flip-flop with asynchronous inputs.**

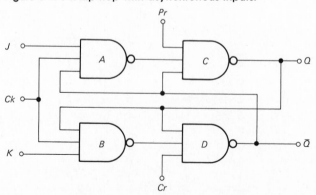

**Table 6-7**
**Asynchronous Inputs State Table**

| Inputs | | | Outputs | | |
|---|---|---|---|---|---|
| Ck | Cr | Pr | Q | $\overline{Q}$ | Result |
| 1 | 1 | 1 | * | * | Enabled |
| 0 | 0 | 1 | 0 | 1 | Cleared |
| 0 | 1 | 0 | 1 | 0 | Preset |

\* Normal J-K flip-flop operation.

vince yourself that this circuit performs the J-K flip-flop function during clock on time with the *Pr* and *Cr* inputs both set to one. (See Problem 6-4.)

Now consider what happens when the clock is off and the *Cr* signal becomes zero. No matter what the state of *J, K, Q,* and $\overline{Q}$, the zero clock input forces the outputs of the first-stage gates to one. Because the *Cr* signal is zero, the output of the gate it controls is also a one, thus setting the $\overline{Q}$ output. This also means that all three inputs to gate *C* (*Pr*, $\overline{Q}$, and the output of gate *A*) are ones. Gate *C* will produce a zero, which clears the *Q* output as expected from a clear input.

Trace the sequence that results during clock off time if *Pr* becomes zero. Table 6-7 summarizes the operation of the asynchronous inputs. Some flip-flops reverse the values of the asynchronous inputs; *Cr* and *Pr* is set to one to clear or preset respectively and to zero to enable normal operation.

**J-K Master/Slave Flip-Flop**

The J-K flip-flop that we analyzed earlier had a problem if we allowed both inputs to become one simultaneously. Often a circuit designer cannot prevent this event, yet he or she obviously does not want to build a race into the equipment. A J-K master/slave flip-flop will solve that problem. The circuit is shown in Fig. 6-10.

**Figure 6-10. J-K master slave flip-flop.**

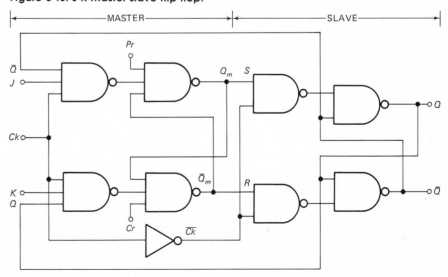

**Table 6-8**
**J-K Master Slave Flip-Flop Expanded State Table**

| During Clock On Time | | | | During Clock Off Time | | | |
|---|---|---|---|---|---|---|---|
| $J$ | $K$ | $Q_n$ | $\overline{Q}_n$ | $Q_m$ | $\overline{Q}_m$ | $Q_{n+1}$ | $\overline{Q}_{n+1}$ |
| 0 | 0 | 0 | 1 | 0 | 1 | 0 | 1 |
| 0 | 0 | 1 | 0 | 1 | 0 | 1 | 0 |
| 1 | 0 | 0 | 1 | 1 | 0 | 1 | 0 |
| 1 | 0 | 1 | 0 | 1 | 0 | 1 | 0 |
| 0 | 1 | 0 | 1 | 0 | 1 | 0 | 1 |
| 0 | 1 | 1 | 0 | 0 | 1 | 0 | 1 |
| 1 | 1 | 0 | 1 | 1 | 0 | 1 | 0 |
| 1 | 1 | 1 | 0 | 0 | 1 | 0 | 1 |

It consists of the previously studied J-K flip-flop with the asynchronous inputs followed by a clocked R-S flip-flop.

During the clock pulse, the $Q$ and $\overline{Q}$ outputs of the slave cannot change because the inverter disables that portion of the circuit, but $Q_m$ and $\overline{Q}_m$ of the master follow J-K logic. At the end of the clock pulse, the inputs to the slave are enabled, then $Q_m$ and $\overline{Q}_m$ are transferred into the slave flip-flop. The outputs stabilize during the time that the clock is off.

Table 6-8 shows the states for that sequence. The intermediate values of $Q_m$ and $\overline{Q}_m$ at the time the clock pulse terminates are listed. Although Table 6-8 seems to be identical to the J-K flip-flop state table, the race condition has been eliminated. The intermediate values are not gated into the slave until after the master has been disabled. So changing values of the slave outputs do not get fed back to the master until it is too late for them to influence the outputs.

This means that the master receives its information on the positive leading edge of the clock pulse, while the slave is activated and receives its information on the negative trailing edge.

### J-K Flip-Flop Review

1. Describe the method for presetting and clearing a flip-flop.
2. Define race condition.
3. Explain how races can be eliminated in the J-K flip-flop.
4. List the types of flip-flops used in the construction of the J-K master/slave flip-flop.

### D FLIP-FLOP

**Table 6-9**
**Flip-Flop Compressed State Table**

| $D$ | $Q_{n+1}$ | $\overline{Q}_{n+1}$ |
|---|---|---|
| 1 | 1 | 0 |
| 0 | 0 | 1 |

The D flip-flop can be constructed from a J-K flip-flop or an R-S flip-flop. Our example in Fig. 6-11 uses the former. We have used integrated circuit modules, in this case an inverter and a J-K flip-flop, to build the more complex D flip-flop.

Analysis of the D flip-flop is so simple that an expanded state table is unnecessary. We can proceed directly to a compressed state table. Because the inverter is between the $J$ and $K$ input terminals, we are limiting the input states to those of rows 2 and 3 of Table 6-6. Our D flip-flop operates in only a portion of the J-K states. Table 6-9 lists these states.

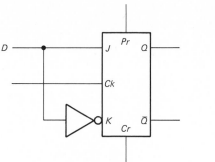

Figure 6-11. D flip-flop.

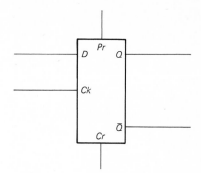

Figure 6-12. Symbol for a D flip-flop.

We see that the $Q$ output states are the same as the $D$ input. Another name for this device is a delay flip-flop, because the signal is delayed by the circuit propagation time before it appears at the output. The D flip-flop symbol is shown in Fig. 6-12. The 7474 flip-flop in the next section is an example of a D flip-flop.

**T FLIP-FLOP** The T flip-flop is another useful sequential circuit. Its construction is even more straightforward than that of the foregoing one. The $J$ and $K$ terminals are simply wired together as illustrated in Fig. 6-13$a$.

The compressed state data can be read from Table 6-6. We know that both $J$ and $K$ must be equal, so we use the first and last rows of that table to find the T flip-flop states.

Every time the $T$ input is a one, the outputs reverse or toggle their states. Otherwise, there is no change. Table 6-10 shows the operational states. The $T$ or toggle flip-flop symbol is shown in Fig. 6-13$b$. The T flip-flop is not available commercially because it is so easy to make your own.

**Table 6-10
T Flip-Flop Compressed State Table**

| $T$ | $Q_{n+1}$ | $\overline{Q}_{n+1}$ |
|-----|-----------|----------------------|
| 1   | $\overline{Q}_n$ | $Q_n$ |
| 0   | $Q_n$ | $\overline{Q}_n$ |

**TRIGGERING** In our study of flip-flops, we were concerned about the time the outputs changed. The R-S flip-flop required that its inputs be held long enough for the circuit to latch. This was an example of level triggering. Contrast that with the edge triggering of the J-K master/slave flip-flop.

Figure 6-13. T flip-flop. (a) Construction, (b) symbol.

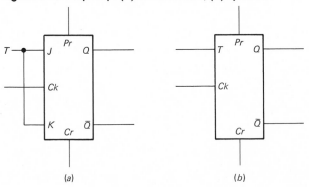

(a)                    (b)

Level triggering requires that one set of inputs be removed before the next is applied. (What would happen if the next input were applied to the $R$ terminal while the $S$ terminal still had the previous input value applied?) The input data cannot change except after the positive clock pulse, and then it can only change once.

If edge triggering is used, only the beginning or end of the pulse matters, not the duration. The input data may change at any time, and the proper outputs will be produced. Two types of edge triggering are used. Positive edge triggering uses the positive going transition of the pulse. This can be either the leading or trailing edge. Negative edge triggering employs the negative going edge of the pulse. Again, this could be either the leading or trailing edge.

**D and T Flip-Flop Review**

1. Describe the purpose of the D flip-flop.
2. Explain why the T flip-flop is called a toggle.
3. Describe how a T flip-flop can be constructed.
4. Name the triggering method which does not depend on input-pulse duration.
5. Distinguish between positive and negative edge triggering.

**INTEGRATED CIRCUIT FLIP-FLOPS**

The flip-flops discussed so far have been constructed from individual gates, but they are also available as integrated circuits. The dual D flip-flop 7474 IC shown in Fig. 6-14a is a typical example.

Figure 6-14. IC flip-flops (a) 7474 dual D, (b) 7476 dual J-K.

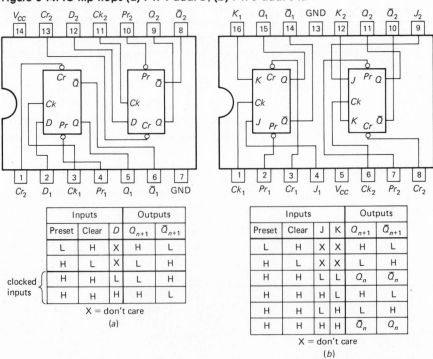

| | Inputs | | | Outputs | |
|---|---|---|---|---|---|
| | Preset | Clear | D | $Q_{n+1}$ | $\bar{Q}_{n+1}$ |
| | L | H | X | H | L |
| | H | L | X | L | H |
| clocked inputs { | H | H | L | L | H |
| | H | H | H | H | L |

X = don't care

(a)

| | Inputs | | | | Outputs | |
|---|---|---|---|---|---|---|
| | Preset | Clear | J | K | $Q_{n+1}$ | $\bar{Q}_{n+1}$ |
| | L | H | X | X | H | L |
| | H | L | X | X | L | H |
| | H | H | L | L | $Q_n$ | $\bar{Q}_n$ |
| | H | H | H | L | H | L |
| | H | H | L | H | L | H |
| | H | H | H | H | $\bar{Q}_n$ | $Q_n$ |

X = don't care

(b)

The package contains two independent flip-flops which are triggered by the leading edge of the clock input. Asynchronous preset and clear inputs are provided. The 7476 dual J-K flip-flop IC of Fig. 6-14$b$ is quite similar to the one shown in Fig. 6-7. The two independent J-K flip-flops have preset and clear inputs.

**CHAPTER SUMMARY**

1. Reset-set flip-flops consist of logic gates connected with feedback loops. The present output state of the gates assists in determining the next output state. This results in a circuit with a memory which can retain its output states when the inputs are removed.

2. Analysis of any sequential circuit begins with an expanded state table which lists all possible input conditions. The next state of the output can be calculated from the present inputs by using Boolean algebraic relationships. A compressed state table, which summarizes the information, can then be derived.

3. Some input combinations produce illogical or invalid outputs. These are forbidden states which must be prevented when the circuit is being designed.

4. Another aspect of sequential circuits is that they introduce delays. A timing diagram is used to analyze the dynamic circuit operation and account for the propagation delays in each element. The design must accommodate the worst-case condition, that is, the slowest sequence in the timing chain.

5. Clocked or synchronous circuits eliminate the designer's problem of deciding how long the inputs must be held constant. The inputs must not change during the positive clock pulse. The clock duration is specified by its pulse width and either its period or its frequency. Analysis of synchronous circuits requires the addition of an intermediate inputs column to the expanded state table.

6. If we want to initialize a flip-flop to a known state, the asynchronous or direct inputs can be used. The flip-flop can be started with either a cleared or preset output.

7. The J-K master/slave flip-flop eliminates the possibility of a race condition when both of the inputs are ones. It consists of a J-K flip-flop which is active while the clock is on followed by an R-S flip-flop which operates while the clock is off.

8. The delay flip-flop transfers the input value to the output terminal after the delay of the propagation period. For this reason, D flip-flops are often used to slow down or store signals that would otherwise be lost.

9. The toggle flip-flop complements the output state whenever a one is applied at the input terminal. It is easily constructed from a J-K flip-flop.

10. Each type of flip-flop uses level or edge triggering. The duration of the pulse becomes important with level triggering; the time of the transition between the high and low levels is used by edge-triggered devices.

**KEY TERMS AND CONCEPTS**

sequential circuit
flip-flops
R-S flip-flops
state table
propagation delay
timing diagram
synchronous and asynchronous circuits
clock pulse width, frequency, and period

J-K flip-flops
invalid inputs
asynchronous inputs
master/slave flip-flops
D flip-flops
T flip-flops
level triggering
edge triggering

## PROBLEMS

6-1. What would happen if the $R$ input in Fig. 6-2 were held for only $1t_{pd}$ rather than $3t_{pd}$? Draw a timing diagram showing $R$, $S$, $Q$, and $\overline{Q}$ to show your answer.

6-2. Develop the compressed state table for the J-K master/slave flip-flop of Fig. 6-10.

6-3. The propagation delay of each gate shown in Fig. 6-15 is $t_{pd}$ and the clock pulse width is $4t_{pd}$. For any combinations of inputs $R$ and $S$, what will be the next states of $Q$ and $\overline{Q}$? Draw expanded and compressed state tables.

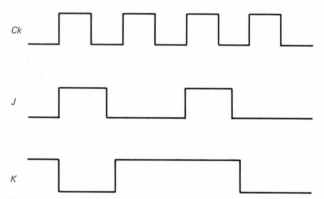

Figure 6-16. Problem 6-5.

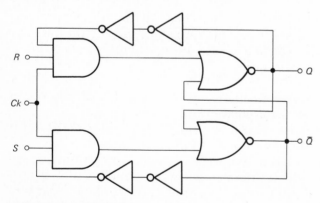

Figure 6-15. Problem 6-3.

6-4. Derive the expanded state table for the J-K flip-flop in Fig. 6-9.

6-5. The waveforms shown in Fig. 6-16 indicate the $J$, $K$, and $Ck$ inputs applied to a J-K flip-flop. Draw the waveforms for $Q$ and $\overline{Q}$. (Assume the clock pulse width is large enough for proper operation.)

6-6. Table 6-6 shows the compressed state table for a J-K flip-flop. Another table, given below, also represents the J-K flip-flop. An $X$ in the table means that it does not matter whether the entry is a one or a zero. It is called a "don't care" condition. The first row indicates that the output state does not change if the $J$ input is a zero and $K$ is either a zero or a one. Show how to obtain this table from the compressed state table.

| $J$ | $K$ | $Q_n$ | $Q_{n+1}$ |
|-----|-----|-------|-----------|
| 0 | X | 0 | 0 |
| 1 | X | 0 | 1 |
| X | 1 | 1 | 0 |
| X | 0 | 1 | 1 |

6-7. A Slobbovian manufacturer builds the Ultra-Good (UG) flip-flop shown in Fig. 6-17 with its state table. Before you buy one, you check it carefully. What do you decide is wrong with it?

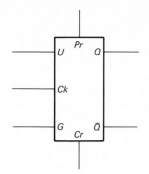

**Figure 6-17. Problem 6-7.**

### State Table

| U | G | $Q_{n+1}$ |
|---|---|---|
| 0 | 0 | $Q_n$ |
| 0 | 1 | $Q_n$ |
| 1 | 0 | $Q_n$ |
| 1 | 1 | 1 |

6-8. Does the circuit in Fig. 6-18 perform the same operation as a T flip-flop? Hint: Construct the state table.

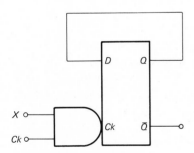

**Figure 6-18. Problem 6-8.**

6-9. What are the next output states for the inputs given below for Fig. 6-19?

| P | $Q_{n+1}$ | $\overline{Q}_{n+1}$ |
|---|-----------|----------------------|
| 0 |           |                      |
| 1 |           |                      |

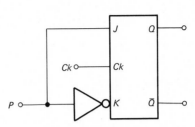

**Figure 6-19. Problem 6-9.**

6-10. Prepare the state table for the circuit shown in Fig. 6-20. The lower input to the AND gate is always a one.

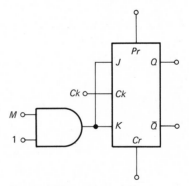

**Figure 6-20. Problem 6-10.**

# EXPERIMENT 6 SWITCH DEBOUNCER

**PURPOSE** To investigate eliminating spurious signals produced by switch closure.

**PARTS LIST**

| Item | Quantity |
|---|---|
| 7400 | 1 |
| 7447 | 1 |
| 7490 | 1 |
| 330-$\Omega$ resistor | 7 |
| 900-$\Omega$ resistor | 2 |
| IEE 1712 LED display | 1 |
| switch | 1 |

**IC DIAGRAMS**

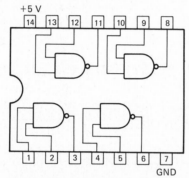

**Figure 6-21. 7400.**

**Note:** This experiment will use the circuit shown in Fig. 6-22 which consists of a counter together with a decoder and a seven-segment LED display. The counter circuit will be fully explained in a later chapter. Here we will just use it as an indicator of results.

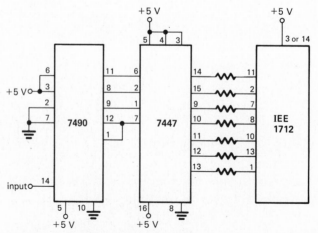

Carefully note the ground and $V_{cc}$ connections on the 7490.
All resistors are 330 $\Omega$.

**Figure 6-22. Decade counter.**

**PROCEDURE**   **Step 1.**   Connect the switch and resistor as shown in Fig. 6-23. Connect the output to pin 14 of the 7490, which is wired in the manner shown in Fig. 6-22. Alternately close and open the switch 10 times and record the number on the LED display.

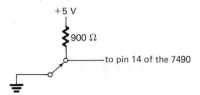

**Figure 6-23. Switch.**

**Step 2.**   Using the 7400 IC, revise the switch circuit to the one shown in Fig. 6-24. After connecting pin 6 of the 7400 to pin 14 of the 7490, repeat the procedure of closing and opening the switch 10 times. Record your results.

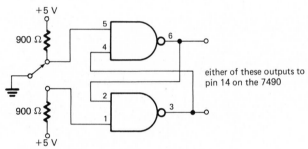

**Figure 6-24. Debounced switch.**

**Step 3.**   Disconnect pin 6 of the 7400 from the 7490 and connect pin 3 of the 7400 in its place. Repeat the measurements of Step 2.

**Step 4.**   Explain how the circuit in Fig. 6-24 was able to debounce the switch. How do the results in Steps 2 and 3 compare?

# CHAPTER SEVEN
# SEQUENTIAL CIRCUITS:
# COUNTERS AND REGISTERS

This chapter extends our study of sequential circuits to counters and registers. Counters and registers are used for digital and arithmetic applications in computers, digital watches, calculators, test equipment, and controllers. Their multipurpose nature makes it possible to combine them with analog circuits to produce hybrid systems. In such applications, the counters and registers perform the operations easily achieved using a digital implementation.

**CHAPTER OBJECTIVES**  In this chapter we will be building counters and registers from combinatorial elements and flip-flops. You will see how the components we studied earlier can be combined to perform the new functions. After completing this chapter, you should be able to:

1. Analyze counters and registers.
2. Discuss binary counter operation and adapt binary counters to other functions.
3. Describe register operation.
4. Distinguish between the various methods of register input and output.
5. Describe the different types of shifting commonly used.

**COUNTERS**  We are surrounded by numbers in our world. Every year more demands are made for computers and calculators. A basic component of these digital devices is the counter which accumulates numbers, times pulse trains, and performs simple arithmetic. All counters can be derived from one basic type, the binary counter.

**Binary Counter** The simplest counters are based on the binary number system. Such counters are limited to a count capacity which is a multiple of two. Figure 7-1 shows a binary counter consisting of three T flip-flops and two AND gates. The pulses that we want to count are applied to the clock input of each flip-flop; thus, this is a synchronous counter. We can determine the maximum number a binary counter can contain by first counting the flip-flops (in this case three) and then using the formula

$$\text{Maximum count} = 2^n \qquad (7\text{-}1)$$

where $n$ is the number of flip-flops. We can see that the counter in Fig. 7-1 can count no higher than $2^3$ or 8. If we want to develop a counter with a higher count capacity, we just increase the number of flip-flop stages.

Just as we did with flip-flops, we will use state tables to analyze counters. Only a minor change is required to adapt a table for use with this circuit. The inputs to the third flip-flop result from the ANDing of the outputs of the first two stages. The output value of the circuit depends on the combination of the outputs from all stages (generated by the upper AND gate). This means that both the intermediate input and the output columns must include the Boolean combinations.

Before we develop the state table, let us form the equations for these values. By inspection of the circuit

$$\begin{aligned} T_0 &= 1 \qquad (7\text{-}2) \\ T_1 &= Q_0 \\ T_2 &= Q_0 Q_1 \\ \text{Output} &= Q_0 Q_1 Q_2 \end{aligned}$$

Now we can proceed to the state table.

When we analyze counters we will usually use only an expanded state table. To keep the notation from getting unwieldy, we do not use the $n$ and $n+1$ subscripts that we used earlier with flip-flops. Instead we refer to the present state and next state of

**Figure 7-1. Binary synchronous count-by-eight circuit.**

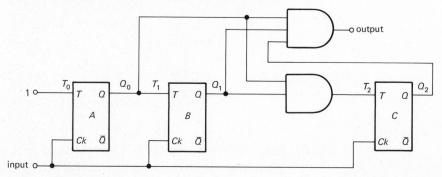

**Table 7-1**
**Binary Counter State Table**

| Present State | | | Intermediate Inputs | | | Next State | | | |
|---|---|---|---|---|---|---|---|---|---|
| $Q_2$ | $Q_1$ | $Q_0$ | $T_2$ | $T_1$ | $T_0$ | $Q_2$ | $Q_1$ | $Q_0$ | Output |
| 0 | 0 | 0 | 0 | 0 | 1 | 0 | 0 | 1 | 0 |
| 0 | 0 | 1 | 0 | 1 | 1 | 0 | 1 | 0 | 0 |
| 0 | 1 | 0 | 0 | 0 | 1 | 0 | 1 | 1 | 0 |
| 0 | 1 | 1 | 1 | 1 | 1 | 1 | 0 | 0 | 0 |
| 1 | 0 | 0 | 0 | 0 | 1 | 1 | 0 | 1 | 0 |
| 1 | 0 | 1 | 0 | 1 | 1 | 1 | 1 | 0 | 0 |
| 1 | 1 | 0 | 0 | 0 | 1 | 1 | 1 | 1 | 1 |
| 1 | 1 | 1 | 1 | 1 | 1 | 0 | 0 | 0 | 0 |

each output. The column headings, as shown in Table 7-1, help us keep this distinction clear. The present state for any combination of the inputs is listed. Since we have three inputs, the present states of the $Q$ outputs, there will be eight combinations. It is convenient to list them in ascending binary numerical order; this prevents omission of one of the combinations. The analysis would be equally correct for any other order.

The intermediate inputs column provides space for recording the value of each $T$ input. The next state column contains the outputs of each flip-flop, as well as the overall circuit output.

The first row is developed by computing the Boolean values of each of the $T$ inputs. Because $T_0$ is "hard wired" to a one input, it will always be one. $T_1$ depends on the value of $Q_0$. Referring to the present state column, we see that $Q_0$ is zero, so $T_1$ is also zero. Using Eqs. 7-2, we compute $T_2$ by ANDing $Q_0$ with $Q_1$. Both $Q$s are zero, thus $T_2$ is zero. Now that all of the intermediate inputs are known, we can determine the next state for the flip-flops.

We recall that the T flip-flop will toggle its output if the input is one and not change otherwise. Looking at the intermediate inputs column, we see that only one input $T_0$ is a one. So the first flip-flop will toggle and the others will stay the same. We can summarize the action as follows:

| Flip-flop | Result of Input | Present State | Next State |
|---|---|---|---|
| A | Toggle | 0 | 1 |
| B | No change | 0 | 0 |
| C | No change | 0 | 0 |

These results are tabulated in the next state columns for each of the $Q$ outputs.

What is the next state at the output terminal? Using our equation and the known next state of each flip-flop, we find that the result is zero. The table also shows this value.

Working row by row, we complete the table. In the second row both $T_0$ and $T_1$ are one. This means that the flip-flops controlled by these inputs will complement their outputs, while the third flip-flop will not change. $Q_0$ changes from its present state of one to zero, and $Q_1$ goes from a zero to a one. $Q_2$ remains zero. The fourth row shows an interesting event. All of the $T$ inputs are ones in that row. The table shows that this produces toggling of every flip-flop in the circuit.

The event that produces a change at the output terminal is in the seventh row. When the next state of all of the $Q$ outputs is one, the ANDing of them will change the overall output from zero to one. In the next row, the output returns to the zero state. Assuming that we start the counter with every flip-flop set to one, we will require eight pulses before the output again becomes one. If we consider the $Q$ outputs to be binary numbers, the counter runs from 0 through 7 ($111_2$). Since this takes exactly eight inputs, we can also call the circuit a *divide-by-eight counter*. Dividers are often used to reduce the frequency of an oscillator to the desired level in digital watches.

What would happen if the flip-flops were not preset to one? This could be the situation, because there are no preset inputs on the flip-flops. If this event should occur, the first time the output changes to one, there may be an error in the count. For example, if flip-flop $C$ were set to one and the others to zero, only two input pulses would produce a one output. After the false output, however, the counter would be in the proper condition to work correctly. A counter with this feature is called *self-starting*. But the designer must remember to discard the first incorrect count if it would result in equipment malfunction.

## Binary Synchronous Decimal Counter

The binary counter is fine if we want to count or divide by powers of two. What if we want another capacity? The count we most often use is ten. The binary count can be readily changed to a decimal count with added circuit elements.

Figure 7-2 shows one example of such a counter. We develop it by selecting a binary counter with a higher capacity than we need, 16 in the decimal counter case; then we "throw away" the extra capacity. Our analysis will show that this is exactly what happens.

The first step is to write the Boolean equations for the intermediate inputs. These are

$$
\begin{aligned}
T_0 &= 1 \\
T_1 &= Q_0 \overline{Q}_3 \\
T_2 &= Q_1 Q_0 \\
T_3 &= Q_2 Q_1 Q_0 + Q_3 Q_0 \\
\text{Output} &= Q_3 Q_0
\end{aligned}
\tag{7-3}
$$

Table 7-2 lists all combination of the present output states and provides space for recording the intermediate inputs and the next states of the outputs. Using Eqs. 7-3, we can determine that the intermediate inputs for the first row are all zero except $T_0$, which is one. The $T_0$ input will toggle the first flip-flop, but the others will remain in their present states.

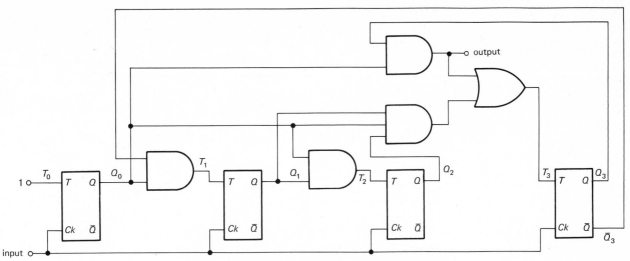

**Figure 7-2. Binary synchronous decimal counter.**

The output changes to one in the ninth row. Then, in the tenth row, it returns to the zero state. Notice that although we only wanted our counter to contain a maximum of ten, we have to consider the results should the present states of the $Q$ outputs be above that number. This situation might happen during initialization. There are no preset inputs to the flip-flops, so the start-up state cannot be guaranteed to be within the limits of 0 through 9 ($1001_2$). We want to be sure that the counter cannot become stuck in the invalid states and never produce the proper counting sequence. We might also say that we are trying to determine if this is a self-starting counter.

**Table 7-2**
**Decimal Counter State Table**

| Present State | | | | Intermediate Inputs | | | | Next State | | | | Output |
|---|---|---|---|---|---|---|---|---|---|---|---|---|
| $Q_3$ | $Q_2$ | $Q_1$ | $Q_0$ | $T_3$ | $T_2$ | $T_1$ | $T_0$ | $Q_3$ | $Q_2$ | $Q_1$ | $Q_0$ | Output |
| 0 | 0 | 0 | 0 | 0 | 0 | 0 | 1 | 0 | 0 | 0 | 1 | 0 |
| 0 | 0 | 0 | 1 | 0 | 0 | 1 | 1 | 0 | 0 | 1 | 0 | 0 |
| 0 | 0 | 1 | 0 | 0 | 0 | 0 | 1 | 0 | 0 | 1 | 1 | 0 |
| 0 | 0 | 1 | 1 | 0 | 1 | 1 | 1 | 0 | 1 | 0 | 0 | 0 |
| 0 | 1 | 0 | 0 | 0 | 0 | 0 | 1 | 0 | 1 | 0 | 1 | 0 |
| 0 | 1 | 0 | 1 | 0 | 0 | 1 | 1 | 0 | 1 | 1 | 0 | 0 |
| 0 | 1 | 1 | 0 | 0 | 0 | 0 | 1 | 0 | 1 | 1 | 1 | 0 |
| 0 | 1 | 1 | 1 | 1 | 1 | 1 | 1 | 1 | 0 | 0 | 0 | 0 |
| 1 | 0 | 0 | 0 | 0 | 0 | 0 | 1 | 1 | 0 | 0 | 1 | 1 |
| 1 | 0 | 0 | 1 | 1 | 0 | 0 | 1 | 0 | 0 | 0 | 0 | 0 |
| 1 | 0 | 1 | 0 | 0 | 0 | 0 | 1 | 1 | 0 | 1 | 1 | 1 |
| 1 | 0 | 1 | 1 | 1 | 1 | 0 | 1 | 0 | 1 | 1 | 0 | 0 |
| 1 | 1 | 0 | 0 | 0 | 0 | 0 | 1 | 1 | 1 | 0 | 1 | 1 |
| 1 | 1 | 0 | 1 | 1 | 0 | 0 | 1 | 0 | 1 | 0 | 0 | 0 |
| 1 | 1 | 1 | 0 | 0 | 0 | 0 | 1 | 1 | 1 | 1 | 1 | 1 |
| 1 | 1 | 1 | 1 | 1 | 1 | 0 | 1 | 0 | 0 | 1 | 0 | 0 |

The row below the double line will have a next state of $1011_2$ instead of returning to a binary number that is less than 9. That happens to be the present state of the next row, and we see that the counter does return to the limits we want ($0110_2$ in this case). The same pattern results in all of the states shown below the double line; however, the output is incorrect in these cases.

Assuming that the counter starts in the $1010_2$ state, it will produce an output of one on the next count. It will become zero on the following input pulse, but the counter will produce another erroneous one output. If we trace the binary operation through the table, we see that the sequence will be

1010, 1011 (output = 1), 0110, 0111, 1000, 1001

(output = 1), 0000, . . .

The count finally resumes a normal sequence after producing two false outputs of one. Starting in some other state will result in some other counting sequence, but in no case will there be more than two false outputs of one. This means that the first two times the output becomes one, they should be ignored. The counter is self-starting.

The method which converts the binary counter to a decimal counter is also apparent in the table. There are two conditions that cause $T_3$ to become one, which complements the $Q$ output of the final stage: (1) either all of the previous flip-flop stages have $Q$ outputs of one, or (2) the first and last flip-flops have $Q$ outputs of one. The first case causes the count to go from $0111_2$ to $1000_2$, which is the normal situation for a binary counter. The other case resets all of the flip-flops to the zero condition, which produces a smaller maximum count than the four-stage capacity. This prevents the count from ever going above nine (except in the initialization sequence described above).

## Ring Counter

Sometimes we do not want to count a sequence of input pulses, but prefer to have a series of one and zero pulses for use in controlling other circuits. This might be the clock pulse train for other synchronous circuits in the unit. The ring counter can be used for this purpose.

As the name suggests, the ring counter just routes its output back to the input terminal. Figure 7-3 gives an example of a simple ring counter. The outputs of the first and second stages are fed back to the input and the counter generates a repeating sequence at the output terminal.

Figure 7-3. Ring counter.

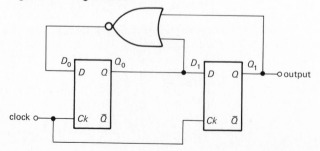

**Counter Review**
1. What is the count capacity of a binary counter with five flip-flop stages?
2. List the steps required to analyze a counter by means of state tables.
3. Define a self-starting counter.
4. Describe the method for converting a binary counter into a decimal counter.
5. Distinguish between a binary counter and a ring counter.

**SHIFT REGISTERS**

Often we want to store a number that is the result of a calculation or some other combination of inputs. If this number is only a single bit, we can use a flip-flop. For longer numbers, registers are used.

**Synchronous Shift Register**

The shift register gets its name from the fact that the data are simultaneously shifted along a chain of flip-flops. Figure 7-4 shows a shift register constructed of D flip-flops. For higher-speed operation, J-K master/slave flip-flops are used instead of D flip-flops to prevent problems associated with propagation delays from stage to stage.

Our analysis of the shift register will be based on the state table, but we need not consider all present states of the flip-flops. Instead we will use the table to see the changes produced by a series of input values. The clear inputs will simplify our analysis. We will assume that the register has been cleared prior to the application of the first input.

Table 7-3 is the state table for this circuit. Let a one be applied to the $D$ input of the first flip-flop. After the delay of the flip-flop, it will cause the $Q$ output to change to a one. Now the input to the second stage is one, but the clock period is selected to be short

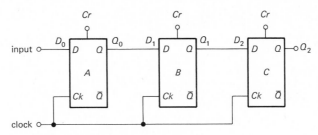

**Figure 7-4. Synchronous shift register.**

**Table 7-3**
**Synchronous Shift Register State Table**

| Present State | | | | Intermediate Inputs | | | Next State | | |
|---|---|---|---|---|---|---|---|---|---|
| Input | $Q_2$ | $Q_1$ | $Q_0$ | $D_2$ | $D_1$ | $D_0$ | $Q_2$ | $Q_1$ | $Q_0$ |
| 1 | 0 | 0 | 0 | 0 | 0 | 1 | 0 | 0 | 1 |
| 0 | 0 | 0 | 1 | 0 | 1 | 0 | 0 | 1 | 0 |
| 1 | 0 | 1 | 0 | 1 | 0 | 1 | 1 | 0 | 1 |

enough to prevent the second flip-flop from being active when $Q_0$ changes state.

Next let a zero be applied to the $D_0$ input when the clock pulse occurs. The one at $D_1$ can now be accepted by that flip-flop, and the next state of the outputs will be $Q_2 = 0$, $Q_1 = 1$, and $Q_0 = 0$. On the next clock pulse, a one is placed on the inputs. It propagates through the flip-flop, changing $Q_0$ to 1; the $D_1$ input changes $Q_1$ to zero, and the $D_2$ input causes $Q_2$ to become one.

As shown in the table, the first one input has moved through each flip-flop. On each clock pulse, it shifts one element down the chain. We see that it takes two clock pulses for the input to move completely through the circuit and become available at the $Q_2$ output.

**Input and Output**  We could only put data into the previous shift register 1 bit at a time. The output took two clock pulses to become available, and then only as a single bit. This type of register is called serial in, serial out.

We can also build registers that take the data several bits at a time and make them available at the outputs in that format. This register would be called parallel in, parallel out.

Since we may have either type of input or output, there are four basic configurations for shift registers:

serial in, serial out (SISO)
serial in, parallel out (SIPO)
parallel in, serial out (PISO)
parallel in, parallel out (PIPO)

More complex registers even combine these possibilities.

Figure 7-5 shows a serial or parallel in, serial or parallel out

**Figure 7-5. Serial/parallel input, serial/parallel output shift register.**

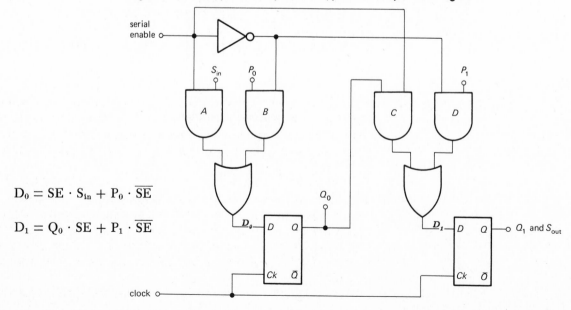

$$D_0 = SE \cdot S_{in} + P_0 \cdot \overline{SE}$$

$$D_1 = Q_0 \cdot SE + P_1 \cdot \overline{SE}$$

**Table 7-4**
**Serial/Parallel Shift Register State Table**

| Inputs | | | | Outputs | |
|---|---|---|---|---|---|
| $S_{in}$ | $P_1$ | $P_0$ | Serial Enable | $Q_1$ | $Q_0$ |
| X | 0 | 1 | 0 | 0 | 1 |
| X | 1 | 1 | 0 | 1 | 1 |
| 0 | X | X | 1 | 1 | 0 |
| 0 | X | X | 1 | 0 | 0 |
| 1 | 1 | 0 | 1 | 0 | 1 |

X = don't care

shift register. The operation of the circuit is shown in Table 7-4.

This circuit has three inputs. The serial input is labeled $S_{in}$, and the parallel inputs $P_0$ and $P_1$. The output can be obtained in serial form at $S_{out}$ (also labeled $Q_1$) or in parallel at $Q_0$ and $Q_1$. The two modes of operation are controlled by the serial enable line. If we place a zero on serial enable, we see that the AND gates $B$ and $D$ pass the $P_0$ and $P_1$ inputs through to the OR gate and then to the flip-flop. The first row of the table shows the result if $P_0 = 1$ and $P_1 = 0$. The $S_{in}$ value is indicated by an X, a "don't care" condition. It may be either zero or one and will not affect the output. That input cannot pass gate $A$ regardless of the value. The second row of the table shows another example of parallel operation.

The next row assumes that the serial enable signal is high. This signal enables gates $A$ and $C$ but disables $B$ and $D$. Whatever input is applied at the $S_{in}$ terminal will appear at the $Q_0$ output of the first flip-flop. We apply another zero to the serial input. The $Q_0$ output shifts to the next stage on the clock pulse and the new input, a zero in row 4, appears at $Q_0$. In two clock pulses, the serial input will be at the $S_{out}$ terminal.

The last row of the table continues the example. By use of the serial enable line, the circuit will operate in any combination of serial or parallel that we desire. The circuit is an unusual example. More often, the circuit designer will select only one method or the other to enter and remove data.

**Shifting Methods**    Now that we understand how shift registers are constructed, let us consider the various types of shifting that can be performed. The bits in the register can be moved either left or right. The circuit in Fig. 7-5 shifted right. Figure 7-6 illustrates other shifting methods.

The original binary contents are shown in the left-hand column. The shift register is 6-bits long. After a 1-bit logical right shift, the result is as shown in Fig. 7-6a. A 1-bit logical left shift produces a completely different number (Fig. 7-6b). One important use of right and left shifting is that we divide or multiply the original number by two when we do the shift. This is seen more easily in decimal.

The original number is $45_{10}$ (ignoring the sign bit for now). After

| | |
|---|---|
| *a.* Original contents<br>101 101 | One-bit logical right shift<br>010 110 |
| *b.* Original contents<br>101 101 | One-bit logical left shift<br>011 010 |
| *c.* Original contents<br>101 101 | Three-bit logical left shift<br>101 000 |
| *d.* Original contents<br>101 101 | One-bit circular right shift<br>110 110 |
| *e.* Original contents<br>101 101 | Two-bit circular left shift<br>110 110 |
| *f.* Original contents<br>101 101<br>↑<br>sign bit | Two-bit arithmetic right shift<br>111 011 |

Figure 7-6. Shift patterns.

a right shift of 1 bit, we have $22_{10}$. This is not exactly half because the portion of the number that is shifted off is lost. This is what computer programmers call *truncation* or *round-off error*. The left shift results in $26_{10}$. This is not the answer we expected. The cause was the bit that had to be dropped off the end. This time we *overflowed* the register because it was not long enough to contain the answer. If we had started with a 7-bit register prior to shifting, the answer would have been $1\ 011\ 010_2 = 90_{10}$. We are not limited to single-bit shifts, as Fig. 7-6c shows.

One way to prevent truncation is to bring the last bit around to the other end of the register rather than let it fall off the end. The next two rows show the results of *circular* or *end-around* shifting. In Fig. 7-6d the one that is truncated on the right is moved into the most-significant-bit position after all of the other bits shift right. We are not limited to single-bit circular shifts either, as shown in Fig. 7-6e.

All of these shifts are useful for moving a bit pattern, but we must not use them if we are concerned with the value of the number. If the original number were to represent a two's complement value, the most significant bit would have to be the sign bit. In the case of Fig. 7-6a, for example, the negative number (sign bit = 1) is changed to a positive number (sign bit = 0).

When we are using the register for arithmetic, in a computer or calculator, we want to preserve the sign. In that case, we use an *arithmetic shift* which drags the sign. In Fig. 7-6f the number is shifted two places to the right, but after each 1-bit shift, the sign value is restored. By converting to decimal, we see that the original number (using two's complement) is −19. After two right shifts (equivalent to dividing by 4) the result is −4. The error is again caused by rounding off; however, the correct sign has been retained after the shifting.

**Register Review**

1. Describe the operation of a synchronous shift register.
2. List the four basic input and output combinations for shift registers.
3. Distinguish between right and left shifting.
4. After three left shifts, four right shifts, and two left shifts by what number has the original value in a 12-bit register been multiplied?
5. Define circular shifting.
6. Explain why it is necessary to drag the sign for an arithmetic shift.

**INTEGRATED CIRCUIT REGISTERS**

The register circuits described in this chapter can also be purchased in the form of integrated circuits. A typical example is the 7496 shift register, shown in Fig. 7-7, which contains five R-S master/slave flip-flops. Because of the parallel preset inputs and parallel outputs, the individual flip-flops are accessible. The register, therefore, can perform any combination of serial or parallel input and output operations.

A low voltage applied to the preset enable line clears all outputs. Data can be applied to either the parallel preset or serial pins. The parallel preset inputs are controlled by the preset enable input; therefore, the clock controls only the serial input.

**CHAPTER SUMMARY**

1. The largest number that a binary counter can contain is $2^n$, where $n$ is the number of flip-flop stages.
2. State tables, slightly modified, are used to analyze the dynamic operation of counters and registers.
3. Counters can be considered to be dividers. A count-by-eight circuit also divides by eight. Dividers are used to reduce the frequency of oscillators.
4. Binary counters can be modified to count by a number that is not a multiple of two by eliminating the unnecessary states. The decimal counter is a common example of this technique.
5. Self-starting counters do not have to be preset, but some of the initial output pulses must be discarded to prevent erroneous results.

**Figure 7-7. 7496 shift register.**

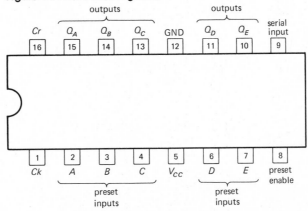

6. Ring counters will generate a continuous pulse train without any input being required. These counters are used to generate clock pulses in some equipment.

7. Shift registers are used to store a numeric value until it is used by other circuits.

8. Inputs and outputs of registers may be either serial or parallel or a combination.

9. There are several shifting methods used. If we are not concerned about the sign bit of a number, logical right and left shifts can be used. Circular shifting preserves the bits that would be truncated in logical shifting. The registers used for arithmetic must perform arithmetic shifts to preserve the sign bit.

**KEY TERMS AND CONCEPTS**

| | |
|---|---|
| synchronous counters | serial and parallel inputs |
| binary counters | and outputs |
| count capacity | logical shifting |
| decimal counters | circular shifting |
| self-starting counters | arithmetic shifting |
| ring counters | truncation |
| shift registers | overflow |

## PROBLEMS

7-1. The clock pulses of the circuit shown in Fig. 7-8 are $1.5t_d$ in duration, where $t_d$ is the maximum propagation delay for any gate or flip-flop in the circuit. (The small circles on the clear inputs of the flip-flops indicate that a zero input will reset the device.) Draw a timing diagram showing $Q_0$, $Q_1$, $Q_2$, and $Q_3$ for the first 16 clock pulses. All flip-flops initially have $Q = 0$, and negative edge triggering is used.

7-2. The R-S flip-flop is removed from the circuit in Fig. 7-8, and points $X$ and $Y$ are connected with a wire. What happens if $FF_3$ takes appreciably longer to clear than $FF_1$ when $Q_1$ is returning to zero?

7-3. The circuit in Fig. 7-8 is restored to that shown (that is, the jumper between $X$ and $Y$ is removed). Complete the state table for the circuit.

**Figure 7-8. Problem 7-1.**

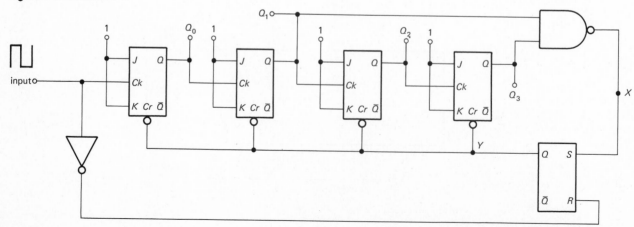

| Present State | | | | Next State | | | |
|---|---|---|---|---|---|---|---|
| $Q_3$ | $Q_2$ | $Q_1$ | $Q_0$ | $Q_3$ | $Q_2$ | $Q_1$ | $Q_0$ |
| 0 | 0 | 0 | 0 | | | | |
| 0 | 0 | 0 | 1 | | | | |
| 0 | 0 | 1 | 0 | | | | |
| 0 | 1 | 0 | 0 | | | | |
| 1 | 0 | 0 | 0 | | | | |
| 1 | 1 | 0 | 1 | | | | |
| 1 | 1 | 1 | 1 | | | | |

7-4. A shift register ring counter is shown in Fig. 7-9. What are the equations for each $D$ input?

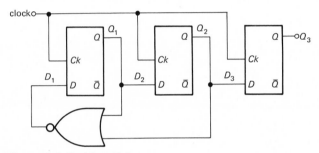

Figure 7-9. Problem 7-4.

7-5. For all possible states of the counter in Fig. 7-9, what next states can this counter assume? (Develop the state table.)

7-6. What is the minimum clock period for proper serial operation of the circuit in Fig. 7-5? Parallel operation? (Assume that all gates and flip-flops have propagation delay time $t_p$.)

7-7. For the shift register shown in Fig. 7-10, write the $T$ input equations for each flip-flop.

Figure 7-10. Problem 7-7.

7-8. Complete the state table for the circuit in Fig. 7-10.

| Present State | | | | Next State | | | |
|---|---|---|---|---|---|---|---|
| $Q_0$ | $Q_1$ | $Q_2$ | $Q_3$ | $Q_0$ | $Q_1$ | $Q_2$ | $Q_3$ |
| 0 | 1 | 0 | 1 | | | | |
| 1 | 0 | 0 | 1 | | | | |
| 0 | 0 | 0 | 0 | | | | |
| 1 | 1 | 1 | 1 | | | | |

7-9. Construct a state table for the counter in Fig. 7-11. All of the T flip-flops are initially cleared.

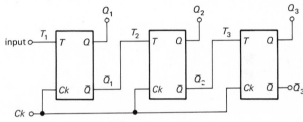

Figure 7-11. Problem 7-9.

7-10. The counter in Fig. 7-12, consisting of J-K flip-flops, is counting a series of input pulses. All flip-flops are initially set to zero. What will the next state of each $Q$ output be for the first 16 pulses?

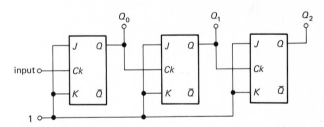

Figure 7-12. Problem 7-10.

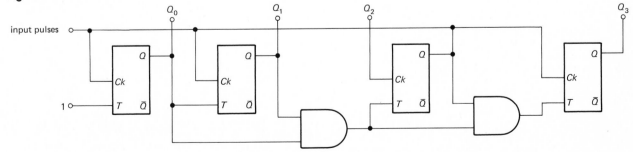

# EXPERIMENT 7 THE DECADE COUNTER

**PURPOSE**   To investigate the operation of a decade counter.

**PARTS LIST**

| Item | Quantity |
| --- | --- |
| 7400 | 1 |
| 7490 | 1 |
| LED | 4 |
| 330-$\Omega$ resistor | 4 |
| 900-$\Omega$ resistor | 2 |
| Switch | 1 |

**IC DIAGRAMS**

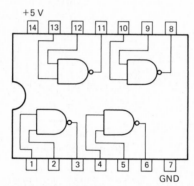

Figure 7-13. 7400.

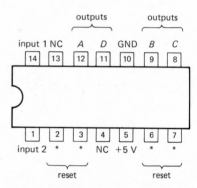

*Pin 2 is $Ro(1)$, pin 3 $Ro(3)$, pin 6 $Rg(1)$, and pin 7 $Rg(2)$.

Figure 7-14. 7490.

**PROCEDURE**   **Step 1.**   Connect the 7490 counter as shown in Fig. 7-15. Recall that the 7400 is acting as a switch debouncer.

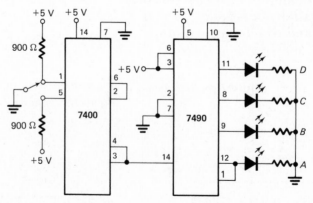

All resistors are 330 $\Omega$.

Figure 7-15. Decade counter experiment.

**Step 2.**   Opening and closing the switch, record the binary values of the outputs.

| | Output LED States | | | |
|---|---|---|---|---|
| Count | D | C | B | A |
| 0 | | | | |
| 1 | | | | |
| 2 | | | | |
| 3 | | | | |
| 4 | | | | |
| 5 | | | | |
| 6 | | | | |
| 7 | | | | |
| 8 | | | | |
| 9 | | | | |
| 10 | | | | |
| 11 | | | | |
| 12 | | | | |

**Step 3.** Reconnect the circuit as shown in Fig. 7-16. (Only pins 1 and 14 on the 7490 are changed.) Repeat Step 2 and record the output values. How do these results compare with those in Step 3? What can you conclude about using pin 1 as an input?

**Figure 7-16. Counter experiment.**

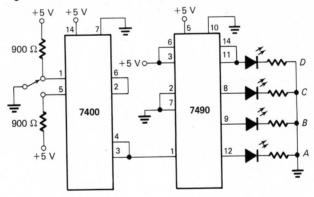

All resistors are 330 Ω.

# CHAPTER EIGHT
# ARITHMETIC CIRCUITS

The advantage of digital systems is that all of the quantities can be readily manipulated by using numeric operations. Addition, subtraction, multiplication, and division of binary numbers are performed by arithmetic circuits in almost all digital equipment. Devices such as arithmetic logic units and calculators provide within a single IC several types of operations which are selected by programmable inputs.

**CHAPTER OBJECTIVES**  Upon completion of this chapter you should be able to:

1. Discuss the combination of gates used to form various types of adders.
2. Describe the methods used to propagate the carries which develop in adders.
3. Describe how an adder can be converted to a subtractor.
4. Describe the operation of binary multipliers and dividers.
5. Distinguish between the actions provided by an arithmetic logic unit and describe how the actions performed depend on the selection inputs.

**ADDERS**  Single-bit binary addition is simple because there are only four possible combinations of zeros and ones to add, as was discussed in Chap. 5. Single-bit binary addition and a truth table for all possible results are shown in Fig. 8-1.

Addition

$$\begin{array}{cccc} 0 & 0 & 1 & 1 \\ +0 & +1 & +0 & +1 \\ \hline 0 & 1 & 1 & 0 \end{array}$$ and a carry of 1

**Truth Table for Addition**

| A | B | Sum | Carry |
|---|---|-----|-------|
| 0 | 0 | 0 | 0 |
| 0 | 1 | 1 | 0 |
| 1 | 0 | 1 | 0 |
| 1 | 1 | 0 | 1 |

Figure 8-1. Single-bit binary addition.

**Half Adder**

Logic equations for the sum and carry can be derived from the truth table. We write an equation for all cases in which the output is to be one. If either input column is a zero in a row with a one output, then that variable must be complemented. For example, the sum is one in rows 2 and 3 of Fig. 8-1. In row 2 the A input is in the zero state and B is a one, so we have $\overline{A}B$. Row 3 also has a one output, but the inputs are in the opposite states of row 2. So the equation for the sum is

$$\text{sum} = \overline{A}B + A\overline{B} \tag{8-1}$$

We have seen this form of Boolean equation before; it is an exclusive OR.

Using the same procedure for the carry output, we see that only row 4 has a one output. The equation is

$$\text{carry} = AB \tag{8-2}$$

Logic equations 8-1 and 8-2 can be converted to circuitry which forms a half adder as shown in Fig. 8-2. A half adder produces the sum on one output line and the carry on another. The symbol for this circuit is a rectangle with four terminals. Inputs are placed on the A and B lines, while the sum and carry are available at the outputs.

Figure 8-2. Half adder. (a) Logic diagram, (b) symbol.

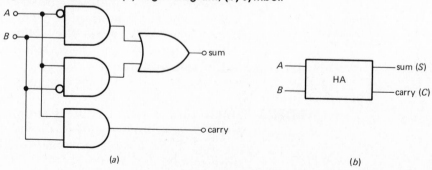

(a)

(b)

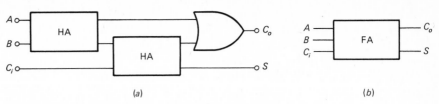

Figure 8-3. Full adder. (a) Logic diagram, (b) symbol.

**Full Adder**

The half adder does not complete the addition process. A carry-in from the digit position immediately to the right of the one being computed must be added to the sum, and a carry-out value from the current digit position must be passed on to the position of the next higher order.

Figure 8-3 shows how two half adders can be combined to perform these functions. The first half adder computes the sum and carry from the $A$ and $B$ inputs. That sum is added to the carry-in ($C_i$) from the next lower digit to compute the final sum. If a carry results from either of the addition operations, it is made available to the next higher digit position on the carry-out ($C_o$) line. The full adder thus computes the complete sum and handles all carry values both into and out of the circuit.

**4-Bit Parallel Adder**

The discussion, to this point, has been concerned with single-bit addition. Adders must be capable of adding numbers consisting of many bits. An example of a 4-bit parallel adder, shown in Fig. 8-4, will illustrate the method for expanding single-bit adders to multiple-bit use.

Bit positions are indicated by subscripts, the least significant bit is bit zero. Corresponding bits of the $A$ and $B$ inputs are applied to the input terminals of four full adders. Each adder computes the sum of $A$, $B$, and the input carry. It then produces an output carry to the next higher order digit and a sum.

Table 8-1 provides an example of the addition of two 4-bit numbers. With inputs of $A = 5_{16}$ and $B = 2_{16}$, the sum is $7_{16}$. Now consider the resulting sum if $A = 7_{16}$ and $B = 6_{16}$. The sum is $D_{16}$ which is not correct. We must use our four-bit word to represent both positive and negative numbers. Because the sign bit is set, we have a negative number. In this problem two positive numbers were added, but the sum was negative. This type of adder error is called *overflow*. The two inputs were too large for the 4-bit adder word length. The user of an adder circuit must prevent all cases of overflow; otherwise the answer will be incorrect.

Figure 8-4. 4-bit parallel adder.

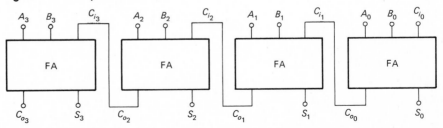

**Table 8-1**
**Example of 4-Bit Addition**

| $A_3$ | $A_2$ | $A_1$ | $A_0$ | | $A = 5_{16}$ |
|---|---|---|---|---|---|
| 0 | 1 | 0 | 1 | | |
| $B_3$ | $B_2$ | $B_1$ | $B_0$ | | $+B = 2_{16}$ |
| 0 | 0 | 1 | 0 | | |
| $S_3$ | $S_2$ | $S_1$ | $S_0$ | $C_{o_3}$ | $S = 7_{16}$ |
| 0 | 1 | 1 | 1 | 0 | |

The 4-bit adder accepted the two inputs at the same time, or in parallel, but the carry from each stage propagated to the next higher digit in a ripple fashion. This type of adder is therefore called a *ripple-carry* adder.

We might also note that the least significant bit adder does not have a carry-in, so a half adder can be used instead of a full adder. Fewer gates would then be needed to build the adder.

The propagation delay of the ripple carry can be reduced by using a *look-ahead carry* instead. This technique forms the carry from each bit position independently of the addition process. A carry-out is generated from each adder stage if one of three conditions is satisfied.

$$C_o = A_n B_n + A_n C_{i_n} + B_n C_{i_n} \qquad (8\text{-}3)$$

where $n$ is the number of the adder stage. Equation 8-3 tells us that there will be a carry-out if both input bits are ones, or if one input is one and there is a carry-in from the previous stage. The look-ahead carry circuitry for a 4-bit adder is shown in Fig. 8-5.

While adders can be built from combinatorial gates, they are also available as single integrated circuits. Figure 8-6 shows the 7483 adder. This IC can add 4-bit binary numbers and provide

**Figure 8-5. Look-ahead carry circuit.**

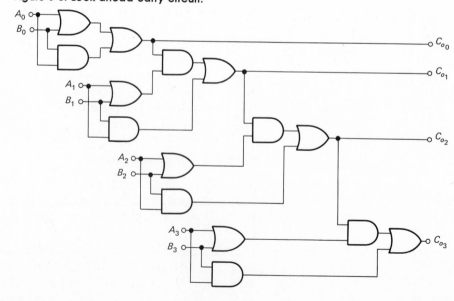

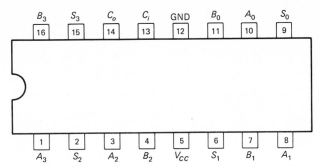

Figure 8-6. 7483 4-bit adder.

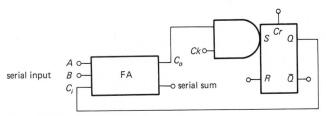

Figure 8-7. Serial adder.

look-ahead carries across the 4 bits. Typical addition time with this circuit is 10 nanoseconds.

**Serial Adder**   Another method of producing multiple-bit sums is to use a serial adder, such as the one shown in Fig. 8-7. The serial numbers are added with the least significant bit first.

After each addition, the sum and carry-out are generated. The carry is stored in a flip-flop until the next addition is performed. The flip-flop must be cleared before each carry is clocked in.

The sum must be used as soon as each bit becomes available. A shift register can be used to store the bits until the entire sum is computed. The size of the shift register and the number of addition cycles are determined by the word size of the numbers.

**Adder Review**   1. Write the Boolean equations for binary addition.
2. Distinguish between a half adder and a full adder.
3. Why is a half adder adequate for the least significant bit position in the 4-bit parallel adder?
4. Distinguish between a ripple carry and a look-ahead carry.
5. Describe the serial adder circuit.

**SUBTRACTORS**   As we explained in Chap. 5, the use of a complement number system together with an adder produces the same functions as a subtractor and does not require special circuitry just for this operation.

Figure 8-8 shows how the 4-bit parallel adder with supplementary inverters can be used as a subtractor. The carry-in to the first stage must be a one. This carry-in produces a two's complement

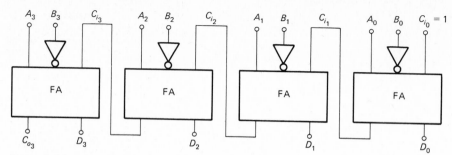

**Figure 8-8. 4 bit parallel subtractor.**

number system. The sum outputs have been relabeled difference outputs $(D)$ on the figure.

Another feature of the circuit is that the final carry-out terminal (which is really a borrow because of the subtraction) contains the sign of the difference. If the final borrow is a zero, the difference is negative; an output of one signifies a positive difference.

An error similar to addition overflow can occur in the subtractor. Consider the subtraction below in a 4-bit register using two's complement arithmetic.

Inputs
$A = 5_{16}$
$B = E_{16}$

| Direct subtraction | Complement (using a 4-bit register) |
|---|---|

$$\begin{array}{cc} 5_{16} & \\ \underline{-E_{16}} & \text{two's complement} \\ -9_{16} & \end{array} \qquad \begin{array}{l} 5_{16} \\ \underline{+2_{16}} \\ 7_{16} \quad \text{incorrect answer} \end{array}$$

The error occurs because the 4-bit word length is not long enough for the magnitude of the difference.

A serial subtractor can also be constructed as shown in Fig. 8-9. The difference is produced with the least significant bit first. A shift register is used to collect the serial results. The flip-flop is also used to produce two's complement arithmetic. The two's complement results from presetting the flip-flop prior to beginning the subtraction process. The flip-flop must also be cleared between each subtraction.

**Subtractor Review**

1. Describe the conversion of the 4-bit parallel adder to a subtractor.

**Figure 8-9. Serial subtractor.**

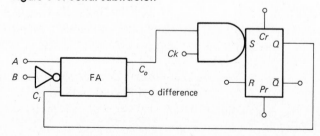

2. Name the input which is used to make the 4-bit parallel sub-tractor perform two's complement arithmetic.
3. Describe the operation of the serial subtractor.
4. List the inputs to the flip-flop in the serial subtractor for proper operation.

**MULTIPLIERS**

Multiplication can be performed by using a series of additions and shifts. Let's look at a 4-bit multiplication problem.

$$
\begin{array}{rl}
A_3\ A_2\ A_1\ A_0 & \text{multiplicand} \\
B_3\ B_2\ B_1\ B_0 & \text{multiplier} \\
\hline
P_{03}\ P_{02}\ P_{01}\ P_{00} & \\
P_{13}\ P_{12}\ P_{11}\ P_{10} & \text{partial products} \\
P_{23}\ P_{22}\ P_{21}\ P_{20} & \\
P_{33}\ P_{32}\ P_{31}\ P_{30} & \\
\hline
P_7\ P_6\ P_5\ P_4\ P_3\ P_2\ P_1\ \ P_0 & \text{product}
\end{array}
$$

We see that two 4-bit numbers multiplied together can produce an 8-bit product.

A $4 \times 4$-bit parallel multiplier can be constructed that is based on the operations shown above, but a simpler circuit can be used instead. The simplest multiplier consists of an adder, shift registers, and control logic as shown in Fig. 8-10. A flow diagram of the circuit actions is also provided in Fig. 8-11.

To understand the operation, let's perform a multiplication. Let

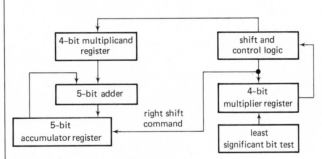

Figure 8-10. 4-bit multiplier logic.

Figure 8-11. 4-bit multiplier flow diagram.

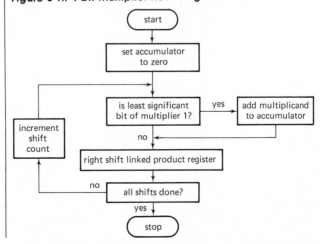

**Table 8-2**
**Multiplication Example**

| Step | Accumulator (A) | Multiplier (MPLR) | Multiplicand (MCAND) | Comments |
|---|---|---|---|---|
| 1 | 00000 | 0011 | 1011 | Start |
| 2 | 01011 | 0011 | 1011 | Add A and MCAND |
| 3 | 00101 | 1001 | 1011 | Right shift A and MPLR |
| 4 | 00101 | 1001 | 1011 | All shifts not done |
| 5 | 10000 | 1001 | 1011 | Add A and MCAND |
| 6 | 01000 | 0100 | 1011 | Right shift A and MPLR |
| 7 | 01000 | 0100 | 1011 | All shifts not done |
| 8 | 01000 | 0100 | 1011 | Do not add |
| 9 | 00100 | 0010 | 1011 | Right shift |
| 10 | 00100 | 0010 | 1011 | All shifts not done |
| 11 | 00100 | 0010 | 1011 | Do not add |
| 12 | 00010 | 0001 | 1011 | Right shift |
| 13 | 00010 | 0001 | 1011 | All shifts done |
| 14 | 00010 | 0001 | 1011 | Stop* |

* The product in the linked A and MPLR registers is 00010 0001 = $21_{16}$.

the multiplicand be $B_{16}$ and the multiplier be $3_{16}$. Table 8-2 shows the contents of each register for each step in the process. (The accumulator and multiplier registers are linked as a 9-bit register to hold the final product.)

The multiplication takes four shifts, and possibly four additions, before the final product is developed. Following the operation in the table, we see that only two additions are required in this problem because the two right-hand bits in the multiplier are ones. The final product is $21_{16}$ ($33_{10}$).

**Multiplier Review**

1. Describe the reason for the product word length being double that of the multiplicand and multiplier in a $4 \times 4$ multiplication.
2. What is the purpose of the least significant bit test in Fig. 8-10a?
3. List the steps in which shifting of the product was performed in the multiplication example.

**DIVIDERS**

A divider can be fabricated by using a binary subtractor together with two shift registers, a storage register, and some combinatorial gates as shown in Fig. 8-12. Each of the operands, in this case a 4-bit divisor and an 8-bit dividend, are placed in their respective registers. The quotient will occupy another register, but the remainder will be stored in the dividend register. The quotient is developed serially.

Division starts with the dividend being entered into the subtractor as a minuend and the divisor as the subtrahend. The difference is computed with the most significant bits of the operands

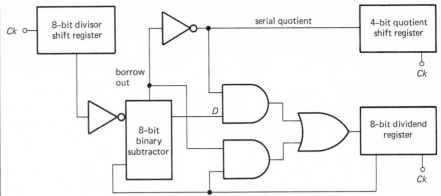

**Figure 8-12. Divider.**

aligned. If a borrow is required in the most significant bit position, one is brought in. For example, let the divisor be $C_{16}$ and the dividend be $9F_{16}$. The first subtraction would be

$$\text{borrow brought-in} \quad \begin{array}{r} ①\,1001\ 1111_2 \\ -1100_2 \\ \hline 1101\ 1111_2 \end{array} \quad \begin{array}{l} \text{dividend} \\ \text{divisor} \\ \text{first difference} \end{array}$$

The complement of the borrow-in is the most significant bit of the quotient. Moreover if the borrow-in is one, the minuend is reentered in the dividend register to be used to generate the next bit of the quotient. If the borrow-in is zero, the new difference is entered in the dividend register to serve as the next minuend instead of the borrow-in.

The circuit is clocked so that the first pulse enters the bit generated for the quotient into its shift register. The divisor register shifts right one bit on each clock pulse, so the divisor is properly aligned for subtraction in the next lower bit position. The process is repeated until the final quotient is developed. The word size of the quotient is equal to the total number of clock pulses used in the division.

## ARITHMETIC LOGIC UNIT (ALU)

Arithmetic logic units are MSI circuits which can perform a large variety of arithmetic operations. A single IC, such as the 74181 shown in Fig. 8-13, can add, subtract, shift, compare magnitudes, and provide many logic operations. The 74181 is programmable. That is, the selection inputs ($M$ and $S_0$ through $S_3$) determine which function will be performed. The function table in the figure lists the operations selected when positive logic is used. If negative logic is chosen, a different function table must be applied.

To prevent confusion between addition and the Boolean OR function, plus is spelled out in the table and the + sign is used to mean OR. The setting of the $M$ input decides whether the ALU will provide Boolean or arithmetic functions. With the $M$ input high, logic functions are provided. For example, setting $M$ high and the four $S$ input bits to $6_{16}$ will cause the ALU to perform an exclusive OR. The output is available at the 4-bit $F$ output termi-

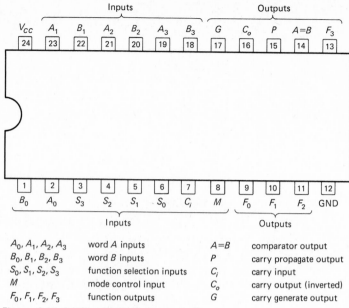

$A_0, A_1, A_2, A_3$   word $A$ inputs    $A=B$   comparator output

$B_0, B_1, B_2, B_3$   word $B$ inputs    $P$   carry propagate output

$S_0, S_1, S_2, S_3$   function selection inputs    $C_i$   carry input

$M$   mode control input    $C_o$   carry output (inverted)

$F_0, F_1, F_2, F_3$   function outputs    $G$   carry generate output

**Figure 8-13. 74181 arithmetic logic unit.**

## Positive Logic Functions

| Selection Inputs | | | | Logic Functions $M = 1$ | Arithmetic Functions $M = 0$ | |
|---|---|---|---|---|---|---|
| $S_3$ | $S_2$ | $S_1$ | $S_0$ | | $C_i = 1$ | $C_i = 0$ |
| 0 | 0 | 0 | 0 | $F = \overline{A}$ | $F = A$ | $F = A$ plus 1 |
| 0 | 0 | 0 | 1 | $F = \overline{A + B}$ | $F = A + \overline{B}$ | $F = A + \overline{B}$ plus 1 |
| 0 | 0 | 1 | 0 | $F = \overline{A}B$ | $F = A + \overline{B}$ | $F = A + \overline{B}$ plus 1 |
| 0 | 0 | 1 | 1 | $F = 0$ | $F = -1$ (2's comp.) | $F = 0$ |
| 0 | 1 | 0 | 0 | $F = \overline{AB}$ | $F = A$ plus $A\overline{B}$ | $F = A$ plus $A\overline{B}$ plus 1 |
| 0 | 1 | 0 | 1 | $F = \overline{B}$ | $F = A + B$ plus $AB$ | $F = A + B$ plus $AB$ plus 1 |
| 0 | 1 | 1 | 0 | $F = A \oplus B$ | $F = A - B - 1$ | $F = A - B$ |
| 0 | 1 | 1 | 1 | $F = A\overline{B}$ | $F = A\overline{B} - 1$ | $F = A\overline{B}$ |
| 1 | 0 | 0 | 0 | $F = \overline{A} + B$ | $F = A$ plus $AB$ | $F = A$ plus $AB$ plus 1 |
| 1 | 0 | 0 | 1 | $F = \overline{A \oplus B}$ | $F = A$ plus $B$ | $F = A$ plus $B$ plus 1 |
| 1 | 0 | 1 | 0 | $F = B$ | $F = A + \overline{B}$ plus $AB$ | $F = A + \overline{B}$ plus $AB$ plus 1 |
| 1 | 0 | 1 | 1 | $F = AB$ | $F = AB - 1$ | $F = AB$ |
| 1 | 1 | 0 | 0 | $F = 1$ | $F = A$ plus $A$* | $F = A$ plus $A$ plus 1 |
| 1 | 1 | 0 | 1 | $F = A + \overline{B}$ | $F = A + B$ plus $A$ | $F = A + B$ plus $A$ plus 1 |
| 1 | 1 | 1 | 0 | $F = A + B$ | $F = A + \overline{B}$ plus $A$ | $F = A + \overline{B}$ plus $A$ plus 1 |
| 1 | 1 | 1 | 1 | $F = A$ | $F = A - 1$ | $F = A$ |

* Each bit is shifted to the next more significant position.

**Table 8-3**
**Magnitude Comparison**
**in the 74181**

| Input $C_1$ | Output $C_o$ | Meaning |
|---|---|---|
| 1 | 1 | $A \leq B$ |
| 1 | 0 | $A > B$ |
| 0 | 1 | $A < B$ |
| 0 | 0 | $A \geq B$ |

nals. Arithmetic functions depend on the carry-in value as well as on the $M$ and $S$ inputs. With carry-in low, the ALU will add the $A$ and $B$ inputs if $M$ is low and $S$ is $9_{16}$. However, the same $S$ and $M$ inputs caused the sum of $A$ and $B$ plus one to be generated if the carry-in is low.

To find if the $A$ and $B$ inputs are equal, the ALU can be used as a comparator. The ALU must be in the subtract mode ($M = 0$, $S = 6_{16}$) and $C_i$ must be high. If the $A$ and $B$ inputs are equal, the $A = B$ output will be high. The $C_i$ and $C_o$ terminals can also be used to compare the magnitudes of $A$ and $B$ by using the ALU in the subtract mode we just discussed. Table 8-3 shows how to decode the relative magnitudes depending on the value of output $C_o$.

Several 74181 ICs can be cascaded to operate on multiple operands of 4-bit word length. Because the $A = B$ output is an open collector, a wired AND can be used to compare the magnitudes of words consisting of more than 4 bits.

**Arithmetic Logic Unit Review**

1. List the functions that an ALU can perform.
2. Define the purpose of the $M$ input.
3. Describe the types of magnitude comparisons that an ALU can make.
4. What two combinations of selection inputs to the 74181 produce outputs of zero regardless of the $A$ and $B$ input values?

**CHAPTER SUMMARY**

1. Binary adders are formed from half adders which produce separate sums and carry-outs. The full adder, built from two half adders, accepts a carry-in from the next lower position and generates a carry-out to the next higher position and a sum.
2. Carries can be propagated in a ripple fashion or, where higher speed is needed, in a look-ahead manner.
3. Serial adders sacrifice speed to reduce the amount of circuitry involved.
4. Simply placing inverters on one input of an adder and properly connecting the carry lines converts an adder to a subtractor.
5. Overflow errors can occur in adders or in subtractors if the numbers used for inputs are not within the range of the devices.
6. Multipliers use a series of adds and shifts clocked by control

logic. In multiplication, the product length is the sum of the word lengths of the multiplier and multiplicand.
7. Dividers use registers, subtractors, and combinatorial logic to perform a series of shifts and subtractions.
8. The arithmetic logic unit provides a programmable adder, subtractor, comparator, and logic network in a single IC.

| **KEY TERMS AND CONCEPTS** | adder | look-ahead carry |
|---|---|---|
| | half adder | serial adder |
| | full adder | subtractor |
| | carry-in and carry-out | multiplier |
| | overflow | divider |
| | ripple carry | arithmetic logic unit (ALU) |

## PROBLEMS

8-1. The inputs to a full adder are listed below. What is the value of the carry-out and the sum?

$$A = 1 \qquad B = 1 \qquad C_i = 1$$

8-2. Complete Table 8-4 for the adder shown in Fig. 8-4.

**Table 8-4**

| $A_3 = 0$ | $B_3 = 0$ | $S_3 =$ | $C_{03} =$ |
|---|---|---|---|
| $A_2 = 1$ | $B_2 = 0$ | $S_2 =$ | $C_{02} =$ |
| $A_1 = 0$ | $B_1 = 1$ | $S_1 =$ | $C_{01} =$ |
| $A_0 = 1$ | $B_0 = 1$ | $S_0 =$ | $C_{00} =$ |

8-3. Using a 4-bit adder, in which of the cases listed below does overflow occur?

a. $A = 6_{16}, B = 7_{16}$
b. $A = 2_{16}, B = 5_{16}$
c. $A = 4_{16}, B = 4_{16}$
d. $A = A_{16}, B = 1_{16}$

8-4. Using the look-ahead carry circuit of Fig. 8-5, find the value of the four carry-out bits if $A = 9_{16}$ and $B = 3_{16}$.

8-5. The inputs to a 7483 adder are listed below. What are the output levels of $S_0$ through $S_3$ and also $C_o$?

| $A_3 A_2 A_1 A_0$ | $B_3 B_2 B_1 B_0$ | $C_i$ |
|---|---|---|
| 0 1 0 1 | 1 0 0 1 | 1 |

8-6. The 4-bit subtractor has an $A$ input of $7_{16}$ and a $B$ input of $3_{16}$. What are the outputs at the difference terminals?

8-7. Prepare a table, similar to Table 8-2 and showing the contents of the multiplier's registers, for the following problem.

$$\begin{array}{r} D_{16} \\ \times\ 7_{16} \\ \hline \end{array}$$

8-8. Using the divider of Fig. 8-12, develop a table showing the contents of each register after each clock pulse for the following problem. The quotient is to be 4 bits in length.

$$C_{16}\overline{)36_{16}}$$

8-9. What is the result at the output terminals of a 74181 ALU with the following inputs?

| $S_3 = 1$ | $A_3 = 1$ | $B_3 = 1$ |
|---|---|---|
| $S_2 = 0$ | $A_2 = 0$ | $B_2 = 1$ |
| $S_1 = 1$ | $A_1 = 1$ | $B_1 = 0$ |
| $S_0 = 1$ | $A_0 = 0$ | $B_0 = 1$ |
| $M = 1$ | $C_i = 1$ | |

8-10. The 74181 is to be used to compare the values of $A$ and $B$ inputs. What can be concluded about the magnitudes of $A$ and $B$ if the inputs and outputs are

| $S_3 = 0$ | $M = 0$ |
|---|---|
| $S_2 = 1$ | $C_i = 1$ |
| $S_1 = 1$ | $A = B = 0$ |
| $S_0 = 0$ | $C_o = 1$ |

# EXPERIMENT 8 ADDERS

**PURPOSE**  To investigate binary adder operation.

**PARTS LIST**

| Item | Quantity |
|------|----------|
| 7482 | 1 |
| LED | 3 |
| 330 $\Omega$ resistor | 3 |
| SPDT switch | 4 |

**IC DIAGRAM**

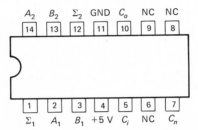

Figure 8-14. 7482.

| Function | MSB | LSB |
|----------|-----|-----|
| Input $A$ | $A_2$ | $A_1$ |
| Input $B$ | $B_2$ | $B_1$ |
| Carry-in | — | $C_i$ |
| Sum | $\Sigma_2$ | $\Sigma_1$ |
| Carry-out | — | $C_o$ |

**PROCEDURE**  **Step 1.**  Connect the circuit shown in Fig. 8-15.

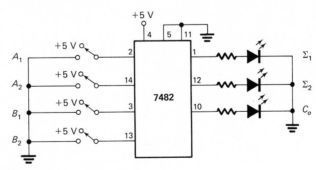

All resistors are 330 $\Omega$.

Figure 8-15. 2-bit adder experiment.

**Step 2.**  Using the switches, complete the positive logic truth table on page 150 showing the conditions of the LED indicators.

| Input Switches | | | | LEDs | | |
|---|---|---|---|---|---|---|
| Input $B$ | | Input $A$ | | | | |
| $B_2$ | $B_1$ | $A_2$ | $A_1$ | $\Sigma_2$ | $\Sigma_1$ | $C_o$ |
| 0 | 0 | 0 | 0 | | | |
| 0 | 0 | 0 | 1 | | | |
| 0 | 0 | 1 | 0 | | | |
| 0 | 0 | 1 | 1 | | | |
| 0 | 1 | 0 | 0 | | | |
| 0 | 1 | 0 | 1 | | | |
| 0 | 1 | 1 | 0 | | | |
| 0 | 1 | 1 | 1 | | | |
| 1 | 0 | 0 | 0 | | | |
| 1 | 0 | 0 | 1 | | | |
| 1 | 0 | 1 | 0 | | | |
| 1 | 0 | 1 | 1 | | | |
| 1 | 1 | 0 | 0 | | | |
| 1 | 1 | 0 | 1 | | | |
| 1 | 1 | 1 | 0 | | | |
| 1 | 1 | 1 | 1 | | | |

**Step 3.** Now connect pin 5 to +5 volts, and repeat the experiment. Compare the table with the one you obtained in Step 2. What is the purpose of the pin 5 input?

# CHAPTER NINE
# MEMORIES

Memories allow digital systems to store (write) and retrieve (read) information. These same functions are performed by flip-flops and registers, as we have seen, but memories provide storage for more than a single bit or word. Most memories are capable or both read and write operations, though a special class of read-only memories is used for storing data that does not require updating. The various construction techniques used to build memories affect their cost, storage capacity, and response time.

**CHAPTER OBJECTIVES**   Upon completing this chapter you should be able to:

1. Distinguish between random-access memories and read-only memories.
2. Describe how data are stored in and retrieved from memories.
3. Describe the programming processes used to store information in read-only memories.
4. Discuss typical methods of organizing memories.
5. Describe the operation of core memories.
6. Discuss the theory of operation for charge-coupled devices and bubble memories.

**SEMICONDUCTOR MEMORIES**   The discussion in this chapter will begin with memories based on semiconductor devices. Other types of memories include magnetic cores and moving-surface memories. Comparisons between semiconductor-type and other memories should make the distinctions clear.

As mentioned earlier most memories are read/write. If the memory can access all of its storage locations in the same amount of time, it is called a random-access memory. The fixed read or write period for this kind of memory is called the *memory-cycle time.*

Contrast this constant access time with the access times for *serial* and *block* memories, which both require variable amounts of time to reach a given storage location. An example of a serial-access memory is the magnetic tape cassette. Information is stored as flux patterns on magnetic material. Cassettes can store $10^6$ to $10^7$ bits and access the data in 10 to 100 seconds. Large disk-drive units are examples of block memories which can store $10^9$ to $10^{10}$ bits and access in about 20 milliseconds.

If the information stored in a memory is retained when power is shut off, the storage is *nonvolatile*. Most moving-surface memories are nonvolatile. Cores are also nonvolatile. In contrast, many semiconductor memories are *volatile*. Memories fabricated from bipolar, PMOS, NMOS, CMOS, and VMOS elements are volatile, whereas charge-coupled devices and bubble memories are nonvolatile. (The VMOS, or V-groove MOS, uses minute indentations etched in the silicon wafer vertical structure. This fabrication technique produces a fast, dense memory configuration. Typical response times are on the order of 45 nanoseconds.)

## RANDOM-ACCESS MEMORIES (RAM)

There are two basic types of semiconductor RAM construction. Just as in the MOS circuits of Chap. 4, RAMs can be either *static* or *dynamic*. Static RAM memories do not require a refresh cycle, but they must always have power. Dynamic RAMs store information in capacitors which allow power to be shut off most of the time, but the charge on the capacitor must be refreshed about 500 times a second.

Memory size is specified by giving two dimensions. For example a $1 \times 16,384$ contains 16,384 one-bit storage locations. Often the same memory size is written $1 \times 16K$. The letter K stands for 1024 bits ($16 \times 1024 = 16,384$). Some writers may use K to mean 1000 bits instead of 1024. Little confusion results regardless of which value is used for K. Sometimes the first dimension is omitted if it is one; for example, a $1 \times 4K$ RAM could simply be referred to as 4K.

## Static MOS RAM

Figure 9-1 shows a static MOS RAM storage cell. This is only a single cell in the entire memory array. The cell uses coincident *x-y* addressing to select each memory location. $Q_1$ and $Q_3$ form an inverter and so does $Q_2$ with $Q_4$. The two inverters are cross-connected into a flip-flop. $Q_5$ and $Q_6$ act as a NAND gate used with the *x-y coincident addressing* scheme. $Q_7$ and $Q_8$ are another NAND gate which is also used in addressing the cell.

Remember that this memory location is only one in a large

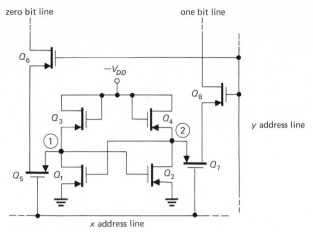

**Figure 9-1. Static MOS RAM cell.**

memory matrix. You can picture the memory as a two-dimensional Cartesian coordinate system with a cell at each intersection on the surface. Just as in the coordinate system, there are many $x$ and $y$ lines, but only one memory cell is placed at the intersection of each $x$ and $y$ addressing line. If a negative voltage $(-V_{DD})$ is applied to only one $y$ address line, transistors $Q_6$ and $Q_8$ of every cell along that line will be turned on because of the negative gate voltage. If one $x$ line is also set to $-V_{DD}$, $Q_5$ and $Q_7$ of all the cells along that line are on. But at only one memory location (where the $x$ and $y$ lines set to $-V_{DD}$ intersect) are all of the selection transistors on. At other cells only two of the four are on if the set $x$ or $y$ line passes through that cell. As we will see below all of those transistors must be on to activate the cell. The memory selection by the use of a negative voltage on the address lines coincident with a single cell give us the name.

We will arbitrarily define the state with $Q_2$ on and $Q_1$ off to mean that a one is stored in the cell. The opposite states of the two transistors will indicate a zero. In the quiescent condition, the $x$ and $y$ address lines are at ground, thus isolating the flip-flop from the bit lines.

To follow the memory-cell operation, assume that initially $Q_2$ is on and $Q_1$ is off. This state produces a voltage of $-V_{DD}$ at point 1 on Fig. 9-1 and 0 volts at point 2. Now if we want to read the contents of the cell, the $x$ and $y$ address lines are pulsed with a negative voltage. This voltage on their gates turns $Q_5$, $Q_6$, $Q_7$, and $Q_8$ on, and so selects this memory cell. Next a voltage of $-V_{DD}$ is applied to both of the bit lines.

Current flows into the 1-bit line because $Q_7$, $Q_8$, and $Q_2$ are on. Very little current (almost none) can flow into the 0-bit line because $Q_1$ is off and point 1 is at $-V_{DD}$ also. The state of the memory contents is read by determining which bit line has current flowing into the cell. The reading of the cell is *nondestructive readout* (NDRO). That is, the value stored in the cell was not altered during the reading process.

Writing into the cell depends on whether a one or a zero is to be stored. To write a one, the $x$ and $y$ address lines are pulsed, and the 1-bit line is grounded. Because point 2 is already at 0 volts, no change in the cell's state occurs. A one had already been stored, so writing in a one for a second time will not have any effect.

Next a zero is to be written. After the $x$ and $y$ address lines are pulsed, the 0-bit line is grounded. This action will pull point 1 to ground, changing the gate voltage to $Q_2$. $Q_2$ is turned off by its grounded gate, and current flow stops causing the voltage at point 2 to switch to $-V_{DD}$. That voltage on the gate of $Q_1$ causes the transistor to turn on. Now the memory cell contains a value of zero.

A typical static MOS RAM might be packaged in a 24-pin DIP and contain 1K to 4K bits. Cycle time is in the range of 200 nanoseconds to 1 microsecond. The outputs are usually TTL and DTL compatible.

## Dynamic MOS RAM

As memory design has evolved, memory size has gotten smaller and fewer transistors are required. Figure 9-2 shows a dynamic RAM which stores information in a small (0.05 picofarad) capacitor. If the charge on the capacitor is high, then a one has been stored. The dynamic memory must be rewritten, or refreshed, about 500 times a second.

Assume that the capacitor is charged to 12 volts and we want to read the memory. The word-read line is pulsed with 12 volts, turning $Q_3$ on. $Q_2$ is on because of the voltage on the capacitor, so applying 12 volts to the data output line causes current to flow into the cell. If the capacitor had been discharged, $Q_2$ would be off and there would be no current.

To write a one, the word-write line is pulsed, turning $Q_1$ on. Then 12 volts is applied to the data input line. Current will flow into the circuit until the capacitor is charged. Writing a zero is accomplished by grounding the data input line, which causes the capacitor to discharge.

An even simpler dynamic memory cell, consisting of only one transistor, is shown in Fig. 9-3, together with a block diagram of its sensing and input/output components. Reading the cell is a two-step process. First the row-selection line is set to $+12$ volts, then the column-selection line is sensed to determine if current is flowing or not. Current flow indicates that the capacitor must have been charged; that is, a one was stored. No current means a zero was in the cell. Reading is nondestructive because the charge on the capacitor is not disturbed.

**Figure 9-2. Dyanmic MOS RAM memory cell.**

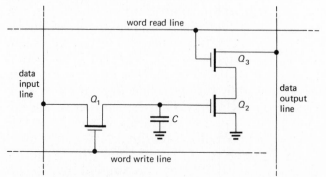

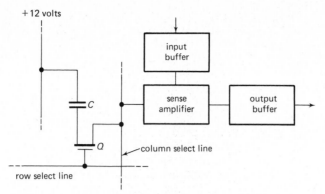

**Figure 9-3. Dynamic MOS memory cell and output logic.**

Writing a zero calls for setting the row-selection line to 12 volts and grounding the column-selection line. This sequence discharges the capacitor. A one is stored by again setting the row-selection line and opening the column-selection line to allow the capacitor to charge.

The sense amplifier detects the presense or absence of current, and thus the content of the cell. The output is passed to the buffer, which stores the information until it can be sent to the next component in the output circuit. Incoming data are stored in the input buffer until the proper time to write, then the sense amplifier either opens or grounds the column selection-line depending on whether a one or zero is to be written into the memory.

**Static Bipolar RAM**  A TTL RAM cell is shown in Fig. 9-4. It consists of two transistors and two resistors. The transistors are connected similarly to $Q_1$ and $Q_2$ in Fig. 9-1 and form a flip-flop. Only one of the two transistors is on; the other one is off because its base is held low by the low collector on the saturated transistor.

Assume that if $Q_1$ is on a one is stored. If the $x$- and $y$-selection lines are at 0 volts, $Q_1$ has a low impedance path to ground. Therefore, the zero and one sense lines have low outputs.

Both the $x$ and $y$ lines are set high to select the cell. The collector current from $Q_1$ will flow out of the one sense line, indi-

**Figure 9-4. Bipolar RAM cell.**

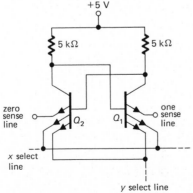

**Table 9-1**
**Memory Technologies**

| Type | Number of Transistors per Cell | Cell Size, mils$^2$ | Access Time, $\mu$s | Power, mW Operate | Power, mW Standby |
|---|---|---|---|---|---|
| NMOS (dynamic) | 2 | 2.3 | 0.3 | 240 | 10 |
| CMOS (static) | 6 | 12.5 | 0.2 | 10 | 2 |
| Bipolar (static) | 6 | 9.8 | 0.06 | 500 | 150 |

cating that a one was stored in the cell. No current flows in the zero sense line because $Q_2$ is off.

Writing a one in the cell requires that the $x$ and $y$ lines be set high and the sense line be grounded; this condition causes base-emitter current to flow in $Q_1$, but $Q_1$ is already on and consequently no change in state occurs. The other sense line is used to write a zero. If the zero sense line is grounded, current begins to flow in the base-emitter junction of $Q_2$, turning it on, and this will cause the base of $Q_1$ to go low and turn $Q_1$ off.

Table 9-1 compares three examples of memory technology. The table shows that it is possible to trade off power for speed. Bipolar memories are fastest and consume the most power.

**RAM Review**

1. Distinguish between a random-access memory and a serial-access memory. How is a block memory different from either of these memories?
2. Define the term volatile with respect to memories.
3. List the differences between static and dynamic RAMs. How are they alike?
4. How many bits does a 4 × 16K memory contain?
5. Define the coincident $x$-$y$ addressing method used for MOS RAMs.
6. Describe the similarities and differences between static MOS and bipolar RAMs.

**READ-ONLY MEMORIES (ROM)**

There are two general types of ROMs in use. The MOS ROM retains data as a stored charge on the gate of each transistor. This kind of ROM is erasable and can be rewritten, or reprogrammed. The MOS ROM is called a programmable ROM (PROM). The other type of ROM is bipolar. The bipolar ROM is permanently altered. Interconnecting links within the chip are broken or left off. There is also a programmable form of the bipolar ROM, but it is not erasable. It can only be written once.

The bipolar ROM can be manufactured (mask programmed) with a pattern stored in the memory cells. In another form of the bipolar ROM, metal (Nichrome) links between transistors are

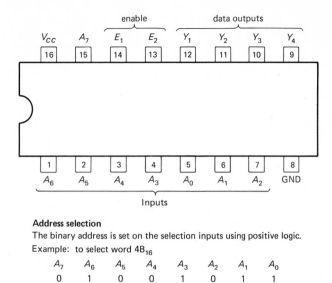

**Address selection**

The binary address is set on the selection inputs using positive logic.

Example: to select word $4B_{16}$

| $A_7$ | $A_6$ | $A_5$ | $A_4$ | $A_3$ | $A_2$ | $A_1$ | $A_0$ |
|---|---|---|---|---|---|---|---|
| 0 | 1 | 0 | 0 | 1 | 0 | 1 | 1 |

**Outputs**

$Y_1$ is the least significant bit of the output, $Y_4$ is the most significant.

**Figure 9-5. 74187 ROM.**

blown open. Other bipolar ROMs are programmed by shorting the semiconductor junctions by means of avalanching or fusing open the crystalline silicon links in much the same way as the metal ones were treated. When they were first developed, there was a problem with regrowth of the blown links; this regeneration would disrupt the programmed pattern of the ROM. Use of silicon links seems to have eliminated the regrowth problem.

## Mask-Programmed ROM

A mask-programmed 74187 ROM is shown in Fig. 9-5. Each customer specifies the 256 4-bit words that are to be written into the ROM. Once written, the memory cannot be changed. The 4-bit word is addressed by setting the eight selection lines to the word number (address). Each output is an open collector, so wired logic can be used with the memory. The access time for the IC is about 40 nanoseconds, and power dissipation is 0.5 milliwatt for each bit in the memory. Both enable bits must be set low for the $Y_1$ through $Y_4$ terminals to generate the output.

## Programmable ROM

The structure of a MOS PROM memory cell is shown in Fig. 9-6. The cross section of the silicon chip reveals that the gate is not connected to any external lead. The silicon gate is said to be isolated in the silicon dioxide, and hence bears the name *isolated gate*.

Writing a one in the memory requires that the gate be charged. The charging is accomplished by avalanche injection of about 30 volts on a machine called a *ROM programmer*. The charged gate will induce a P-channel, as shown in Fig. 9-6b, and the transistor will conduct current from the source to the drain. There will be no current flow in transistors with an uncharged gate. If the mem-

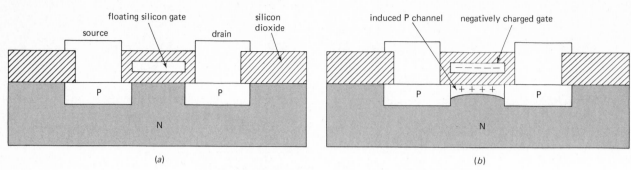

Figure 9-6. MOS PROM. (a) Zero stored, (b) one stored.

ory is to be erased, it is exposed to ultraviolet light which causes a photoelectric current to flow between the gate and silicon substrate. The charge quickly bleeds off, and the memory is ready to be reprogrammed. MOS PROMs have a transparent window above the memory chip so that light can strike it. Because it can be erased by any form of radiation, the MOS PROM is not suitable for use in space, where it would be subjected to many kinds of radiation. Properly sheltered, the PROM will retain its charge for about 10 years.

## ROM Characteristics

The characteristics of the ROM depend on the technology used in its manufacture. MOS ROMs have access times of about 100 nanoseconds when they are used with a 5-volt power supply. They are available in sizes ranging from 1K to 16K. The bipolar ROMs can be accessed in about 50 nanoseconds and come in packages of 256 to 8K bits.

Electrically alterable ROMs (EAROMs) can be used when the data remain constant over long periods of time, but eventually they must be rewritten. These devices are fabricated from a metal nitride oxide semiconductor (MNOS). There are not many applications that use EAROMs today. They are expensive, require excessive time for writing, and have demonstrated low reliability.

## ROM Review

1. Distinguish between the two types of ROMs. Which one is erasable?
2. Describe how a one is written into the isolated-gate PROM. How is a zero stored?
3. If you were designing a new calculator which requires a stored sine/cosine table, which type of ROM would you use?

## RAM ORGANIZATION

Now that you understand the operation of a single memory cell, let's investigate how the cells are organized into memory arrays. Figure 9-7 shows a block diagram of a $1 \times 4K$ memory. The memory designer must efficiently use the pins on the package. Packages with a minimum pin count are most economical and least likely to be damaged. Most important to pin count is the addressing method chosen. The coincident $x$-$y$ addressing used in

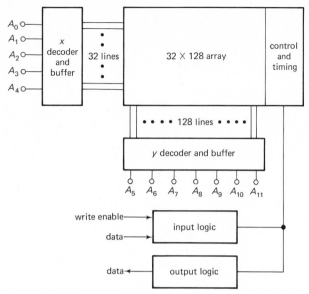

**Figure 9-7. Dynamic RAM organization.**

our study of individual cells allows every bit in the memory of Fig. 9-7 to be addressed by using only 12 bits, $A_0$ through $A_{11}$.

Bits $A_0$ through $A_4$ specify which of 32 ($2^5 = 32$) $x$ rows will be selected, and the 7 bits $A_5$ through $A_{11}$ select which of the 128 ($2^7$) columns will be enabled. Decoding an address requires that the 12-bit code be split into two parts; the least significant 5 bits represent the $x$ row and the most significant bits are the $y$ column.

The $x$ and $y$ decoders are demultiplexers such as were described in Chap. 2. Only one output line from each decoder will be set high and thus will select a single cell in the array. The control and timing logic circuits are used to enable the read and write cycles and also to refresh the contents of the dynamic memory.

The internal timing generator produces three clock phases. In phase, 1 preconditioning of internal circuits is accomplished. During phase 2, data are read or written; and phase 3 is used to initiate refresh. Whether the operation is to be a read or a write depends on the state of the write enable input. A high input enables writing.

Even more pin reduction can be realized by using a *split cycle* for address selection. During the first half of the address-selection cycle the column address is applied to the selection lines. This signal is often designated $\overline{CAS}$. Then the row address, $\overline{RAS}$, is put on the selection lines for the second part of the cycle. The two-wave or split-address method allows a 64K memory to be addressed with only eight pins. In that case, the 64K memory would be organized into 256 rows and 256 columns ($2^8 \times 2^8$).

**CORE MEMORIES** Small ferrite toroids, or cores, are commonly used in high-speed electronically alterable memories for both minicomputers and larger computers. Memory systems ranging from small 1K scratchpad size to large bulk memories of 5000K storage capacity have been built by using cores.

A large number of cores is required in building a memory because each core stores only 1 bit. A memory requires $W \times L$ cores,
with $W$ representing the number of words and $L$ the word length
in bits, as shown in Fig. 9-8a. Most core memories use a
*coincident-current matrix* system for core selection; this system is
similar to the coincident $x$-$y$ address selection method used in
semiconductor memories.

Two different core-winding configurations are shown in Fig.
9-8b. If an $x$ current and a $y$ current flowing through a core in the
same direction are sufficient to equal the write current (that is, the
current necessary for the core to switch states), the coincident $x$
and $y$ currents are said to address the core. As shown in Fig. 9-8c,
the core characteristic switching curve requires a current more
negative than that of point $A$ to switch to the zero state or more
positive than that at point $B$ to cause switching to the one state.
When enough current flows in the wires threading through the
core, the core is magnetized in the direction indicated by the current polarity.

**Figure 9-8. Core memories. (a) Number of cores, (b) core windings, (c) switching characteristics.**

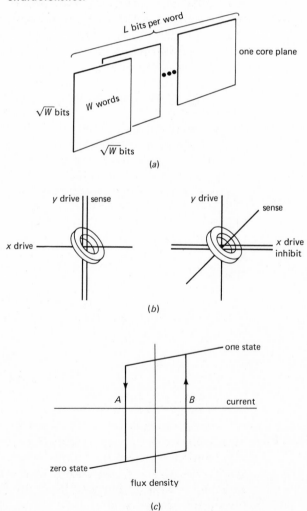

**Reading Core Memory**

Reading the stored data in a core is *destructive readout.* It is accomplished by writing a zero into the selected core address. If the core was in the one state, flux reversal results. This change in flux causes a pulse on a sense line which can be detected at the sense terminals. If the core was already in the zero state, no flux reversal occurs and there is only a small pulse on the sense line. The pulse amplitude of a core switched from the one state will be much greater than that of one already in the zero state, so the data in the core can be found by noting the pulse amplitude. (Typical ratios between pulse amplitudes in the one and zero states may be as low as $2:1$ or $3:1$.) Before the memory cycle is complete, the original content of the cell is restored by rewriting.

In most core memories, as shown in Fig. 9-9, the value of the write current is divided in two; the $x$ winding carries half of the write current and the $y$ winding supplies the remainder. Thus, only the core threaded by a coincident $x$ and $y$ current will be addressed. The $2 \times 2$ core plane shown will serve as an example. Let the $x_2$ and $y_1$ windings each have half the current required to write a one placed in them. Only core number 1 will have enough current to switch to a one. Core 2 and 4 only have half the required switching current, so they remain in their previous states. Core 3 has no current flowing through it because neither the $x_2$ nor the $y_1$ windings pass through it. Note that there is only one sense line required for the entire plane. The address of the core being read is known by the $x$ and $y$ lines selected.

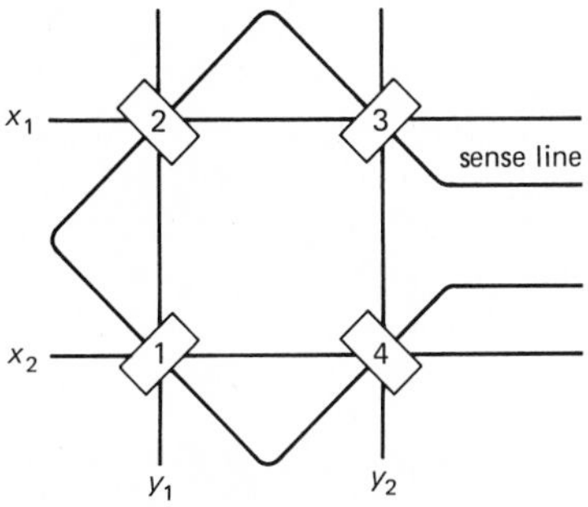

Figure 9-9. 2x2 core plane.

**Core Memory Organization**

The three basic memory organizations used for cores are shown in Fig. 9-10. These are two-dimensional (2D), three-dimensional (3D), and $2\frac{1}{2}$ dimensional ($2\frac{1}{2}$D). The 2D system is easily wired, but is limited to a single plane. For that reason, it is suitable only for scratchpad memories of less than 1K capacity. Each plane of the 3D system has a sense line and an inhibit line. Inhibit lines are wired to oppose either the $x$ or the $y$ drive line. The inhibit lines are set to address the correct plane by placing an opposing half switching current on all but one of them. The inhibit lines cancel the drive current on the $x$ or $y$ line parallel to them on all but the one plane addressed. The $2\frac{1}{2}$D system is a combination of the other two. It is not as complex as the 3D system yet has more capacity than the 2D memory. The $x$ line passes through all of the memory planes, while each plane has its own set of $y$ lines. A single sense line may be used for all planes, and the inhibit line is not required.

**Core Memory Review**

1. How many cores would an 8K memory with 16-bit word lengths contain?
2. Describe the coincident-current addressing method used on core memories.
3. Describe the method used to read core memories. Why is it called destructive?
4. Distinguish between 2D, 3D, and $2\frac{1}{2}$D memory organizations.
5. Define the purpose of the inhibit line. Why is it only necessary on 3D memories?

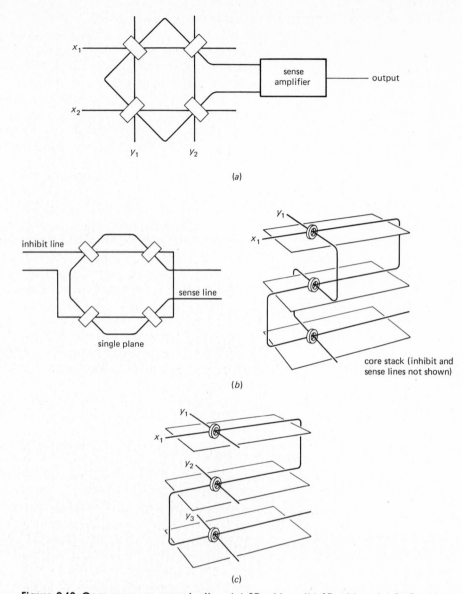

Figure 9-10. Core memory organization. (a) 2D wiring, (b) 3D wiring, (c) 2½D wiring.

**CHARGE-COUPLED DEVICE (CCD) MEMORIES**

CCD memories provide serial access to each word. The bits move serially through an array of 64 or more locations between the times when data are written and when they become available for reading. Figure 9-11 shows two CCD memory arrays. The synchronous parallel-serial-parallel memory accepts data in 64-bit parallel format. The data are then serially transferred as single bits through each of the 64 columns in the array. Each of the 64 columns can store 64 bits, so the total capacity is 4096 bits.

The charge of the stored information is held at nodes in the memory. These nodes have low capacitance, so the signal is not attenuated as it would be in a RAM, and therefore the amplifiers and refresh circuitry can be simpler. As each bit reaches the regeneration circuits, it is available at the parallel output; alternatively, the data can be recirculated to the top of the memory and

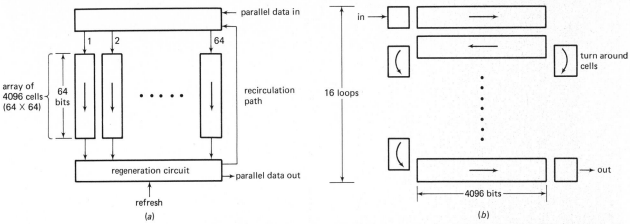

**Figure 9-11. CCD memories. (a) Synchronous parallel-serial-parallel, (b)synchronous serpentine.**

**Figure 9-12. CCD memory (*Fairchild Camera and Instrument Corporation*).**

kept in storage. The access time is a product of the number of locations in the column and the cycle time needed to move one bit position down the column. This time is usually 100 microseconds to 1 millisecond.

The serpentine CCD memory shifts the bits along loops then uses turnaround cells to bring the bits into the next lower loop. The memory shown has a 64K (16 × 4096) capacity. Such memories can be built on a 3.5 × 5 millimeter chip. Figure 9-12 shows a photomicrograph of a 64K memory. The CCD memory has a smaller area per cell than the RAM. Because of the serial nature of CCD memories, address decoding is also simpler.

## BUBBLE MEMORIES

Microscopic bubbles, or magnetic domains, can be used to store data in special memories. The bubbles form in a magnetic film which is exposed to magnetic lines of force perpendicular to the film plane. Domains of one polarization (say downward) are stable within an area on the film of opposite polarization (upward). These domains can be moved by using weak magnetic fields at right angles to the main field. By organizing the domains, bubbles are formed. The stored pattern can be made nonvolatile by using permanent magnets as the source of the perpendicular field. The memory designer designates the presence of a domain to represent a one, so the absence of a domain means a zero. By using electromagnetic loops on the surface of the film, the domains can be generated or removed. Rotating magnetic fields are used to shift the domains along fixed patterns, or loops. The patterns are established by electrodes shaped like Ts or chevrons.

Figure 9-13 shows a bubble-memory configuration. The memory is organized serially with an access time of about 100 microseconds. The major loop of the memory contains one data block. To write, the serial input is applied to the generation head. After all bits have entered the major loop, they are simultaneously trans-

**Figure 9-13. Bubble memory.**

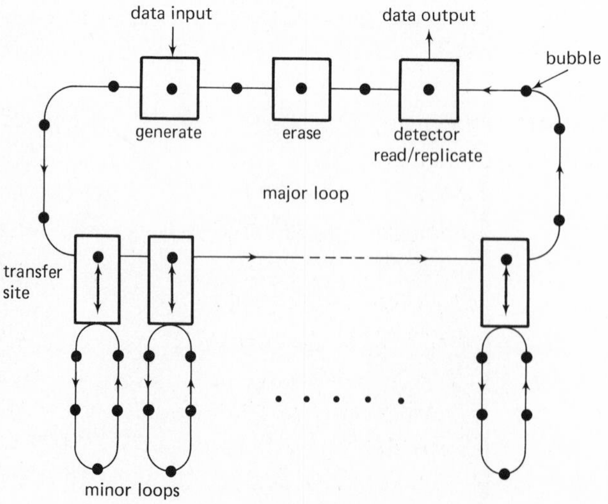

ferred to the minor loops (one bit to each loop). Each minor loop circulates the bubbles within that loop.

A reverse process is used to read the memory. After simultaneous transfer from the minor loops to the major loop, each bubble passes under the detector. The output is serial. Bubbles in the major loop can be regenerated, erased, or rewritten. The memory size is the product of the number of bubble sites per minor loop and the number of minor loops.

**CHAPTER SUMMARY**

1. Most memories can both store and retrieve data, but read-only memories can be used to store unchanging data.
2. Semiconductor memories are random access. The time required to address any storage location is equal to that required to address any other location.
3. If the memory retains its information without power, it is nonvolatile. Volatile memories must remain under power at all times.
4. Semiconductor RAMs may be static or dynamic. Dynamic RAMs require periodic refresh cycles, but use less power.
5. Coincident $x$-$y$ address selection is the most commonly used method for RAMs.
6. Bipolar RAMs use two transistors which form a flip-flop.
7. MOS ROMs may be erased and rewritten, while bipolar ROMs are permanently programmed.
8. Memories are organized to minimize the number of pins needed to address each cell. Minimum pin count can be achieved by using split-cycle address selection.
9. Core memories use ferrite toroids magnetized in one of two directions. Addressing is by coincident current selection. Core memory reading is destructive and requires a write cycle after each read.
10. The organization of core memories can be 2D, 3D, or $2\frac{1}{2}$D.
11. CCD memories use serial storage and retrieval. The information moves through columns or loops and may be regenerated.
12. Magnetic bubble memories use magnetic domains grouped into circulating loops. Magnetic fields control the formation and movement of the bubbles.

**KEY TERMS AND CONCEPTS**

memory
write
read
random-access memory (RAM)
serial-access memory
block-access memory
access time
volatile and nonvolatile memory
static MOS RAM

dynamic MOS RAM
coincident $x$-$y$ addressing
bipolar RAM
read-only memory (ROM)
programmable ROM (PROM)
electrically alterable ROM (EAROM)
memory organization
split-cycle addressing
core memory

coincident $x$-$y$ current addressing

destructive and nondestructive readout (NDRO)

2D, 3D, and 2½D memories

CCD memories

bubble memories

## PROBLEMS

9-1. In Fig. 9-1, transistors $Q_8$, $Q_1$, and $Q_6$ are on. What would be the result of setting the $x$ address and both bit lines to $-5$ volts? (Let $V_{DD} = -5$ volts.)

9-2. The dynamic memory cell of Fig. 9-2 has 12 volts placed on the word-read line and also on the word-write line. What would be the outcome if the capacitor were charged and the output line were connected to the input line?

9-3. The bipolar RAM has a zero stored in it. In which sense line of Fig. 9-4 would current flow if the $y$ select line were grounded and the $x$ select line set high?

9-4. A partial listing of the 74187 ROM contents is given below. What would be on each of the four output lines for the following inputs? What is the total power consumption of the ROM?

**Partial ROM Contents**

| Address$_{16}$ | Contents$_{16}$ |
|---|---|
| B7 | 6 |
| B8 | 3 |
| B9 | F |
| BA | 7 |
| BB | D |
| BC | 1 |

| | $A_0$ | $A_1$ | $A_2$ | $A_3$ | $A_4$ | $A_5$ | $A_6$ | $A_7$ | $E_1$ | $E_2$ |
|---|---|---|---|---|---|---|---|---|---|---|
| Input 1 | 0 | 1 | 0 | 1 | 1 | 1 | 0 | 1 | 0 | 1 |
| Input 2 | 0 | 0 | 1 | 1 | 1 | 1 | 0 | 1 | 0 | 0 |

9-5. Refer to Fig. 9-7.
 a. Which specific $x$ and $y$ lines are selected for address $1738_{10}$? ($x$ lines are numbered 0 to $31_{10}$ and $y$ lines 0 to $127_{10}$)
 b. $x$ line $29_{10}$ and $y$ line $89_{10}$ being selected correspond to which decimal address?

9-6. A 2½D core memory uses 16-bit words. Total memory capacity is 65,536 bits and there are the same number of rows and columns in the array.

 a. How many memory planes are used in the memory?
 b. How many $x$ (row) address lines are used in each plane? In the entire memory?
 c. How many $y$ (column) lines are used in each plane? In the entire memory?

9-7. A certain 3D core memory uses 15 address bits to reference each of its 30-bit words. How many bits does the memory contain?

9-8. Using a split addressing cycle, a MOS RAM integrated circuit requires seven address pins. Words are 4-bits long.

 a. How many $x$ address lines are required for the RAM?
 b. How many $y$ address lines?
 c. What is the total bit capacity of the memory?

9-9. A 4K bipolar RAM is used to store single-bit quantities. The RAM does not use split-cycle addressing. If there are four $x$ row selection address bits, how many $y$ address bits are used to reference the memory?

9-10. Associated with many memories are two registers used for addressing and reading or writing. The memory address register (MAR) holds the address of the word that is currently being written or read. The memory buffer register (MBR) holds the data being written into or read out of the memory. A small memory segment is shown on page 167. After the sequence of events listed, what is the final content of each memory location?

| Address$_{16}$ | Initial Content$_{16}$ |
|---|---|
| 1000 | AF |
| 1001 | 21 |
| 1002 | 5C |
| 1003 | 21 |
| 1004 | 59 |
| 1005 | 77 |

| Event | MAR$_{16}$ | MBR$_{16}$ | Write Enable |
|---|---|---|---|
| 1 | 1003 | 72 | on |
| 2 | 1001 | 16 | on |
| 3 | 1003 | 44 | on |
| 4 | 1005 | 44 | off |
| 5 | 1003 | 77 | off |
| 6 | 1000 | 77 | on |

# EXPERIMENT 9 RAM OPERATION

**PURPOSE**   To investigate the operation of a random-access memory.

**PARTS LIST**

| Item | Quantity |
|---|---|
| 7489 | 1 |
| LED | 4 |
| 330-$\Omega$ resistor | 4 |
| DPDT switch | 9 |

**IC DIAGRAM**

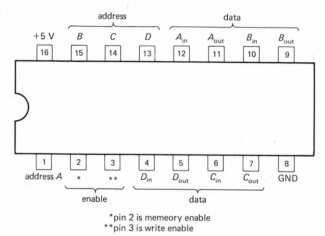

Figure 9-14. 7489.

### Function Table

| Function | *Pins | | | |
|---|---|---|---|---|
| | $D$ | $C$ | $B$ | $A$ |
| Data input | 4 | 6 | 10 | 12 |
| Data output | 5 | 7 | 9 | 11 |
| Address | 13 | 14 | 15 | 1 |

\* $A$ is the least significant bit and $D$ is most significant.

**PROCEDURE**   Memory enable (pin 2) is grounded during normal operation. Write enable (pin 3) must be grounded to write, $+5$ volts to read. The 16 storage locations (0 to $F_{16}$) can each hold one 4-bit word.

**Step 1.**   Connect the circuit as shown in Fig. 9-15.

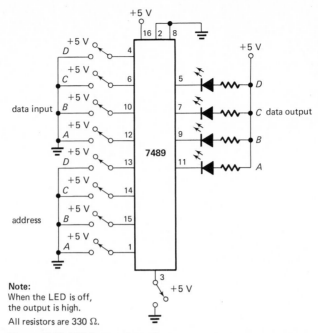

**Figure 9-15. RAM experiment.**

**Step 2.** Ground the switch connected to pin 3. Write the number 0 through $F_{16}$ in memory addresses 0 through $F_{16}$, respectively, using the data input and address switches.

**Step 3.** Read each address in turn by setting the proper combination of input switches. (You must connect the switch on pin 3 to +5 volts first.) Record your results.

**Step 4.** Momentarily disconnect pin 16 from the power supply. Repeat Step 3. What does this tell you about the 7489 RAM?

# CHAPTER TEN
# LINEAR CIRCUITS

Linear circuits are characterized by having outputs that are directly proportional to their inputs. Most analog circuits are linear, at least over a major portion of their operating range. The basic linear circuit is the operational amplifier, or *op amp*. These amplifiers are available in small, highly reliable, and economical integrated circuits. Op amps are used in many ways, but this chapter will focus on their use in pulse applications. The use of linear circuits as triggers and timers will be covered as well. The conversion of signals from analog to digital form and vice versa involve yet another important class of linear circuits which will be discussed.

**CHAPTER OBJECTIVES**  After completing this chapter, you should be able to:

1. Name the characteristics of an ideal operational amplifier and discuss how these change in real devices.
2. Distinguish between the inverting and noninverting inputs to operational amplifiers.
3. Discuss the use of operational amplifiers for pulse applications.
4. Describe the power-supply requirements of operational amplifiers.
5. Discuss the operation of a Schmitt trigger.
6. Describe the 555 integrated timing circuit and indicate how the timing period is controlled by the selection of external components.

**7.** Discuss the operation of digital-to-analog (D/A) and analog-to-digital (A/D) converters.

**OPERATIONAL AMPLIFIERS**

Op amps were originally the primary components of analog computers. Together with a feedback network, the high-gain amplifiers performed such operations as adding, subtracting, integrating, and differentiating. Although op amps are still used for these functions, we will be interested in them for their use in circuits with pulse inputs or outputs. Figure 10-1 shows an op amp packaged much like a transistor. Op amps are also available as DIPs.

The symbol for an op amp is shown in Fig. 10-2a. There are two input terminals. The one marked with a minus sign is the inverting input; the other, with the plus sign, is the noninverting input. Why the terminals are given those names will become clearer in the next section. The input voltage $v_i$ is defined as

$$v_i = v_1 - v_2 \qquad (10\text{-}1)$$

The amplifier has a voltage gain $A_v$, thus the output voltage must be

$$v_o = A_v v_i \qquad (10\text{-}2)$$

An equivalent circuit for the op amp input is shown in Fig. 10-2b. The input voltages, $v_1$ and $v_2$, are measured relative to ground. The input resistance of the amplifier is represented by $R_i$. Figure 10-2c is equivalent to the amplifier output. A voltage source of $A_v v_i$ is the output voltage, and $R_o$ is the output resistance of the op amp.

Two precisely balanced positive and negative voltages are needed in the op amp power supply. Two ways of providing

**Figure 10-1. Operational amplifier (*Burr-Brown*).**

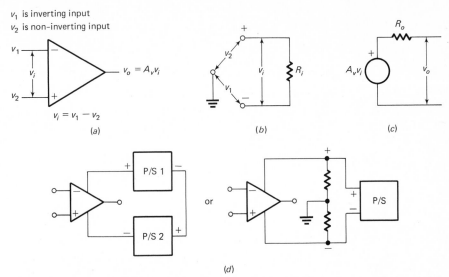

$v_1$ is inverting input
$v_2$ is non-inverting input

$v_o = A_v v_i$

$v_i = v_1 - v_2$

(a)

(b)

(c)

(d)

**Figure 10-2. Ideal operational amplifier (a) Symbol, (b) equivalent input circuit, (c) equivalent output circuit, (d) power-supply configurations.**

power to an op amp are shown in Fig. 10-2d. Separate supplies connected at a common ground can be used. Alternatively two identical resistors allow a single power supply to provide the required voltages. The resistor values must remain in balance in spite of temperature changes.

## The Ideal Op Amp

As a first approximation, we can examine the characteristics of an idealized amplifier. These characteristics help us to understand how an op amp performs in a circuit. Table 10-1 lists the features that we would find in an ideal device.

Let's examine a circuit to understand what Table 10-1 means. Figure 10-3 shows the basic op amp *inverting circuit*. Because the input resistance is infinite, all of the input current must pass through $R_2$, and none enters the op amp. With the feedback resistor in place, voltage gain in the ideal op amp becomes

$$A_{vf} = -R_2/R_1 \qquad (10\text{-}3)$$

In a practical op amp, however, the actual input and output re-

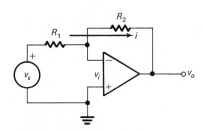

**Figure 10-3. Basic inverting op amp circuit.**

## Table 10-1
## Ideal Op Amp Parameters

| | |
|---|---|
| Input resistance ($R_i$) | $\infty$ |
| Output resistance ($R_o$) | 0 |
| Voltage gain ($A_v$) | $-\infty$ |
| Bandwidth | $\infty$ |
| Perfect balance | If $v_1 = v_2$, then $v_o = 0$ |
| Drift with temperature change | none |

sistances are not those listed in Table 10-1; therefore the voltage gain is not infinite. Even so, Eq. 10-3 turns out to be a reasonable approximation. Note that the negative sign in the equation means inversion has taken place.

Contrast the inverting circuit with the one shown in Fig. 10-4. Here the *noninverting* amplifier input has been used. The amplification with feedback is

$$A_{vf} = (R_1 + R_2)/R_1 \qquad (10\text{-}4)$$

This configuration is sometimes called a *differential amplifier* because

$$v_o = A_{vf}(v_1 - v_2) \qquad (10\text{-}5)$$

Again real op amps closely approximate Eqs. 10-4 and 10-5.

### Analog Comparator

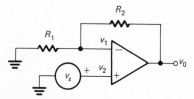

**Figure 10-4. Noninverting op amp circuit.**

Often we will want to compare two voltages to determine their relative magnitudes. Say we have a temperature sensor that generates a voltage proportional to the temperature. When the temperature sensor reports a voltage that represents 60°C, a heating coil is to be switched off. A second voltage, called the reference ($V_{\text{ref}}$) is constantly held at the 60°C value and applied to the differential amplifier circuit of Fig. 10-4. (The reference voltage must be within the manufacturer's specification of the common-mode range.)

Assuming a supply of 5 volts and an amplifier voltage gain of about 2500, the transfer characteristics for the comparator are shown in Fig. 10-5. Either input terminal can be connected to the reference voltage and the other to the sensor output ($v_s$). As the

**Figure 10-5. Comparator transfer characteristic curves.**

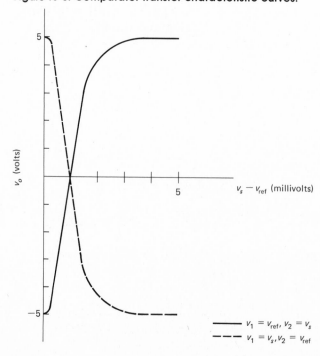

figure shows, the output drops to 0 volts when the difference between the two inputs is about 1 millivolt. If $v_2$ is the reference voltage, the output is at the maximum negative value until $v_s$ is within about 2 millivolts of the reference. Then a rapid change in the output takes place. The output rises almost linearly to its maximum positive value as the difference of the two voltages approaches zero. If $v_1$ is the reference voltage, the transfer characteristics just reverse polarity.

**Zero-Crossing Detector**

How could we find when the output of the comparator in the previous section reached exactly 0 volts? The zero-crossing detector circuit shown in Fig. 10-6a could be used. Basically the circuit is a differential amplifier with a reference voltage of zero. Every time the input voltage passes through zero the output voltage swings to its other extreme value. Another use of the zero-crossing detector is to generate square waves from a sine wave input.

The waveforms for the circuit are shown in Fig. 10-6b. The output square wave is a result of the transfer characteristics of the analog comparator with a reference of 0 volts. The resistor and capacitor form a differentiator which generates a pulse that decays

**Figure 10-6. Zero-crossing detector (a) Circuit, (b) waveforms.**

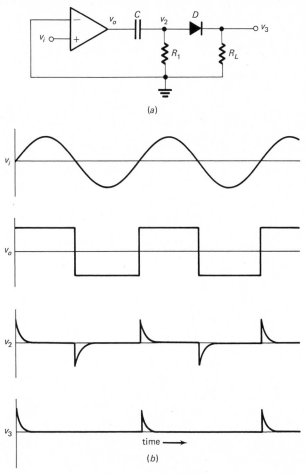

to zero every time $v_o$ changes polarity. The diode acts as a rectifier and only passes the positive going pulses (that is, every time the input crosses zero from below) to the load. Which of these waveforms ($v_0$, $v_2$, or $v_3$) is most useful depends on the specific application.

## Sample-and-Hold

When a voltage must be converted from analog to digital form, it must be sampled periodically. The sampled voltages are then held constant as an input to an A/D converter. The converter will be discussed in one of the following sections. Here we will consider the sampling of the signal and holding it at a constant voltage.

A simplified version of a sample-and-hold circuit is shown in Fig. 10-7a. Sampling is provided by closing the switch. The capacitor charges to the signal voltage ($v_s$) and holds the charge after the switch is opened. Of course, this circuit is much too slow for practical use.

Figure 10-7b adds a MOSFET and an op amp to provide the necessary switching speed. A negative input is applied to the gate of $Q_1$ to turn the transistor on. At that time, the capacitor charges with a time constant corresponding to the capacitor and the resistance of $Q_1$. Because $Q_1$ is on its resistance is low, so this time is almost instantaneous. The input signal hardly changes during the charging period.

Next $Q_1$ is switched off, blocking the input signal. The capacitor is isolated from the load through the op amp. The output voltage will be the voltage on the capacitor referenced to ground.

The speed of the sample-and-hold circuit in reacting to the input is called its *aperture time*. The specifications for aperture time establish a maximum delay between the control pulse application to the switching transistor and the time the transistor turns on. Typical asperture times are on the order of 100 nanoseconds.

Another important measure of the sample-and-hold performance is the *acquisition time*. Acquisition time is the period necessary for the capacitor to charge from one level of holding voltage to the new value of the input after the transistor switches on.

The isolation provided by the op amp can be a potential problem if the capacitor is greater than 0.05 microfarad. If the output should be short-circuited or the power supply abruptly turned off while the capacitor is charged, damage may result. This problem can be eliminated by inserting a 10-kilohm resistor between the capacitor and the op amp input for protection.

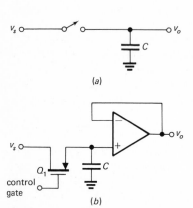

**Figure 10-7. Sample-and-hold. (a) Simplified circuit, (b) practical circuit.**

## Monostable Multivibrator

Monostable multivibrators, or *one-shots*, have one stable state and one temporarily stable state. The circuit shown in Fig. 10-8 remains in the stable state until triggered. Then it changes to the temporary state for a certain time and finally reverts to the stable state.

Assuming that the circuit is initially in its stable state, $C_1$ is clamped at 0.7 volt by $D_1$ and the output voltage is at some positive voltage, say 5 volts. Resistors $R_2$ and $R_3$ are equal in value.

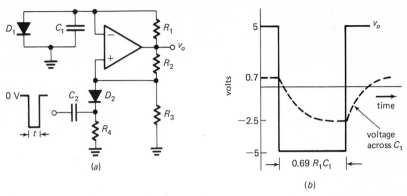

**Figure 10-8. Monostable multivibrator. (a) Circuit, (b) voltage waveforms.**

Using a negative trigger produces an instantaneous voltage of $-2.5$ volts on the cathode of $D_2$ and makes it conduct. The input causes the op amp comparator to switch its output to $-5$ volts. $D_1$ is then reverse biased and the voltage across $C_1$ approaches $-2.5$ volts. The differential amplifier will produce a $+5$ volt output at that point. Then $C_1$ again can charge through $R_1$ toward $+2$ volts, but it is stopped at $0.7$ volt by the clamping action of $D_1$.

It can be shown that the one-shot stays in the temporary state for a time of $0.69R_1C_1$. This time is much longer than the width of the trigger pulse. The one-shot effectively expands the duration of the trigger long enough for other circuits to respond. This feature can also be used to convert many short-duration pulses, switch contact "bounce" for example, into a single pulse of longer duration.

**Op Amp Review**

1. List the features of an ideal op amp.
2. Distinguish between the characteristics of the inverting and noninverting inputs to an op amp.
3. Describe the operation of an op amp used as an analog comparator.
4. Describe how the comparator may be converted to detect when the input signal amplitude is zero.
5. Why is the switch in the simplified example replaced by a MOSFET in a practical sample-and-hold circuit?
6. List ways in which the temporary state of the monostable multivibrator, which stretches the trigger pulse, can be used.

**SCHMITT TRIGGER**

Inputs of rectangular pulse trains have been used throughout our discussions on pulse circuits. Up to this point we have not described how these pulse trains were generated. One device that is widely used to generate rectangular pulses is the Schmitt trigger. The trigger is available as an IC, but for illustrating how the device works consider the circuit in Figure 10-9a. The input signal is a sine wave.

As the input to the circuit becomes high, the output of inverter 1 goes low. The instant this happens, inverter 2 begins to go high, as shown in Fig. 10-9b. A high output from inverter 2 is fed back

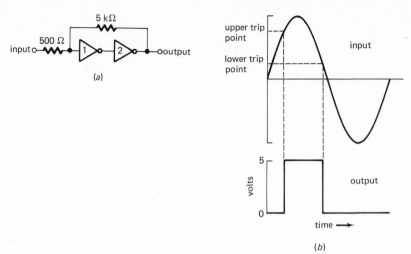

Figure 10-9. Schmitt trigger, (a) Circuit, (b) voltage waveforms.

through the 5-kilohm resistor pulling the input up at a faster rate.

Now the state of the input begins to change as the sine wave approaches zero. As the input voltage falls, nothing happens until the biasing on the input to inverter 1 can change state. When inverter 1 does change state, the second inverter quickly goes low. Feeding back the low voltage accelerates the grounding of the input.

Examining the voltage diagram more closely, we see that there are two points on the input sine curve that cause a change in the output. The upper trip point occurs when the voltage is positive going and the Schmitt trigger switches to the 5-volt output state. The rapid switching gives the output waveform a steep rising edge. As the input peaks and decreases to the lower trip point, the output is forced to 0 volts again. The output wave has a nearly vertical falling edge. The difference between the two tripping voltages is called the *hysteresis zone*. In this manner the Schmitt trigger can convert sine waves, or other slowly varying signals, to trains of square waves.

**Schmitt Trigger Review**

1. Describe the operation of the Schmitt trigger when a high input is applied.
2. Define the term hysteresis.
3. Describe the output waveform generated by a Schmitt trigger with a triangular wave input.

**THE 555 TIMER**

The 555 IC is a widely used DIP that can perform a variety of timing functions. An internal block diagram of the 555 is shown in Fig. 10-10. The 555 consists of two comparators, an R-S flip-flop, an inverter (which also acts as a buffer), and a discharge transistor. The voltages are TTL compatible.

The input to comparator $A$ establishes the threshold voltage for the timer. If the threshold input is above ⅔ the supply voltage (the second input to comparator $A$), the output of that comparator

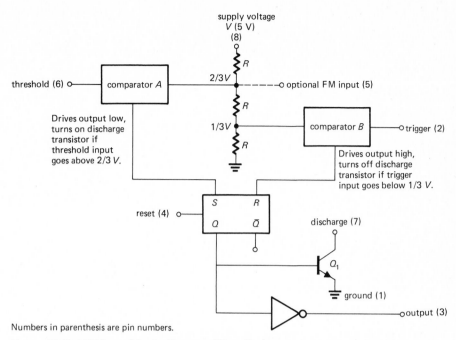

Numbers in parenthesis are pin numbers.

**Figure 10-10. 555 timer block diagram (*Signetics*).**

places a high on the S input of the flip-flop. The output of the flip-flop is driven high. This signal is inverted to produce a final low output.

The trigger input to comparator B is used to drive the 555 output high. If the trigger input is less than ⅓ the supply voltage (the reference voltage for comparator B), the R input to the flip-flop has a high signal that makes the Q output low. The inverter then causes the output to rise to the high state.

The reset input can be used to return the 555 to the low output state. An optional FM input is also supplied. The 555 appears in many applications. Two of them are described in the following sections.

## The 555 Astable Multivibrator

The 555 can provide a pulse train output when connected as an astable multivibrator as depicted in Fig. 10-11a. In following the discussion, refer to the diagrams for the capacitor and output voltages in Fig. 10-11b.

Assume that initially the output is high, the charge on the capacitor is low, and the discharge transistor is not conducting. The capacitor will begin charging through $R_1$ and $R_2$ toward the supply voltage of +5 volts. When the voltage across the capacitor reaches 3⅓ volts (⅔ of the supply voltage), comparator A senses the level. The comparator output goes high, producing a low output. The discharge transistor is turned on, this allows the capacitor to discharge through $R_2$.

As the capacitor discharges it eventually reaches 1⅔ volts. This input causes comparator B to produce a high output and return the circuit to its initial state. The process then repeats as $Q_1$ is off and the capacitor charges through $R_1$ and $R_2$ again.

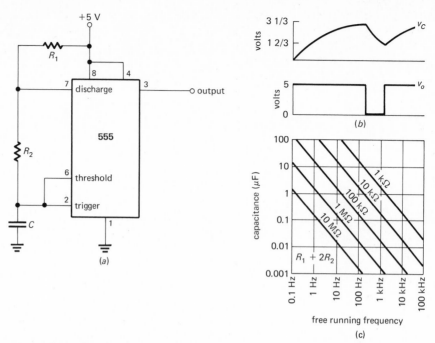

Figure 10-11. 555 used as an astable multivibrator. (a) Circuit, (b) voltage wave-forms, (c) operation frequency (*Signetics*).

The best results are obtained if the capacitor is larger than 1 microfarad and $R_2$ is much larger than the value of $R_1$; for example, if $R_2 = 1$ megohm and $R_1 = 1$ kilohm. Then the output waveform will be almost symmetrical.

A series of equations is available to determine the parameters of a 555 used in this manner. The curves relating the frequency of the output pulses, the capacitor value, and the sum of $R_1$ and $R_2$ are shown in Fig. 10-11$c$. Additional parameters may be found by using these equations.

$$\text{Charge time (output high)} = 0.69\,(R_1 + R_2)C \qquad (10\text{-}5)$$

$$\text{Discharge time (output low)} = 0.69R_2C \qquad (10\text{-}6)$$

$$\text{Period} = 0.69\,(R_1 + 2R_2)C \qquad (10\text{-}7)$$

$$\text{Frequency} = 1.45/(R_1 + 2\,R_2)C \qquad (10\text{-}8)$$

$$\text{Duty cycle} = \text{Time high/Time low} \qquad (10\text{-}9)$$
$$= (R_1 + R_2)/R_2$$

The value of $R_1 + R_2$ must not exceed 3.3 megohm or fall below 1 kilohm. The minimum value suggested for the capacitor is 500 picofarads.

**The 555 Monostable Multivibrator**

The 555 can be used as a monostable multivibrator performing the same function as the op amp version previously discussed. A circuit diagram for this application is shown in Fig. 10-12$a$. The voltages across the capacitor and the output are shown in Fig. 10-12$b$. Initially the output level is ground. The application of a negative going external trigger to the 555 causes the trigger comparator to

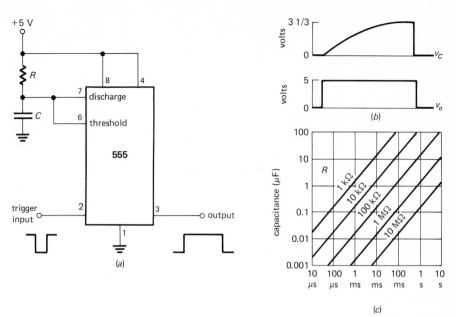

Figure 10-12. 555 used as a monostable multivibrator. (a) Circuit, (b) voltage wave-forms, (c) time delay (*Signetics*).

change the output to +5 volts and turn the discharge transistor off.

The capacitor can now charge through the resistor. When it reaches 3⅓ volts (⅔ supply voltage) the output of the threshold comparator changes state. This high output from the comparator causes the output to go low and $Q_1$ to turn on, discharging the capacitor to ground. The cycle cannot repeat until the next external trigger input.

The time duration of the high output state is determined by the values of the capacitor and resistor as shown in Fig. 10-12c. The trigger input must be held at 5 volts until it is initiated by dropping to ground. Of course, the trigger pulse (or series of pulses) must be shorter than the output pulse period. A maximum trigger duration of less than ¼ the output pulse duration is recommended.

The resistor must be between 1 kilohm and 3.3 megohms and the minimum capacitor value is 500 picofarads. The time duration of the output pulse can also be calculated by using the equation

$$\text{Pulse duration} = 1.1\,RC \qquad (10\text{-}10)$$

A duty cycle of not more than 80 percent with resistors greater than 100 kilohms, or 50 percent with smaller values, is recommended.

**555 Timer Review**

1. Distinguish between the purposes of the two comparators in the 555.
2. If $R_1 + R_2$ is 1 megohm and $C$ is 500 picofarads, what is the frequency of the 555 astable multivibrator?
3. Describe the charging and discharging of the capacitor used with the 555 astable multivibrator in terms of its effect on the output level.

**4.** When the output of the 555 monostable multivibrator is zero, what is the charge on the capacitor?

## DIGITAL-TO-ANALOG (D/A) CONVERTERS

If we are to use digital equipment to control and monitor analog processes, obviously we must be able to convert signals from one type to the other. This section describes digital-to-analog conversion and the following section discusses the reverse process.

The input to most D/A converters is either binary or BCD. The output is an analog voltage corresponding to the digital input. We can write the output in terms of the digital input as

$$v_o = (k_{n-1}2^{-1} + k_{n-2}2^{-2} + k_{n-3}2^{-3} + \cdots + k_0 2^{-n})v_{\text{ref}} \quad (10\text{-}11)$$

where $k_{n-1}$ = the most significant bit of the input
$k_{n-2}$ = the second most significant bit of the input
$k_{n-3}$ = the third most significant bit of the input
$k_0$ = the least significant bit of the input
$v_{\text{ref}}$ = a reference voltage

We see from Eq. 10-11 that if the most significant bit ($k_{n-1}$) were a one and all the rest zeros, the output voltage would be half the reference voltage ($v_{\text{ref}}/2$).

As another example of the use of Eq. 10-11, let the 5-bit input be $1\ 0001_2$. Then

$$v_0 = (1)(2^{-1}) + (0)(2^{-2}) + (0)(2^{-3}) + (0)(2^{-4}) + (1)(2^{-5})]v_{\text{ref}}$$
$$= (\tfrac{1}{2} + \tfrac{1}{32})v_{\text{ref}}$$
$$= \tfrac{17}{32} v_{\text{ref}}$$

If we arbitrarily set the reference at 32 volts, the output is 17 volts.

## Weighted-Resistor D/A Converter

Fig. 10-13a illustrates a simplified D/A converter using a series of weighted resistors; that is, the resistor values of the converter are related by powers of 2. Here the reference voltage is selected to be −10 volts. The parallel input is applied to the control terminals of electronic switches. Each switch is on with a one input and turned off by a zero input.

The op amp converts the parallel currents from each branch into an output voltage. Because of the almost infinite input impedance of the op amp, the output voltage will be

$$v_o = (5 \times 10^3)i \quad (10\text{-}12)$$

which is proportional to the sum of the currents.

The operation of the D/A converter is straightforward. Consider a D/A converter with a 5-bit input. If only the most significant bit is one and all others are zero.

$$i = -10\ \text{V}/10\ \text{k}\Omega$$
$$= -1\ \text{mA}$$

then

$$v_o = (5 \times 10^3)(-1 \times 10^{-3})$$
$$= -5\ \text{V}$$

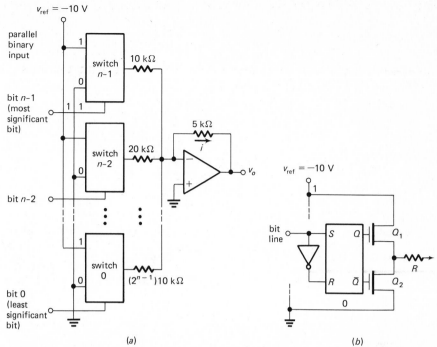

**Figure 10-13. Weighted-resistor D/A converter. (a) Circuit, (b) implementation of the electronic switch.**

This result is half the reference voltage, just as Eq. 10-11 predicts.

Now let all 5 input bits be set to one. The output, using Eq. 10-11, is

$$v_0 = [(1)2^{-1} + (1)2^{-2} + (1)2^{-3} + (1)2^{-4} + (1)2^{-5}] - 10 \text{ V}$$
$$= -10 \, (\tfrac{1}{2} + \tfrac{1}{4} + \tfrac{1}{8} + \tfrac{1}{16} + \tfrac{1}{32}) \text{ V}$$
$$= -10 \, (^{31}/_{32}) \text{ V}$$
$$= 9.69 \text{ V}$$

Note that although the input is at its maximum value, the output is one least significant bit ($^1/_{32}$) less than the reference voltage. We get the same answer by summing the currents in Fig. 10-13$a$ and using Eq. 10-12.

$$i = -(1 + {}^1\!/_2 + {}^1\!/_4 + {}^1\!/_8 + {}^1\!/_{16} \text{ mA})$$
$$= -1\,{}^{15}\!/_{16} \text{ mA}$$
$$v_0 = (5 \times 10^3)(+1\,{}^{15}\!/_{16} \times 10^{-3}) \text{ V}$$
$$= +9.69 \text{ V}$$

The construction of a digital switch to perform the indicated operation is not difficult, as Fig. 10-13 $b$ demonstrates. The bit line is used as an input to an R-S flip-flop operated as a D flip-flop. The switch output voltage will be $-10$ volts if $Q_1$ is on (a one input to the flip-flop causes this) or ground if $Q_2$ is on. The accuracy and stability of a weighted-resistor flip-flop depends on the absolute accuracy of the resistor values. These resistors must also retain their proper weighted relationship with changes in temperature.

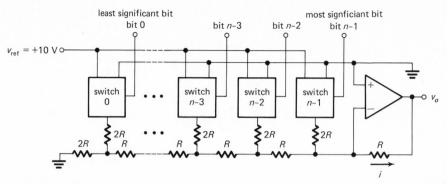

**Figure 10-14. Resistance-ladder D/A converter.**

**Resistance-Ladder D/A Converter**

Another common type of D/A converter is shown in Fig. 10-14. This converter has the advantage of using only two different resistor values (designated $R$ and $2R$) regardless of bit position. The use of identical resistors means that each bit supplies the same amount of current.

Analysis of the resistance-ladder D/A converter is somewhat more complicated than that of the previous type. We will derive an equivalent resistance for the resistor ladder and then simplify by finding Thevenin's equivalent of the resulting circuit.

The final output voltage is simply the summation current ($i$) times the feedback resistor ($R$) across the op amp. Consider the case when all bits except the most significant are off. That means all of the $2R$ resistors, except the one on switch $n - 1$, are connected to ground through their respective switches, as shown in Fig. 10-15$a$.

Working from the left side of the ladder, we can develop an equivalent resistance by looking for parallel and series combinations. We first have two $2R$ resistors in parallel. The equivalent resistance is simply $R$, which is in series with another resistor of value $R$. The series resistance is then $2R$. Continuing this process,

**Figure 10-15. Resistance-ladder D/A converter analysis (bit $n - 1 = 1$). (a) Switch diagram, (b) lumped resistance, (c)simplified circuit.**

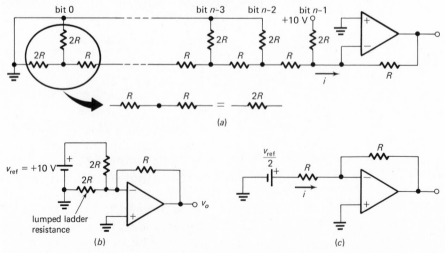

we see that the equivalent resistance of the entire ladder to the left of the one resistor attached to the supply voltage is $2R$. Thus the ladder reduces to the circuit of Fig. 10-15$b$.

Forming Thevenin's equivalent for Fig. 10-15$b$, we arrive at the circuit in Fig. 10-15$c$. Note that the equivalent voltage source is $v_{ref}/2$. Then, because of the almost infinite input impedance of the op amp,

$$v_o = iR$$

where

$$i = (v_{ref}/2)R$$

so

$$v_o = -[(v_{ref}R)/2]R$$

The negative output is a result of the inverting op amp.

$$v_o = -v_{ref}/2$$
$$= -5\text{ V}$$

the desired result when only the most significant bit is set.

Next consider the case when only bit $n - 3$ is one and all others are zeros. Figure 10-16$a$ shows the circuit with the switches eliminated. The ladder to the left of bit $n - 3$ can be reduced to $2R$ just as in the previous case. Figure 10-16$b$ shows the situation with

**Figure 10-16. Resistance-ladder D/A converter analysis (bit $n - 3 = 1$). (a) Switch diagram, (b) lumped resistance, (c) Thevenin's equivalent, (d) simplified circuit.**

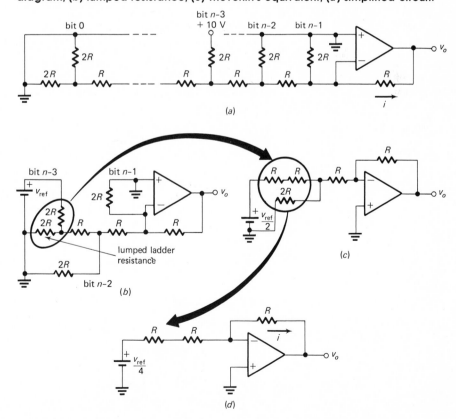

(a)

(b)

Figure 10-17. D/A converters. (a) High-resolution 16-bit converter, (b) internal circuitry (*Micro Networks Corporation*).

the other resistors redrawn to show the parallel and series relationships. Figure 10-16c is the effect of taking a Thevenin's equivalent of the two parallel 2R resistors and the power supply. The supply voltage must be divided by 2. Why?

The 2R resistor across the op amp terminals can be removed because the potential across the input terminals is 0 volts. (Since no current flows, the 2R resistor has no effect on circuit performance.) A second Thevenin's equivalent circuit is used to develop the final configuration of Fig. 10-16d.

The current into the resistor across the op amp is found to be

$$i = (v_{\text{ref}}/4)(1/2R)$$
$$= v_{\text{ref}}/8R$$

and the output voltage

$$v_o = iR$$
$$= -(v_{\text{ref}}/8R)R$$
$$= -v_{\text{ref}}/8$$
$$= -1\tfrac{1}{4} \text{ V with } v_{\text{ref}} \text{ of 10 V}$$

This is the result expected from Eq. 10-11.

Practical D/A converters are not usually constructed of discrete resistors. Instead, they are available in modular form as shown in Fig. 10-17. The module in Fig. 10-17a is a high-resolution 16-bit D/A converter. Figure 10-17b shows another module with the internal circuitry visible. Several parameters are used to specify D/A converter performance.

*Full-scale range* of a D/A converter is its output analog voltage, or current, span: for example, 10 volts in Fig. 10-14. The *resolution* of a converter is expressed as the number of states into which the full scale output may be divided, or resolved. Generally resolution is expressed as a number of bits, so a D/A converter with 10-bit resolution has $2^{10}$ output states. For the 10-volt range, the difference between each state of a converter with 10-bit resolution would be $10/2^{10}$ or 9.8 millivolts. The *nonlinearity* is the maximum deviation from a straight line between the end points of the D/A converter range. Of course, nonlinearity must be small for acceptable operation.

**D/A Converter Review**

1. Define the output voltage of a D/A converter by means of an equation involving the reference voltage and the digital input.
2. Indicate the method of determining each of the resistor values in the weighted resistor D/A converter.
3. Discuss the purpose of the op amp in the weighted-resistor D/A converter.
4. Describe the digital switch implementation used in the weighted-resistor and resistance-ladder D/A converters.
5. If only bit $n - 1$ of the input to the resistance-ladder D/A converter is one and all others are zero, why can all of the resistors to the left of the $n$-2 switch be converted to an equivalent resistance of 2R? (See Problem 10-7.)
6. Define the terms full-scale range, resolution, and nonlinearity.

## ANALOG TO DIGITAL (A/D) CONVERTERS

Now let's examine the method for converting an analog input to a digital value. In using circuits with A/D converters, the input voltage must be held constant during the period the converter is operating. The sample-and-hold circuit, that we studied earlier, is used to prevent this analog input from varying.

A modular A/D converter with the top of the package removed is shown in Fig. 10-18.

### Counter A/D Converter

Figure 10-18. A/D converter (*Micro Networks Corporation*).

One way of achieving A/D conversion is to use a counter combined with a D/A converter. This circuit also illustrates a typical use of the D/A converter. As Fig. 10-19 demonstrates, the analog input is applied to the noninverting input of the op amp comparator. A clock with equally spaced pulses is used as the input to the counter.

In operation, a clear pulse is applied to reset the counter before conversion begins. As long as the analog input voltage $v_a$ is greater than the digital-to-analog converter output voltage $v_d$ the op amp will have a high output. The $v_d$ voltage is the analog representation of the present count of the number of pulses applied to the counter. After the clear pulse, $v_d$ will be zero, so the output of the op amp is high gating the next clock pulse into the counter.

The counter will increment to one and the D/A converter will change that value to an analog voltage. The comparator again determines which of the voltages is larger. If $v_a$ is again greater, the AND gate remains enabled and the process repeats. Eventually the D/A output voltage will exceed the analog input, and the comparator output will switch to the low state. The low input disables the gate and the clock input to the counter, which stops incrementing. The digital value is available at the output terminals.

The conversion is a stairstep progression, as Fig. 10-20 shows. The digital voltage increments one level after each clock pulse. When the digital value exceeds the analog input the counter stops. The accuracy of the A/D converter depends on the size of the voltage steps generated by the counter. For fine resolution many small voltage increments are necessary.

**Figure 10-19. Counter A/D converter.**

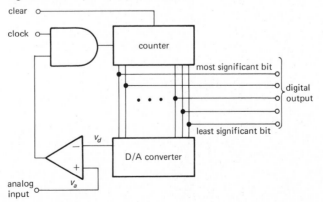

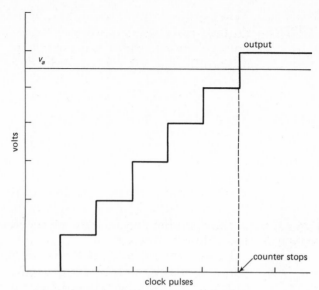

**Figure 10-20. Counter A/D converter voltages.**

## Successive-Approximation A/D Converter

A binary ladder is used to generate voltages one bit at a time to compare against the analog input in the *successive-approximation* A/D converter. As shown in Fig. 10-21, the most significant bit is compared first, followed by the next lower bit until the least significant bit is compared.

Assume that a 4-bit successive-approximation A/D converter is being used. The flip-flops then provide voltages as follows.

flip-flop $A$:   1 V
flip-flop $B$:   2 V
flip-flop $C$:   4 V
flip-flop $D$:   8 V

If an input of 6 volts is applied, flip-flop $D$ is turned on. But the 8 volts it generates is greater than the input, so flip-flop $D$ is turned off by the control logic. Next, flip-flop $C$ is set and the 4 volts it generates is less than the input, so that flip-flop is left on. The remaining flip-flops are tested as shown in Table 10-2. The final result is an output with only flip-flops $B$ and $C$ set. The binary output is thus $0110_2$, which equals the input voltage.

**Figure 10-21. Successive-approximation A/D converter.**

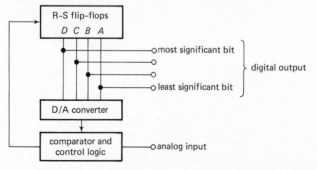

**Table 10-2**
**Successive-Approximation A/D Converter Operation**

| Flip-Flop | Voltage Generated, V | State After Comparison |
|:---:|:---:|:---:|
| D | 8 | off |
| C | 4 | on |
| B | 6 | on |
| A | 7 | off |

**Simultaneous A/D Converter**

If the speed of conversion is important, the serial methods used in the other A/D converters may not be acceptable. An all at once conversion can be used if the cost of additional comparators, resistor networks, and control circuitry is justified.

A *simultaneous* A/D converter is shown in Fig. 10-22. In this example, the resistor network divides the 8-volt reference voltage into 1-volt increments. The analog voltage is the other input to the comparators. If the input is 7 volts, comparators $A$ through $G$ will have a high output and the remaining one a low output. The decoder circuitry will convert this input to $0111_2$.

**Figure 10-22. Simultaneous A/D converter.**

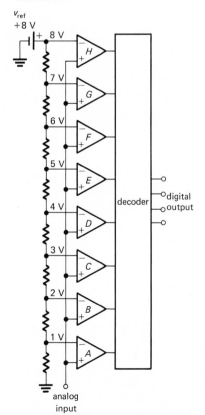

**A/D Converter Review**

1. Name the devices often used to prevent the input voltage to an A/D converter from varying during the conversion time.
2. Describe the relationship of the input voltages to the op amp output in Fig. 10-19.
3. Can the digital output of the counter A/D converter ever be greater than the analog input voltage? Can it be less?
4. Describe the states of the flip-flops in the successive-approximation A/D converter if the input is 14 volts.
5. Which comparators have high outputs if the input to the simultaneous A/D converter is 3 volts?

**CHAPTER SUMMARY**

1. Linear circuits are distinguished by an output that is directly proportional to the input. Most analog circuits are linear.
2. Op amps are general-purpose components that were originally used in analog computers. The characteristics of an ideal op amp are infinite input resistance and bandwidth, zero output resistance, minus infinity voltage gain, perfect balance, and no drift with temperature.
3. Practical op amps are close enough in performance to ideal op amps to use the same feedback gain equations.
4. One input to the op amp produces an inverted output, while the other is noninverting.
5. The op amp can be used as an analog comparator to determine which of two voltages is larger. The comparator can also detect zero crossings of the input voltage.
6. Sample-and-hold circuits are often used together with A/D converters. Important sample-and-hold parameters are aperture time and acquisition time.
7. Monostable multivibrators, or one-shots, are used as pulse expanders and also to combine several triggers into a single pulse.
8. The Schmitt trigger converts slowly varying inputs into a train of rectangular pulses. Its operation in a hysteresis zone provides the two output states.
9. Its flexibility makes the 555 timer IC a good choice for use as either an astable multivibrator or a monostable multivibrator. The output pulse timing can be adjusted by simply changing the resistors and capacitors used with the 555.
10. D/A converters develop an output voltage that is proportional to the digital input. The proportionality constant depends on the reference voltage. Weighted resistors and ladder networks are common D/A circuits.
11. Analog-to-digital converters often include D/A converters in their design. A/D converters may use a counter, successive approximations, or simultaneous operation in developing their output.

**KEY TERMS AND CONCEPTS**

linear circuit
operational amplifier (op amp)
ideal op amp

inverting and noninverting op amp inputs
analog comparator
zero-crossing detector

sample and hold

aperture and acquisition time

monostable multivibrator or one-shot

Schmitt trigger

hysteresis zone

555 timer

digital-to-analog (D/A) converter

weighted-resistor D/A converter

resistance-ladder D/A converter

D/A full-scale range, resolution, and nonlinearity

analog-to-digital (A/D) converter

counter A/D converter

successive-approximation A/D converter

simultaneous A/D converter

## PROBLEMS

10-1. Draw the output voltage waveform and voltage levels for the circuit in Fig. 10-23. Indicate on the output voltage diagram when $D_1$ and $D_2$ are forward and reverse biased.

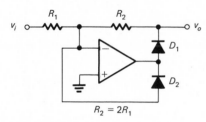

$R_2 = 2R_1$

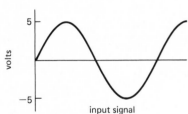

input signal

Figure 10-23. Problem 10-1.

10-2. Given the input signal to the circuit in Fig. 10-24, draw the output waveform. (The RC discharge time constant for the circuit is 1 millisecond.)

Figure 10-24. Problem 10-2.

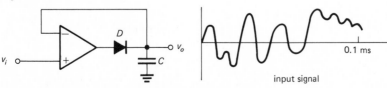

input signal

10-3. Explain why the time that the output signal of the 555 astable multivibrator (Fig. 10-11$a$) is in the high state is always longer than the time it is in the low state.

10-4. Draw a circuit diagram showing pin numbers and all resistor and capacitor values for a 555 astable multivibrator with $R_2 = 1$ megohm, a duty cycle of 2, and a discharge time of 411 milliseconds. What is the free-running frequency of the output?

10-5. If the frequency of a 555 IC used as an astable multivibrator has a frequency of 10 kHz, what is the period? What is the charge time? ($R_1 = 1$ kilohm, $R_2 = 4.5$ kilohms)

10-6. Using the 555 as a monostable multivibrator, what size resistor should be used with a 700-picofarad capacitor to produce a 7-millisecond time delay?

10-7. A 10-bit resistance-ladder D/A converter has an input of $100_{16}$. Draw a diagram for the equivalent resistor network similar to that of Fig. 10-16$b$, and then use Thevenin's theorem to reduce it to simplest form. What is the output voltage if the reference voltage is 10 volts?

10-8. Assuming that the least significant bit in Fig. 10-20 represents 0.1 volt, how many counts are required before the counter stops with an input of 3.05 volts?

10-9. Which flip-flops in the successive-approximation A/D converter are left on if the input is 14.18 volts?

10-10. What are the output states of each comparator in Fig. 10-22 with an analog input of 6.98 volts?

# EXPERIMENT 10  555 TIMER

**PURPOSE**   To investigate the 555 timer used as an astable multivibrator.

**PARTS LIST**

| Item | Quantity |
|---|---|
| 555 | 1 |
| 15-kΩ resistor | 1 |
| 68-kΩ resistor | 1 |
| 100-kΩ resistor | 1 |
| 330-Ω resistor | 1 |
| 1-MΩ resistor | 1 |
| 10-$\mu$F capacitor | 1 |
| 4.7-$\mu$F capacitor | 1 |
| 2.2-$\mu$F capacitor | 1 |
| LED | 1 |

All capacitors are tantalum.

**IC DIAGRAM**

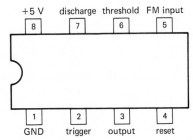

Figure 10-25. 555.

**PROCEDURE**   **Step 1.**   Connect the 555 timer as shown in Fig. 10-26. The output of the timer goes to the LED to indicate the state of the output.

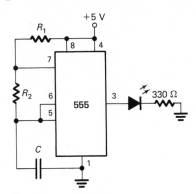

See table for values of $R_1$, $R_2$, and $C$.

Figure 10-26. Timer experiment.

**Step 2.**   For each of the resistor and capacitor combinations below, use a watch with a second hand to count the number of pulses produced in 60 seconds by the astable multivibrator.

| Step | $R_1$ | $R_2$ | $C$ |
|------|-------|-------|-----|
| 2a | 15 k$\Omega$ | 68 k$\Omega$ | 10 $\mu$F |
| 2b | 15 k$\Omega$ | 68 k$\Omega$ | 4.7 $\mu$F |
| 2c | 15 k$\Omega$ | 68 k$\Omega$ | 2.2 $\mu$F |
| 2d | 100 k$\Omega$ | 1 M$\Omega$ | 10 $\mu$F |
| 2e | 100 k$\Omega$ | 1 M$\Omega$ | 4.7 $\mu$F |
| 2f | 100 k$\Omega$ | 1 M$\Omega$ | 2.2 $\mu$F |

**Step 3.** Convert the counts per minute to hertz by dividing by 60. Using the equations in this chapter, calculate the theoretical frequency for each of these cases.

| Step | Actual Frequency | Theoretical Frequency | Percent Error |
|------|------------------|-----------------------|---------------|
| 2a | | | |
| 2b | | | |
| 2c | | | |
| 2d | | | |
| 2e | | | |
| 2f | | | |

What is the percent error in each of these cases?

**Step 4.** Graph the actual values, using a format similar to that in Fig. 10-11c. Why do these values differ from the theoretically calculated ones?

**Step 5.** For the case $R_1 = 15$k$\Omega$, $R_2 = 68$k$\Omega$, and $C = 10\mu$F, what are the charge time, discharge time, period, and duty cycle for the multivibrator?

# CHAPTER ELEVEN
# APPLICATIONS

The individual integrated circuits and modules that we have studied are building blocks which can be used in many kinds of equipment. For example, displaying numerical information to the operator of a hand-held calculator, digital multimeter, or digital watch is one use of decoders and timing circuits. The operations of calculators depend on arithmetic logic units, registers, and combinatorial gates. Digital multimeters must convert analog signals to digital ones. Counters and registers are the heart of digital watches and clocks. Studying these uses of digital and linear circuits will show how they are typically applied in equipment.

**CHAPTER OBJECTIVES** After completing this chapter you should be able to:

1. Distinguish between light-emitting diodes, liquid-crystal displays, and gas-discharge displays and explain the principles of operation for each.
2. Discuss the basic types of light-emitting diode displays.
3. Describe the methods used to drive the various types of displays.
4. Describe the construction of a logic probe.
5. Discuss the operation of a digital multimeter.
6. Discuss the use of counters, registers, and displays in a digital clock.
7. Describe how a simple hand-held calculator works.

**DISPLAYS**  This section will discuss how the outputs of logic circuits can be presented to human beings by means of several kinds of *alphanumeric* (letters and numbers) displays. The discussion will include light-emitting diodes, liquid-crystal displays, and gas-discharge displays.

**Light-Emitting Diode (LED)**

Figure 11-1. LED circuit.

The LED is similar to an ordinary diode because it will carry current in only one direction: that is, when it is forward biased. In addition a LED emits light in the forward biased condition. The simple LED is about the size of a flashlight bulb and has anode and cathode leads extending from the transparent package. Figure 11-1 shows the LED symbol and proper circuit polarities.

A current-limiting resistor is used to minimize drain on the power supply. For a typical red gallium arsenide phosphide (GaAsP) LED the voltage drop is about 1.8 volts. This means that when TTL-compatible 5-volt power supplies are used the resistor drop should be about 3.2 volts. Satisfactory operation of the LED requires from 5 to 40 milliamperes of current. Because the current value is not critical, resistors in the range of 100 to 500 ohms are suitable. The largest resistor that produces adequate light intensity should be chosen.

The circuit in Fig. 11-1 can also be used as a logic probe to determine the states of the pins on ICs. After the power-supply lead to the 5-volt source is connected, the other lead (shown grounded in Fig. 11-1) is used to touch the IC pin. If the pin is in the low state, the LED lights. A high state will cause the LED to remain off. If a series of pulses is the signal on the pin, the LED will blink if the frequency is less than 25 hertz, otherwise the LED intensity will be dimmer than its fully on state. Figure 11-2 shows a much more sophisticated logic probe being used to test an in-place IC.

Figure 11-2. Logic probe (*Hewlett-Packard*).

Figure 11-3. Seven-segment LED display (National Semiconductor).

**Seven-Segment LED Display.** By forming the LEDs into bars a seven-segment display representing numbers and some letters can be built. See Fig. 11-3. Every segment is an individual LED requiring its own current-limiting resistor.

There are two basic types of seven-segment displays: *common anode* and *common cathode*. As Fig. 11-4a shows, the common-anode configuration has a single anode lead, but each segment LED has its own cathode. Figure 11-4b shows the common-cathode display which reverses the lead situation. A truth table for the seven-segment display inputs and outputs is listed in Fig. 11-5. Note that each LED segment is lettered to identify it and the various segments combine to form the digits 0 through 9. Other displays may be capable of forming some letters and a decimal point (DP) as well.

Operation of the common-anode display requires that each of the cathodes be grounded through a current-limiting resistor to light the corresponding segment, as shown in Fig. 11-6a. Groups of segments are lighted by grounding several cathodes. Decoder/driver ICs which accept BCD or binary inputs and ground the appropriate cathodes are available. The 7447 shown in Fig. 11-6b performs the BCD to seven-segment conversion for a common-anode display. The current-limiting resistors must be inserted between the 7447 and the LED display.

Other decoder/drivers such as the 7448 shown in Fig. 11-7b, may be used with a common-cathode display of Fig. 11-7a. In this case the pull-up resistors are used between the seven-segment display and the decoder/driver. By pulling up the voltage, each segment in the display is caused to glow with more intensity.

**Multiple-Digit Display.** Most numeric displays consist of more than one digit; such displays are used in calculators and digital watches. Figure 11-8a shows a photograph of a four-digit display, and Fig. 11-8b illustrates the pin connections for a two-digit dis-

Figure 11-4. Seven-segment display configurations. (a) Common anode, (b) common cathode.

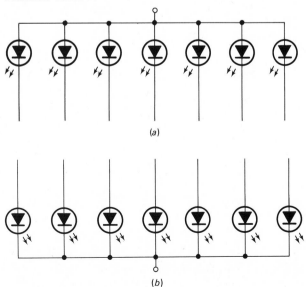

(a)

(b)

| Decimal number | Display | Binary | a | b | c | d | e | f | g |
|---|---|---|---|---|---|---|---|---|---|
| 0 | 0 | 0000 | 1 | 1 | 1 | 1 | 1 | 1 | 0 |
| 1 | 1 | 0001 | 0 | 1 | 1 | 0 | 0 | 0 | 0 |
| 2 | 2 | 0010 | 1 | 1 | 0 | 1 | 1 | 0 | 1 |
| 3 | 3 | 0011 | 1 | 1 | 1 | 1 | 0 | 0 | 1 |
| 4 | 4 | 0100 | 0 | 1 | 1 | 0 | 0 | 1 | 1 |
| 5 | 5 | 0101 | 1 | 0 | 1 | 1 | 0 | 1 | 1 |
| 6 | 6 | 0110 | 0 | 0 | 1 | 1 | 1 | 1 | 1 |
| 7 | 7 | 0111 | 1 | 1 | 1 | 0 | 0 | 0 | 0 |
| 8 | 8 | 1000 | 1 | 1 | 1 | 1 | 1 | 1 | 1 |
| 9 | 9 | 1001 | 1 | 1 | 1 | 0 | 0 | 1 | 1 |

**Figure 11-5. Seven-segment display truth table.**

play, although digits of ten or more may be arranged in the same fashion.

The anodes of Fig. 11-8b are used to select the segments of each digit, while the cathodes determine which of the two digits will be selected. This example therefore consists of 14 segments and two decimal points.

Operation of the multiple-digit display uses a decoder/driver such as the 7448 connected to the proper anode pins together with pull-up resistors. Each cathode is grounded after the anodes se-

**Figure 11-6. Common anode display. (a) Lighting the number 8, (b) BCD-to-seven-segment decoder/driver.**

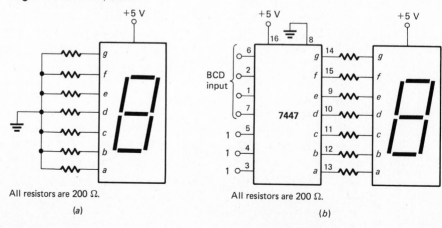

All resistors are 200 Ω.

(a)

All resistors are 200 Ω.

(b)

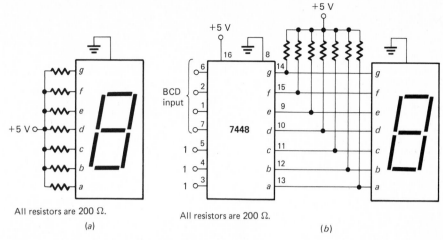

**Figure 11-7. Common cathode display. (a) Lighting the number 8, (b) BCD-to-seven-segment decoder/driver.**

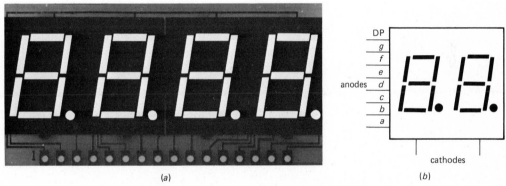

**Figure 11-8. Multiple-digit display (*National Semiconductor*).**

**Figure 11-9. Dot-matrix display. (a) Column and row assignment, (b) lighting the letter A.**

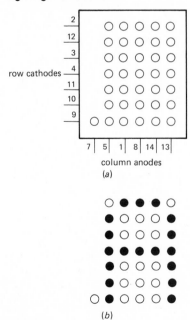

lecting the segments for that digit are set by the decoder/driver. The cathodes are scanned with a sequencing circuit, either from left to right or right to left. Scanning, or multiplexing, the cathodes rapidly enough, causes both digits in the display to glow steadily.

**Dot-Matrix Display.** A matrix of LEDs arranged in 7 rows by 5 columns can be used to display all numbers, letters, and special characters. This flexibility does have a price in that more complex circuitry is needed to decode and drive the display. Figure 11-9a shows a dot matrix. A decimal point is provided to the left of the character. An example of displaying the letter "A" is shown in Fig. 11-9b.

The rows are controlled by cathode leads, and the columns are selected by the anodes. A dot-matrix generator like the Fairchild Semiconductor 3257 can be used to convert 64-character ASCII codes to the 5 × 7 pattern and drive the display. In operation, each row (cathode) is controlled by the driver and the columns (anodes) are sequenced fast enough to prevent flickering. In this way, each dot in the matrix is refreshed many times a second, if it is lighted.

**Table 11-1**
**Ripple Blanking Truth Table**

| Inputs | | Outputs | |
|---|---|---|---|
| RBI | Digit | RBO | Segments |
| 0 | 0 | 0 | off |
| 0 | 1–9 | 1 | enabled |
| 1 | 0 | 1 | enabled |
| 1 | 1–9 | 1 | enabled |

**Automatic Blanking.** When a number is displayed in a multiple-digit readout, we want all leading zeros to the left of the decimal point turned off. That is, any zero to the left of the highest order nonzero digit should not light. It may be desirable to also blank trailing zeros to the right of the decimal point. For example, we want to see 912.25 instead of 00912.2500.

Some displays provide special pins for blanking signals used to perform this function. The pins are labeled ripple blanking in (RBI) and ripple blanking out (RBO). Table 11-1 is a truth table for this function. We see that if RBI and the digit are both zero, the display is turned off and RBO is set to zero. Otherwise, the display will indicate the selected digit.

Figure 11-10 shows how the blanking pins are wired. In the example to the left of the decimal point, RBI into the $10^3$ digit display is grounded. Because the digit is zero, the digit is blanked and RBO is also zero. The $10^2$ display acts in the same manner, but the $10^1$ display has a digit of 7. So RBO is set to 1. This input into

**Figure 11-10. Automatic blanking.**

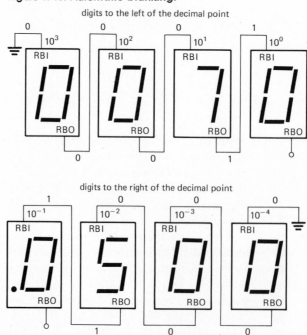

the $10^0$ display causes it to light even though the digit is zero. So the number that appears is 70. To the right of the decimal point, the grounded input into the $10^{-4}$ display causes it to blank. The RBO = 0 blanks the $10^{-3}$ display with its zero digit, too. A digit of 5 in the $10^{-2}$ display causes it to light and produce an RBO output of one. That input into the $10^{-1}$ display causes the zero to light. The number lighted will be .05.

**Liquid-Crystal Display (LCD)**   You are probably familiar with the use of LCDs in calculators, meters, wall and table clocks, portable laboratory instruments, panel meters, and appliance control panels. LCDs do not glow like LEDs, but rely on either ambient light or an external bulb for visibility. The LCD is actually a sandwich of liquid-crystal material, about 1 mil thick, between two glass plates.

Two basic types of LCDs have been produced. In the earlier version, the liquid-crystal material consists of rodlike molecules that are normally perpendicular to the glass plates. Light easily passes through this orderly arrangement. When the molecules are subjected to an electric field, their alignment breaks down, creating turbulence and scattering light. The turbulence makes the liquid crystal layer opaque.

New field-effect, or *nematic,* liquid-crystal displays are more reliable. They use two polarizing screens at right angles to polarize the light passing through the cell. The display looks black until the orientation of the crystals is changed by an electric field. The twisting or nematic effect causes a rotation in the polarized light that makes the affected portions of the crystal layer appear to be clear.

Characters are formed by etching a clear conductive electrode which is applied to the front glass panel. Typically, seven segments are provided for each digit. The segments are designated *a* through *g*, just as with LED displays. LCDs are available in either transmitting or reflecting models. The transmitting type requires an illumination source behind the display to transmit light to the viewer. A mirror finish behind the reflecting LCD collects ambient light and reflects it back.

LCDs can be driven by MOS IC decoder/drivers. Multiple-digit LCDs cannot be scanned like LEDs, so they must be driven in parallel. Economical multiple LCDs therefore are limited in

**Figure 11-11. LCD decoder/driver.**

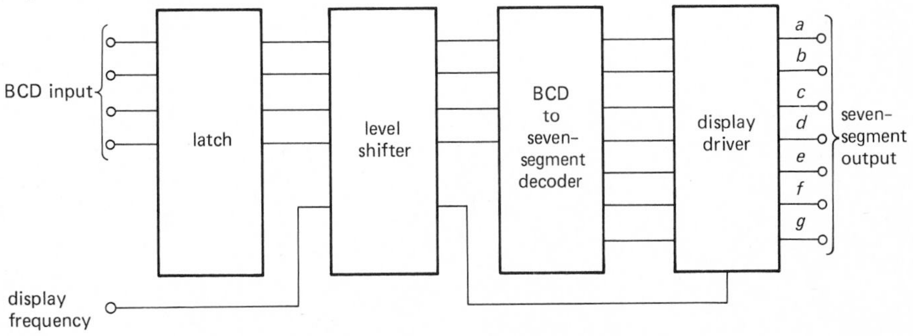

the number of digits to keep costs down. Less power is required by the LCDs than LEDs, so the former are attractive in applications which use batteries.

The MOS or CMOS decoder/driver for LCDs provides a low-frequency ac drive. This drive is required for reliable long-term operation. Figure 11-11 shows a typical decoder/driver. The TTL-compatible input is raised to a higher voltage (usually 15 to 30 volts) by the level shifter. After the decoder converts the BCD to those of the seven segments to be selected, a driver is used to power the display. The ac input controls the driver frequency.

## Gas-Discharge Display

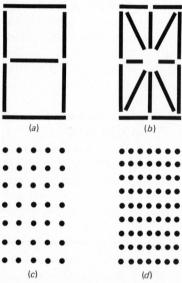

Figure 11-12. Gas-discharge display formats. (a) Seven-segment, (b) 16-segment, (c) 5 × 7 dot matrix, (d) 7 × 9 dot matrix.

When short text readouts of 32 to 256 characters are required on panel displays, gas-discharge displays become economical. Formats are not limited to seven segments or 5 × 7 dot matrices, but also include 7 × 9 dot matrices and 16-segment displays, as shown in Fig. 11-12. The variable format makes it possible to display numbers, letters, script characters, and foreign alphabets. Usually gas-discharge display inputs use a subset of the ASCII code applied on six parallel lines. Fairly elaborate control and character generation circuits, as well as refresh memory, are required with the gas-discharge display panel.

The display uses ionized gas to light the characters. Individual gas-filled cavities, in the shapes of segments or dots, are placed between the front and rear glass plates. Each cavity is crossed by a vertical and a horizontal electrode which together form an addressing matrix. When the two electrodes addressing a cavity (each carrying half the firing voltage) are carrying voltage, current flows through the gas. Outer-shell electrons in the gas are excited to higher energy states. When the electrons fall back to their original states orange light is emitted. Filters can be placed over the panel to convert the orange light to red or amber. A green character display is produced by coating the front glass with a phosphor which absorbs ultraviolet and releases secondary photons in the green region of the spectrum. With proper filtering, several different colors can be obtained on a single panel.

## Display Review

1. List the distinguishing characteristics of LEDs, LCDs, and gas-discharge displays.
2. Why is the polarity of the LED power supply important?
3. Describe the purpose of the current-limiting resistor in Fig. 11-1.
4. Distinguish between common anode and common cathode seven-segment LED displays. Why is the 7447 used with one and the 7448 with the other?
5. Discuss the multiplexed technique used to light multiple-digit seven-segment LED displays.
6. Describe the dot-matrix LED display. Why is it more expensive to use than a seven-segment display?
7. Define the term automatic blanking. How do RBI and RBO control lines provide this capability?
8. Distinguish between transmitting and reflecting LCDs.
9. List the advantages of gas-discharge displays.

## OTHER APPLICATIONS

### Digital Multimeter (DMM)

A meter that converts an analog voltage input to a digital readout can readily be constructed by using a combination of the devices covered in this and previous chapters. As Fig. 11-13 shows, the multimeter is based on the A/D converter. The analog input is forwarded to the sample-and-hold circuit. Control and timing sections provide the signals necessary for the proper sequence of events. After sampling, the signal is changed to BCD by the A/D converter and the digital output is stored in the buffer register. The BCD code for each digit is fed to a separate decoder/driver which lights the appropriate segments of one of three display digits.

### Digital Clock and Watch

An entire clock or watch function can be implemented on a single chip, as Fig. 11-14 shows. Typically, the watch chips run on batteries, whereas clocks accept 50- or 60-hertz ac power. Four- to six-digit readout in either 12- or 24-hour formats are commonly used.

A digital clock block diagram is shown in Fig. 11-15. Here the 60-hertz power also supplies the oscillator for the clock. Battery-powered wristwatches use a separate high-frequency quartz oscillator. The 60-hertz sine wave is shaped into square waves suitable for use in the digital gates and counter. The input gate selects either the 50- or 60-hertz operating frequency and also provides inputs for setting the clock ahead or back and for holding the value constant for synchronization.

A series of dividers converts the 60- or 50-hertz input into hours, minutes, and seconds. The first divider converts the power-supply frequency to one pulse per second. This would be a divide by 60 if the input were 60 hertz, or divide by 50 otherwise. This is followed by a division by 60 to convert seconds to minutes. As there are 60 minutes in one hour, the third divider provides the hours output. The selectable divide by 12 or 24 determines whether the clock is to use the 12- or 24-hour day. A wristwatch requires more

**Figure 11-13. Simplified digital multimeter block diagram.**

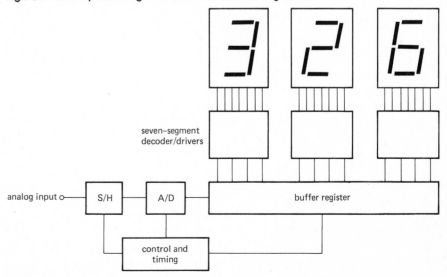

seven–segment decoder/drivers

analog input ○— S/H — A/D — buffer register

control and timing

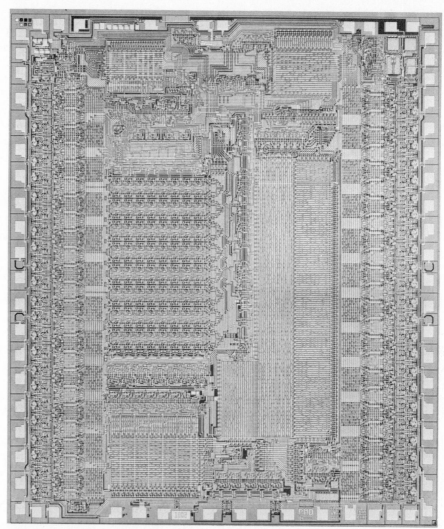

**Figure 11-14. Digital watch chip (*Precision Micro Design, Inc.*).**

divisions to reduce the high frequency of the oscillator to 1 hertz, but after that the sequence of operations is similar to that explained for the clock.

Each time unit is forwarded to the display multiplexer which has a frequency of 1 kilohertz. The multiplexer connects each seven-segment display in sequence. The digit decoder/driver selects which digit is to be lighted while the segment decoder sets the segments for that digit. The display is scanned from right to left; first the seconds, then the minutes, and finally the hours. At the 1-millisecond multiplexer interval, each digit is lighted $1000/6 = 167$ times a second, so the digits appear steady.

**Hand-Held Calculator**   Such sophisticated functions have been implemented in compact calculators that some of these arithmetic machines are almost as powerful as computers. A block diagram for a basic calculator is shown in Fig. 11-16. The keyboard input is multiplexed to the calculator integrated circuit. When a key is pressed, it grounds a

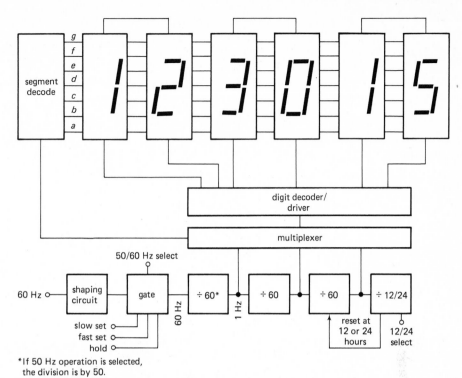

**Figure 11-15. Digital clock block diagram.**

signal line sending that information to the control section. The output of the calculator chip controls a display panel in the same manner that we saw before.

The calculator IC uses one or more registers to perform arithmetic functions in the ALU. In more expensive versions, a decimal point position register is also included for floating point operations.

**Figure 11-16. Calculator block diagram.**

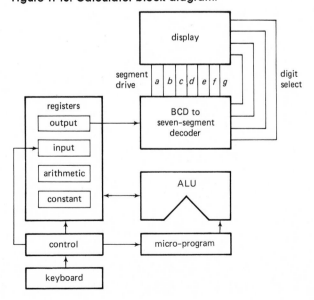

Most keyboards are low-cost, so the switches are not debounced. A timed keyboard debounce feature is often supplied on the chip. When a key closure is sensed, a clock starts a time interval. Any change which occurs in the input during this time period resets the timer to zero, so an input is accepted only after a minimum noisefree period and after all transient noise has disappeared.

The input and output registers buffer the incoming and outgoing data. Constants, such as $\pi$, can be entered during the arithmetic operation in their own register. All steps of the mathematical operation are controlled by the microprogram. (Microprogramming will be explained in the next chapter.) The ALU steps through the specified sequence of the microprogram to execute the command. The results are then sent to the display section.

## Applications Review

1. Describe the sequence used by a DMM in measuring the line voltage on a transformer in a digital clock.
2. Describe the purpose of the shaping circuit in the digital clock.
3. With a 60 hertz input, what unit of time is generated after the signal passes through the first two dividers ($\div 60$) in a digital clock?
4. Name the section of the calculator IC that specifies the sequence of operations for the ALU to perform.

## CHAPTER SUMMARY

1. LEDs, LCDs, and gas-discharge displays are commonly used for presenting limited amounts of alphanumeric information.
2. LEDs are similar to ordinary diodes in that they only carry current in one direction. When LEDs are forward biased they emit light in the visible spectrum.
3. A limiting resistor is used with the LED to minimize the power consumption.
4. Seven-segment displays consist of LEDs formed into bars. Common anode and common cathode configurations are commercially available. The digit-forming segments are labeled *a* through *g*, and an IC decoder/driver is used to convert a BCD or binary input to the signals necessary to light the correct segments.
5. Multiple-digit displays are usually multiplexed so that each digit is only lighted a portion of the time. The repetition rate is so fast that the eye sees a steady illumination.
6. LED dot-matrix displays can generate letters, numbers, and special characters. More external circuitry is used for their control than is needed in simpler LED displays.
7. Automatic blanking of multiple-digit displays removes leading and trailing zeros.
8. Liquid-crystal material reacting to electric fields comprises another display technology which provides low-power operation. Both transmitting and reflecting LCDs are made.
9. Short text readouts with varied character formats can be built by using gas-discharge displays. From 32 to 256 characters may be presented on a single panel.

10. Digital multimeters use an A/D converter together with a sample-and-hold circuit and numeric display to measure analog inputs.

11. A series of frequency dividers form the main logic section of digital watch and clock integrated circuits.

12. Varying in capability from simple four-function to programmable models, hand-held calculators use much the same type of logic as computers.

**KEY TERMS AND CONCEPTS**

displays
light emitting diodes (LED)
logic probe
seven-segment LED display
common anode and common cathode LED displays
decoder/driver
multiple-digit display

dot-matrix display
automatic blanking
liquid-crystal display (LCD)
gas-discharge display
digital multimeter (DMM)
digital clock and watch
hand-held calculator

## PROBLEMS

11-1. Find the current in the following circuits using red GaAsP LEDs.

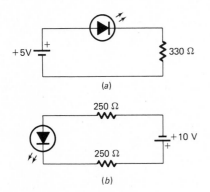

Figure 11-17. Problem 11-1.

11-2. What would be the state of the LED in a logic probe if the probe were applied to the output of the circuit in Fig. 10-11a? (Let $C = 1$ $\mu$F and $R_1 + R_2 = 1$ M$\Omega$)

11-3. For a minimum current drain (5 milliamperes) what is the size of the resistor that should be used in Fig. 11-1? What resistor value would produce maximum brightness of the LED (limit current to 40 milliamperes)?

11-4. Draw a diagram, similar to Fig. 11-6a, showing supply voltages, resistor values, and ground connections for the common anode seven-segment display to light only the segments for the number 3.

11-5. Repeat Problem 11-4 for a common anode configuration to display only the number 7.

11-6. If the input to the 7447 in Fig. 11-6b is 6, which output pins on the decoder/driver are high?

11-7. What BCD input to the 7448 of Fig. 11-7b would cause the following segment output? $a$ low, $b$ high, $c$ high, $d$ low, $e$ low, $f$ high, $g$ high.

11-8. How much power is consumed in the current-limiting resistors of the common anode display in Fig. 11-6b when the number 1 is displayed? When 8 is displayed?

11-9. If the frequency input to the digital clock in Fig. 11-15 is actually 59.8 hertz, how large an error accumulates in the readout after exactly 7 days?

11-10. Suppose the owner of the digital clock mistakenly selected the 50-hertz option on the gate, although the input was actually 60 hertz. If he starts the clock precisely at 12:04:10, what time does the clock display 24 hours later?

# EXPERIMENT 11 LEDs

**PURPOSE**  To investigate LEDs and the difference between common anode and common cathode LED displays.

**PARTS LIST**

| Item | Quantity |
|---|---|
| 7447 | 1 |
| 7448 | 1 |
| IEE 1712 LED display | 1 |
| MAN 74 LED display | 1 |
| 330-$\Omega$ resistor | 7 |
| 1-k$\Omega$ resistor | 1 |
| LED | 1 |
| SPDT switch | 4 |

**IC DIAGRAMS**

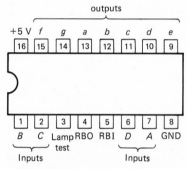

*A* is the least significant bit of the input, *D* is the most significant bit.

**Figure 11-18. 7447 and 7448.**

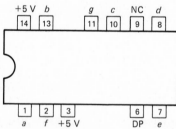

Pins 4, 5 and 12 not provided.

**Figure 11-19. IEE 1712 LED display.**

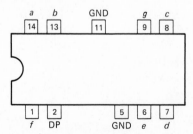

Pins 3, 4, 10 and 12 not provided.

**Figure 11-20. MAN 74 LED display.**

**PROCEDURE**   **Step 1.**   Build the circuits shown in Fig. 11-21a through 11-21d. Record whether the LED is on or off and the relative intensity for each case.

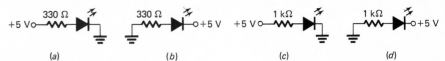

**Figure 11-21. LED experiments.**

Explain your results.

**Step 2.**   Connect the IEE 1712 common anode display as shown in Fig. 11-22. Why does the display show the number 4?

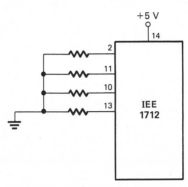

All resistors are 330 Ω.

**Figure 11-22. Common anode LED display experiment.**

**Step 3.**   Connect the 7447 and the IEE 1712 LED display as shown in Fig. 11-23. Record the results for each switch combination. Explain the display readings.

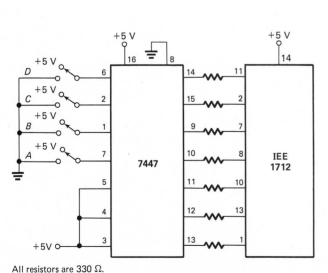

All resistors are 330 Ω.

**Figure 11-23. Common anode LED decoder/driver experiment.**

| Switches | | | | LED Display |
|---|---|---|---|---|
| **D** | **C** | **B** | **A** | |
| 0 V | 0 V | 0 V | 0 V | |
| 0 | 0 | 0 | 5 | |
| 0 | 0 | 5 | 0 | |
| 0 | 0 | 5 | 5 | |
| 0 | 5 | 0 | 0 | |
| 0 | 5 | 0 | 5 | |
| 0 | 5 | 5 | 0 | |
| 0 | 5 | 5 | 5 | |
| 5 | 0 | 0 | 0 | |
| 5 | 0 | 0 | 5 | |
| 5 | 0 | 5 | 0 | |
| 5 | 0 | 5 | 5 | |
| 5 | 5 | 0 | 0 | |
| 5 | 5 | 0 | 5 | |
| 5 | 5 | 5 | 0 | |
| 5 | 5 | 5 | 5 | |

**Step 4.** Connect the 7448 IC and the common cathode MAN 74 display as shown in Fig. 11-24. Record the LED reading for each switch combination listed below. Explain your results.

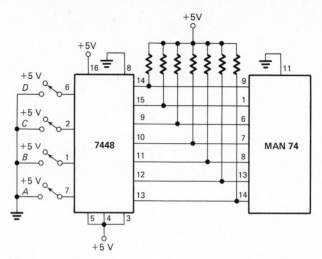

All resistors are 330 Ω.

**Figure 11-24. Common cathode LED decoder/driver experiment.**

| Switches | | | | |
|---|---|---|---|---|
| **D** | **C** | **B** | **A** | **LED Display** |
| 0 V | 0 V | 0 V | 0 V | |
| 0 | 0 | 0 | 5 | |
| 0 | 0 | 5 | 0 | |
| 0 | 0 | 5 | 5 | |
| 0 | 5 | 0 | 0 | |
| 0 | 5 | 0 | 5 | |
| 0 | 5 | 5 | 0 | |
| 0 | 5 | 5 | 5 | |
| 5 | 0 | 0 | 0 | |
| 5 | 0 | 0 | 5 | |
| 5 | 0 | 5 | 0 | |
| 5 | 0 | 5 | 5 | |
| 5 | 5 | 0 | 0 | |
| 5 | 5 | 0 | 5 | |
| 5 | 5 | 5 | 0 | |
| 5 | 5 | 5 | 5 | |

# CHAPTER TWELVE
# MICROPROCESSORS
# AND MICROCOMPUTERS

A microprocessor is a programmable integrated circuit manufactured on from one to three chips. The ALU, registers, address and data bus, instruction set, and control logic are supplied on the chips. The all-in-one microcomputer, on the other hand, includes a microprocessor along with input/output capability, ROM and possibly RAM memory, and a clock oscillator. The operation of both the processor and computer is introduced in the following sections.

An understanding of any digital computer requires knowledge of both hardware and software, so basic programming concepts are also presented in this chapter.

**CHAPTER OBJECTIVES** Upon completing this chapter you should be able to:

1. List the components of a microprocessor.
2. Name the registers used to hold data and instructions in the microprocessor.
3. Describe the control section of the microprocessor and explain how a microprogram specifies the sequence of events to be executed.
4. Distinguish between the operations performed in the arithmetic section.
5. Draw a block diagram of a microprocessor.
6. Explain the meaning and use of the status register flags.

7. Describe the timing and sequence of instruction execution.
8. Distinguish among the various operand addressing methods used in microprocessors.
9. Discuss the types of instructions commonly found in microprocessor repertoires and give examples of each.
10. Define the meaning of bit-sliced microprocessor architecture.
11. Distinguish between programmed input/output, interrupts, and direct memory access.
12. Describe the operation of a universal synchronous/asynchronous receiver transmitter.

## MICROPROCESSOR REGISTERS

The microprocessor provides some or all of the arithmetic and control sections needed in a computer. Microprocessors come with various word sizes ranging from 1 to 16 bits. In this chapter we will use an 8-bit (also called a *byte*) word size as an example. The conclusions we reach are generally applicable to other word lengths as well.

The microprocessor registers are used to temporarily store the instructions to be executed and the data being used in the arithmetic or Boolean operation, and also to buffer control information.

### Accumulator

The main arithmetic register is the 8-bit accumulator, often called the A register. The accumulator is used to hold the result of an arithmetic or Boolean function performed by the ALU. Its name follows from its accumulating of results. Some processors may have more than one accumulator, in which case each register is given a distinguishing number such as $A_1$, $A_2$, . . . . The accumulator is also used to read or write memory data. Reading and writing is required in input/output instructions as well, so the A register may be involved in these operations.

### Index Register

The 8-bit index register, often used together with the accumulator, can be used to increment or decrement quantities or memory addresses. The index register—we will refer to it as the X register—is convenient to apply as the counter in repetitive operations. In some microprocessors the functions of the accumulator and the index registers are combined in one register. The combined form is called a general register.

### Memory Address Register

The memory address register (MAR) should already be familiar to you from our study of memories. The MAR word size depends on the number of memory cells. A register of $n$ bits can address a maximum of $2^n$ words. We will use a 16-bit MAR as our example, and that memory can contain no more than 65,536 ($2^{16}$) words. The address of every word moving from memory or to memory must pass through the MAR.

### Instruction Register and Program Counter

Two closely associated registers are the instruction register and the program counter register. The instruction register (IR) holds the 8-bit instruction currently being interpreted. The program counter (PC) contains the memory address of the next instruction to be executed. The program counter serves an analogous function for instructions to that of the MAR for data. Therefore, the program counter has the same word size as the MAR, 16 bits. Once the starting address of the program has been loaded into the program counter, its contents are normally incremented by one after each instruction cycle.

**Stack**   The stack is actually a file of 8-bit registers that can be used by the processor for storage. The length of the stack specifies the number of registers in the file. The stack can be visualized by comparing it with the spring-loaded plate servers found in many cafeterias. When the top plate is removed the next one pops up. If clean plates are placed on top, the bottom plates are pushed down.

Only information on the top of the stack is available. If you want to read that information, the stack is "popped" and the contents of the top register are made available. Placing information on the stack is called a "push". All of the stack contents are moved down one position by the pointer to receive data being pushed on the stack. If more information is placed on the stack than there are registers to hold it, the last word placed on the stack is lost.

This type of stack structure is called first-in-last-out (FILO) because the newest information is always available on top. A stack pointer register is used to keep track of the location for the latest data place on the stack. Figure 12-1 shows examples of pushing and popping the stack. Two errors can occur in stack operations. If more items are pushed on the stack than it can hold, a *stack overflow* error will result. Popping an empty stack causes the *stack underflow* condition.

**Figure 12-1. FILO stack.**

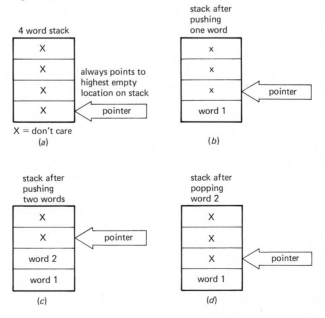

**Register Review**

1. List the way in which each microprocessor register functions.
2. Describe the relationship between the accumulator and the ALU.
3. Why can the memory address register be considered the key to memory?
4. Discuss the use of the program counter and instruction register to sequence through a computer program.
5. Define pushing and popping a stack.

## CONTROL SECTION

The control section maintains the correct timing and sequence in the microprocessor. The sequence is driven by the contents of the instruction register. Each instruction is actually a bit pattern that generates a series of enabling signals throughout the processor. The following discussion on microprogramming will delve deeper into the decoding of instructions. Here, let's briefly consider the events that take place during the instruction cycle.

Each instruction requires one or more clock periods to complete execution. The timing pulses are generated by a crystal oscillator, which, together with the clock logic, forms the master clock. The clock period in typical microprocessors is 100 nanoseconds to 1 microsecond. The clock logic may or may not be on the microprocessor chip.

Every instruction cycle consists of fetching and executing the instruction. During the instruction fetch portion of the cycle, the instruction is read from memory. Table 12-1 lists the steps necessary to obtain the instruction. First, the contents of the program counter are transferred to the memory address register. The word in that memory location (the instruction) is sent to the memory buffer register and then to the instruction register. Finally, the program counter is incremented.

During instruction execution, the instruction is decoded. Instruction execution may require another memory reference to get the data, or operand, to be processed or, alternatively, to write data into memory.

**Table 12-1**
**Instruction Fetching**

| Step 1 | (PC) → MAR |
| Step 2 | (MAR) → memory |
| Step 3 | (MBR) → IR |
| Step 4 | (PC) + 1 → PC |

MBR is the memory buffer register
→ means "is transferred to"
(Z) means the contents of register Z

**Control Section Review**

1. Describe the two parts of the instruction cycle.
2. List the events required to fetch the instruction.
3. Why is the program counter incremented after fetching the instruction?

## ARITHMETIC SECTION

Data is manipulated in the microprocessor section consisting of the ALU and its arithmetic registers. The ALU operates on an entire memory word in parallel. In our example, an 8-bit ALU will be used. As we have seen, the ALU performs binary addition and subtraction, Boolean operations, and complementing. More complex operations, such as multiplication, require additional external circuitry. A basic microprocessor with arithmetic and control sections, registers, and an internal bus is shown in Fig. 12-2a. The internal bus is the pathway for all signal transfer within the microprocessor.

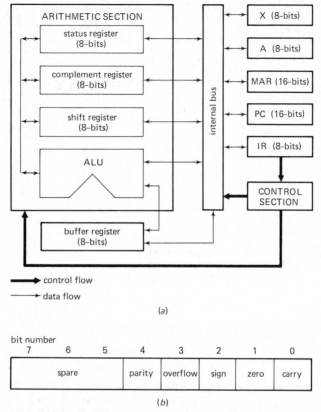

Figure 12-2. Microprocessor. (*a*) Architecture, (*b*) status register.

The *complement* register is used to hold the results of a complement operation. We have already studied the ALU and the *shift* register found in the arithmetic section. The *status* flags register is new, however. Each bit in this register is called a *flag* because the individual bit settings signal a specific condition.

Only certain microprocessor instructions change the status flags and there is little uniformity among the status indications in various microprocessors. Usually one flag bit will indicate the *carry status*. If that bit is set, there was a carry-out from the high-order bit during the last arithmetic instruction. The *zero status* flag indicates that the last arithmetic result was zero when the flag is set. The content of the sign bit in the ALU is transferred to the *sign status* flag. The *overflow* flag is set when an overflow error resulted from the last operation. A *parity* flag would be set to one to show that the last byte had incorrect parity when it was checked. (Parity is simply used to show whether the data contained an odd or even number of ones. For example $0111\ 1000_2$ has even parity. Data are often sent with odd parity. If the parity is even when they are received, one or more bits must have changed state since the data originated.) The status flags are shown in Fig. 12-2*b*.

**Arithmetic Section Review**

1. List the components of the arithmetic section in the microprocessor.

2. Describe the purpose of the complement register.
3. Discuss the purpose of the overflow flag in the status register.
4. Define the term even parity.

**MICROPROCESSOR PACKAGING**

Microprocessors are usually manufactured as DIPs. Figure 12-3 shows the chip for the INTEL 8748 8-bit microprocessor. Included on the chip is 1K of EPROM and 64 words of RAM. The chip also provides 27 input/output lines and contains internal clock logic.

Typically, a microprocessor is a 40-pin DIP. One or two pins are dedicated to power-supply inputs. (For instance, the 8748 uses one pin for the power-supply voltage.) One pin is used for ground and another often for the clock input. Given the MAR in our microprocessor, we can tell that 16 pins are needed for the memory address output. Data input/output uses another eight pins. One or more pins are needed to determine whether the memory reference is for reading or writing. The remaining pins are associated with the control signals used for input and output.

Figure 12-3. 8748 Microprocessor (*Intel Corporation*).

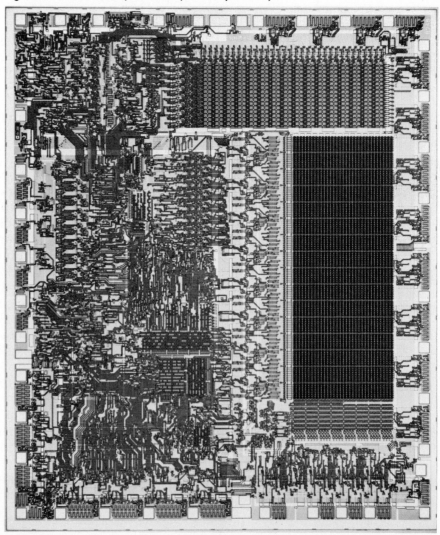

**MICROPROGRAMMING** The earlier discussion on instruction execution introduced the concept of microprogramming. Each instruction in the computer instruction set, such as right shift the contents of the A register, requires a series of commands to move or operate on the data.

Consider the "right shift" instruction. The microprogram steps necessary for its execution are illustrated in Fig. 12-4. All registers, except for the program counter and A register were cleared prior to this sequence. The instruction fetch sequence listed in Table 12-1 is another example of a microprogram. The instruction fetch is completed before the execution microprogram begins, as shown in Fig. 12-4a. A brief review of the instruction-fetching steps will explain the current contents of the registers. The program started at address $2000_{16}$. This is the original value in the program counter that was sent to the memory address register to obtain the instruction. The contents of cell $2000_{16}$ were transferred to the instruction register and the program counter was incremented to $2001_{16}$.

The bits in the instruction are a coded message to control the start of the right shift microprogram. (The code $15_{16}$ means right shift the A register.) First, the content of the A register is gated onto the internal bus and then into the shift register (Figs. 12-4b and 12-4c). The register is commanded to shift right (Fig. 12-4d). Then the data are placed on the bus and finally returned in their shifted form to the A register (Figs. 12-4e and 12-4f).

Five microprogram steps were necessary to execute the instruction. At the completion of the instruction execution the shift register still has the result, but this will be overwritten during the next shift operation. Because detailed knowledge of the internal signal and information flow is required, microprogramming a computer is a significant effort. Normally the programmer need not be concerned with the microprogram. The microprogram is automatically accessed by the processor in response to each instruction.

**Timing** The steps in the microprogram are controlled by the master oscillator. A microprocessor usually develops a series of multiphase clock pulses from the oscillator. During each phase only a particular microprogram can be completed. For example, instruction fetching can be limited to the first clock phase. Reading memory to obtain the operand or perform a data input may be limited to phase 2. Phase 3 is used for executing arithmetic or logical instructions, and data are stored in memory during phase 4. So several clock cycles are required to complete one program instruction.

**MICROCOMPUTER ARCHITECTURE** The microprocessor is used in conjunction with memories and input/output circuitry to perform useful calculations. The interconnections of a microcomputer are often referred to as the *architecture*. Figure 12-5 shows the architecture of a microcomputer with RAM and ROM memories. The processor transfers information between memories and input/output equipment by means of the 8-bit system data bus, but the specific memory addresses involved in either ROM or RAM are passed over the 16-bit address bus.

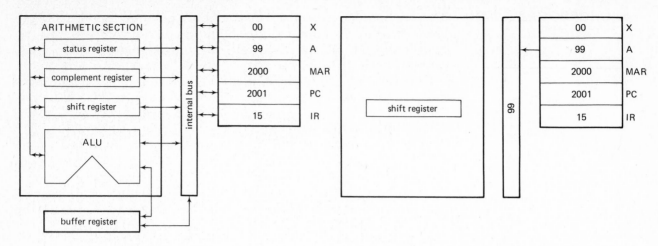

(a) Instruction has been fetched.

(b) Step 1. Contents of A register moved to the bus. (Only the registers involved in the operation are shown.)

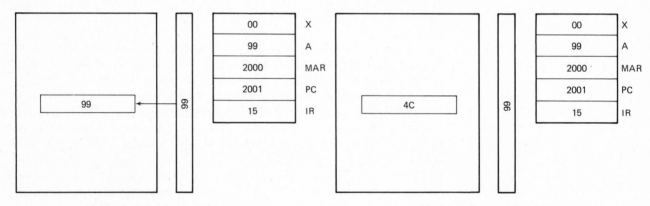

(c) Step 2. Data moved to shift register.

(d) Step 3. Register shifts right.

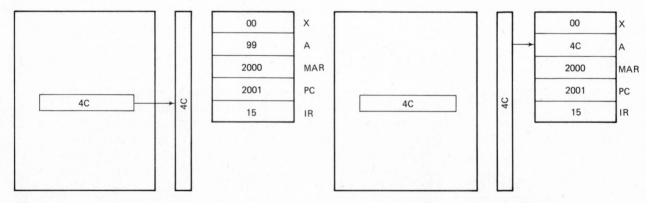

(e) Step 4. Data is placed on the bus.

(f) Step 5. Results are transferred to the A register.

**Figure 12-4. Instruction execution.**

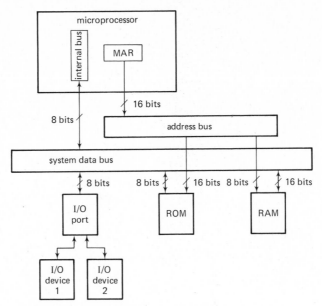

**Figure 12-5. Microprocessor architecture.**

Instead of the fixed size registers and ALU used in our example, the registers and ALU can be divided into 2-bit or 4-bit segments that can be combined into words of various sizes. This technique is used in *bit-sliced* microprocessor architectures. A microprocessor with a word length up to 32-bits can be constructed by combining the appropriate number of slices.

## Microprogramming and Architecture Review

1. List the sequence of microprogram operations needed to complement the accumulator contents.
2. Describe the function of the internal bus in microprocessor operations.
3. Explain the reason for one instruction needing several clock cycles during execution.
4. Describe the need for a 16-bit address bus in an 8-bit microprocessor.

## INPUT/OUTPUT (I/O)

There are three methods for exchanging information between the processor and its outside environment. Programmed I/O transfers data under control of the computer instructions, so the external logic is commanded by the program. Contrast programmed I/O with interrupts where the external logic forces an input data exchange although the processor was not expecting it. Most complex of the I/O methods is direct memory access which moves data to and from memory without involving the microprocessor in the data transfer.

## Programmed I/O

Most commonly microprocessor I/O involves serial data transfer. As Fig. 12-6 shows, the serial data stream is converted to parallel before it is placed on the system bus. The serial data may be trans-

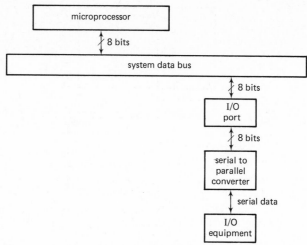

**Figure 12-6. Programmed I/O architecture.**

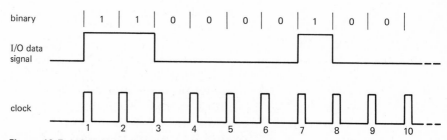

**Figure 12-7. I/O timing diagram for serial data transfer.**

ferred either *synchronously* or *asynchronously*. The difference in the two methods is that every synchronous data exchange begins with one or two unique sync character codes. In either case the transfer is timed by clock pulses, that is each data bit is valid during one clock period, as Fig. 12-7 shows.

The frequency of the data transfer is specified by a *baud rate*. For example a 300-baud serial synchronous data rate is equivalent to 300 bits per second.

**Universal Synchronous/ Asynchronous Receiver Transmitter (USART)**

A USART chip can be used to provide the I/O interface for the microcomputer, but one USART is necessary on each serial I/O channel. The USART is usually available in the form of a 28-pin DIP. During input operations the USART receives the serial data bit and shifts it into a received data buffer register as shown in Fig. 12-8. When the 8-bit register is full, the data are forwarded to the data bus buffer located inside the USART. From there it is moved on the system data bus under microprocessor control and into the A register. Finally the data word is stored in memory. If more than one word is to be transferred, the process repeats.

To send information, output data are moved from memory to the A register, as shown in Fig. 12-9. Then they are placed on the system data bus. The parallel data from the bus move to the

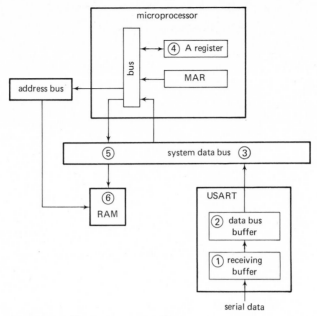

**Figure 12-8. Input data operations.**

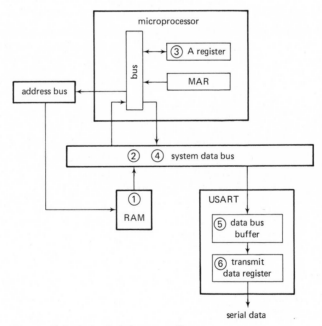

**Figure 12-9. Output data operations.**

USART data bus register and are then sent to the transmit data buffer. From the buffer, they are shifted, one bit at a time, out of the USART to the I/O equipment.

**Interrupts**  When a computer system is used in *real-time* operations, the processor must be notified of unscheduled events from the outside. Interrupt signals are used for this function. An interrupt request

**Table 12-2**
**Interrupt Servicing Microprogram.**

| | |
|---|---|
| Step 1 | Store the contents of the A register, program counter, and status flags. Sometimes memory is used for storage. Alternatively, the stack can be employed. |
| Step 2 | Load the program counter with the address of the interrupt-handling program. |
| Step 3 | Execute the interrupt-handling program. |
| Step 4 | Restore the contents of the A register, program counter, and status flags. |

signal is transmitted to the processor by an external system bus control line. The microprocessor, under program control, can accept or reject the interrupt. If the interrupt is accepted, the processor sets the interrupt acknowledge signal and enters an interrupt-handling microprogram. When the external device senses the acknowledge signal, the device transfers the input data to the I/O port.

Remember that the interrupt was unscheduled, so the microprocessor must suspend whatever it has been doing prior to servicing the interrupt. Table 12-2 lists the microprogram steps for interrupt processing. First, the processor and arithmetic registers must be saved in memory. Then the program counter and other registers are loaded with the address and data of the *interrupt-handling* program. After that program has completed processing and interrupt, the registers are reloaded with their original contents so that the main program can resume executing at the same point where it left off. Figure 12-10 illustrates the transfer of control from the main program to the interrupt handler and back again.

Instead of using software to process the interrupt, a hardware control unit could be substituted, but additional microprocessor logic would then be required. For this reason software processing is most commonly found. To make the programming task simpler,

**Figure 12-10. Interrupt processing.**

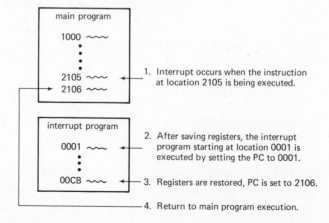

the microprocessor can implement *vectored interrupts*. Vectored interrupts are particularly convenient when more than one I/O device can generate an interrupt. Depending on the device that causes the interrupt, the vectored interrupt feature will select the appropriate address to load into the program counter. Thus the vectored interrupt points out the proper servicing routine.

When more than one interrupt can occur, some priority scheme is necessary. If two interrupts happen simultaneously, the one with highest priority gets first access to the processor. Because only the highest priority interrupting device will have its service request honored, the other interrupt may be held waiting (*queued*) or can simply be ignored. One type of interrupt priority assignment honors the I/O port with the highest number in case of simultaneous interrupts.

**Direct Memory Access (DMA)**

Using a direct access to memory, an external device can read or write data and bypass the microprocessor entirely. The advantage of DMA is that the processor is not involved in I/O operations. Its disadvantage, as we shall see, is the more sophisticated I/O device necessary. Use of DMA is most common when the processor would otherwise be overloaded executing its program and managing I/O.

The scheme used for DMA is called *memory-cycle stealing*. As the timing diagram in Fig. 12-11 shows, the external equipment sets a memory request signal high when it wants to access memory. The microprocessor logic responds with an acknowledge signal. The signal is an automatic response by the microprogram and does not require execution of an I/O instruction by the processor. (Until the acknowledge signal becomes high the requesting device must wait.) While the I/O device is referencing memory, the processor can perform any operation except using memory, hence the term cycle stealing. Some processors allow the device to continue to use memory for many cycles; others only allow a single memory reference before the processor regains control, as our example shows.

Once the information transfer is complete, the I/O device drops the request and the processor again uses memory. A device which

Figure 12-11. Memory-cycle stealing timing diagram.

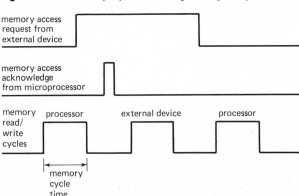

uses DMA must have the same memory logic as the processor, That, is the device needs a memory address register, counter to keep track of the number of words to read or write, status register, I/O clock, and control logic.

**Input/Output Review**

1. List the I/O methods used by microprocessors.
2. Distinguish between synchronous and asynchronous serial I/O.
3. Describe the function performed by a USART during data input. During output.
4. List the sequence of events that an interrupt triggers if it arrives while the microprocessor is executing another program.
5. Define the term vectored interrupt.
6. Why are interrupt priorities necessary?
7. List the signals required to access memory directly.

**PROGRAMMING**

A program that is stored in memory consists of a series of binary words. In this form the instructions are called a machine-language program. Sometimes programmers will mentally convert the binary instructions to octal or hexadecimal and still refer to them as machine code. While perfect for computer execution, machine code is difficult for humans to understand. For ease of programming, mnemonic titles are often assigned to the instructions. For example the machine code for an addition instruction in one microprocessor is $86_{16}$, but it is much easier for a programmer to remember the mnemonic ADD. Special computer programs, called *assemblers*, translate the mnemonics into machine-code instructions.

Even more powerful languages, called *compiler* or *high-order languages*, allow the programmer to code in mathematical or Englishlike statements. Then a compiler program converts the statement to machine code. For example, the single statement

$$X = (Y**2 + Z)/14$$

causes a large number of machine-code instructions to be generated. This conversion would include instructions to

1. Obtain the quantity $Y$ from its memory location.
2. Multiply $Y$ by itself (the double asterisk means raise $Y$ to the power following; 2 in this case).
3. Obtain $Z$ from memory.
4. Add $Z$ to the previous result.
5. Divide the result by $14_{10}$.
6. Store the answer in a new memory cell which will be designated $X$ for the remainder of the program.

A program written in either assembler or compiler statements is called the *source-coded* version. After assembling or compiling, the machine code is called the *object* program. Regardless of how the machine-code object program is generated, it must be loaded into memory before it can be executed. A program is usually pro-

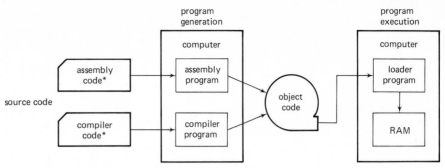

*May be on paper tape, magnetic tape, punched cards, or other media

**Figure 12-12. Program generation and execution.**

vided in ROM with the microprocessor to load programs. After the program is loaded, an operator manually places the first program address in the program counter register and presses the run button. Figure 12-12 is a symbolic representation of the programming, loading, and execution steps.

**Instruction Repertoire**  Almost every computer has a different set of instructions, so only by studying his or her particular machine does a programmer learn its instruction repertoire. To give an idea of the capability of microprocessors, examples of some typical instructions (not for any specific machine) will be discussed.

For ease in understanding, a set of abbreviations and symbols listed in Table 12-3 will be used. Every instruction consists of two

**Tale 12-3**
**Instruction Notation**

| Symbol | Meaning |
|--------|---------|
| A | accumulator |
| MAR | memory address register |
| PC | program counter |
| X | index register |
| M | main memory |
| ( ) | contents of. Examples: (A) means the contents of the accumulator, (M 1000) means the contents of memory cell $1000_{16}$. |
| $\longrightarrow$ | transferred to. Example: (M 1000) $\rightarrow$ A means the contents of cell $1000_{16}$ are transferred to the accumulator. |
| M( ) | memory-indexed. Example: M 1000 (X) is the memory cell designated by the sum of $1000_{16}$ and the contents of the X register. If (X) $\doteq$ $10_{16}$ the memory cell $1010_{16}$ would be indicated. |

parts. The *operation* or *op code* and the *operand.* The op code designates the function to be performed such as add or store, while the operand indicates the data to be used in the instruction execution. The operand may come from memory, be contained in a register such as the A register, or be unnecessary—as in the halt instruction.

**Accumulator Instructions.** One of the most basic computer instructions is to read data from memory and place it in the accumulator. The *load accumulator* or *LDA* instruction is used for this purpose. An explanation and example are given below.

**Load A instruction**
**LDA 5000**

Meaning
(M 5000) → A

| *Prior to execution* | *After execution* |
|---|---|
| (PC) = 1000 | (PC) = 1001 |
| (A) = 00 | (A) = 7F |
| (M 5000) = 7F | (M 5000) = 7F |

Another common operation is storing the accumulator contents in memory. The *store accumulator* operation provides this capability.

**Store A instruction**
**STA 0770**

Meaning
(A) → M 0770

| *Prior to execution* | *After execution* |
|---|---|
| (PC) = 1000 | (PC) = 1001 |
| (A) = FC | (A) = FC |
| (M 0770) = 10 | (M 0770) = FC |

**Index Register Instructions.** Loading and storing the index register are operations similar to those for the accumulator.

**Load X Instruction**
**LDX 7303**

Meaning
(M 7303) → X

| *Prior to execution* | *After execution* |
|---|---|
| (PC) = 1000 | (PC) = 1001 |
| (X) = 06 | (X) = FF |
| (M 7303) = FF | (M 7303) = FF |

**Store X Instruction**
**STX 1234**

Meaning
(X) → M 1234

| *Prior to execution* | *After execution* |
|---|---|
| (PC) = 5000 | (PC) = 5001 |
| (X) = 01 | (X) = 01 |
| (M 1234) = CC | (M 1234) = 01 |

**Arithmetic and Logic Instructions.** A wide range of Boolean and mathematical operations is usually provided in the microprocessor repertoire. Along with addition, subtraction, AND, OR, and complement functions, the processor may also be capable of multiplication, division, and exclusive ORing. If the latter types of instructions are not provided, simple programs can be written to do these operations in *software*.

| Add Instruction | Meaning |
|---|---|
| **ADD 0100** | (M 0100) plus (A) → A |

| *Prior to execution* | *After execution* |
|---|---|
| (PC) = 6000 | (PC) = 6001 |
| (A) = 07 | (A) = 18 |
| (M 0100) = 11 | (M 0100) = 11 |

Note that the original A register value is lost.

| Subtract Instruction | Meaning |
|---|---|
| **SUB 1400** | (A) minus (M 1400) → A |

| *Prior to execution* | *After execution* |
|---|---|
| (PC) = 1000 | (PC) = 1001 |
| (A) = 0F | (A) = 07 |
| (M 1400) = 08 | (M 1400) = 08 |

Subtraction uses two's complement arithmetic. The original A register value is lost.

| AND Instruction | Meaning |
|---|---|
| **AND 2346** | (A) AND (M 2346) → A |

| *Prior to execution* | *After execution* |
|---|---|
| (PC) = 1000 | (PC) = 1001 |
| (A) = 06 | (A) = 00 |
| (M 2346) = F0 | (M 2346) = F0 |

| OR Instruction | Meaning |
|---|---|
| **OR 2346** | (A) OR (M 2346) → A |

| *Prior to execution* | *After execution* |
|---|---|
| (PC) = 1000 | (PC) = 1001 |
| (A) = 06 | (A) = F6 |
| (M 2346) = F0 | (M 2346) = F0 |

**Jump Instruction.** Normally instructions are executed in sequential order, but it may be necessary to break out of the sequence to begin a different program segment. The jump instruction allows the programmer to specify any address to be the source for the next instruction.

**Jump Instruction**                 Meaning
**JMP 4000**                         $(M\ 4000) \to PC$

*Prior to execution*                 *After execution*
$(PC) = 1000$                        $(PC) = 0030$
$(A) = 14$                           $(A) = 14$
$(M\ 4000) = 30$                     $(M\ 4000) = 30$

Cell $0030_{16}$ has the address of the next instruction to be executed in it, because the address placed in the PC is the location for the following instruction.

**Branch Instruction.**  Suppose a programmer wanted to perform a series of instructions a specified number of times and then go to some other portion of the program. By using the index register with a branch instruction, the count can be maintained for the proper number of repeated passes then another program referenced. This instruction is often called an indexed skip.

**Branch Instruction**               Meaning
**ISZ**                              $(X) - 1 \to X$
                                     if $(X) = 0$ then $(PC) + 2 \to PC$
**Case 1 (no skip)**                 otherwise $(PC) + 1 \to PC$
*Prior to execution*                 *After execution*
$(PC) = 1000$                        $(PC) = 1001$
$(X) = 02$                           $(X) = 01$

**Case 2 (skip)**
*Prior to execution*                 *After execution*
$(PC) = 1000$                        $(PC) = 1002$
$(X) = 01$                           $(X) = 00$

In case 2 the instruction in cell $1001_{16}$ is skipped over. The programming example which follows will demonstrate the usefulness of the indexed skip used together with the jump instruction.

**Halt Instruction.**  After the program has run to completion, the microprocessor can be stopped. The operator can restart the program by hitting the run button.

**Halt Instruction**                 Meaning
**HLT**                              $0 \to$ run flip-flop

**Operand Addressing**  All of the instructions shown so far have used operands obtained from memory. This method is called *directly addressing* the operands. Operands may also be obtained from several other sources. Before describing the other cases, let's consider one detail of the instruction format that has been ignored till now. The address must contain 16 bits, as we know, from the PC and MAR word lengths. How do we form a 16-bit address for the instruction using only an 8-bit word?

As Fig. 12-13 depicts, this is done by devoting three memory

| memory cell *m* | op code |
|---|---|
| memory cell *m*+1 | most significant half of operand address |
| memory cell *m*+2 | least significant half of operand address |

**Figure 12-13. Direct operand addressing.**

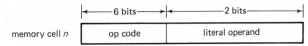

| memory cell *n* | op code | literal operand |
|---|---|---|

**Figure 12-14. Literal operand.**

words to store the instruction. The first memory location contains the op code. The following cell is the most significant bits of the address with the least significant bits in the third memory cell. If we use this instruction format, then the previous statement regarding incrementing the program counter must also be modified. Rather than incrementing the counter by one, which would be the address of the most significant half of the operand address, the PC must count up by three.

A simpler form of addressing uses *literal* operands. The operand is actually part of the instruction in this format. Literal operands are often used when the quantity involved is a constant; for example, adding 2 to the A register. Figure 12-14 shows this type of addressing as the instruction would appear stored in memory. The literal quantity cannot be more than 3 because it is limited by a 2-bit length.

Another source for the operand may be a register. We may load the A register with the content of the index register or vice versa, for example. This is the *register-to-register* operand format.

A powerful addressing technique, called *indexed addressing*, adds the content of the index register to an originating memory address. This form of addressing is often used to process tables of numbers in memory. The programming example in this chapter demonstrates the convenience of indexed addressing.

How does the microprocessor know which addressing method the programmer wants to use? In addition to the instruction op code, the programmer specifies a modifier to indicate the source for the operand. If no source is given (as in the preceding instruction examples) the processor will default to using direct addressing. Examples of the operand modifiers are

| Type | Instruction Example | Contents of X | Operand Source |
|---|---|---|---|
| Direct | ADD 1000 | FF | (M 1000) |
| Literal | ADD L, 2 | FF | Literal; the operand is 2. |
| Register | ADD X | FF | (X) |
| Indexed | ADD I, 1000 | FF | (M 10FF). The contents of X are added to $1000_{16}$. |

**A Sample Program**  A small program will put all of the microprocessor concepts together. Assume that a company uses a microcomputer to calculate its payroll records for 10 employees. A program is needed to credit each employee with one hour's work.

A flowchart for our program is shown in Fig. 12-15. The present number of hours worked by each employee is stored in a memory table. The first step in the program will be to set the index to 10 ($OA_{16}$), that is the number of workers. The current hours credited to each worker must then be read from the table, incremented, and replaced in the same location in the table. The index counter is decremented and the process repeated for the remaining workers. (Because our counter starts at 10 and counts down, we will work from the bottom of the table to the top.) After all of the workers have received credit for the hour, the process stops. Decrementing, checking the counter, and branching when the count is zero is a *looping* process.

The microprocessor program is listed in Table 12-4. The memory table is listed in Table 12-5. The first instruction sets the index

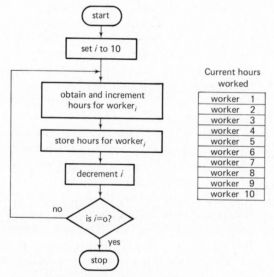

Figure 12-15. Sample program flowchart.

**Table 12-4**
**Sample Microprocessor Program**

| Step | Instruction | Result |
|------|-------------|--------|
| 1 | LDX 1000 | $0A \rightarrow X$ |
| 2 | LOOP LDA L, 1 | $1 \rightarrow A$ |
| 3 | ADD I, 1000 | (M 1000 (X)) plus (A) $\rightarrow$ A |
| 4 | STA I, 1000 | (A) $\rightarrow$ M 1000 (X) |
| 5 | ISZ | Decrement X. If (X) = 0 skip the next step. |
| 6 | JMP LOOP | Loop to next worker |
| 7 | HLT | Stop |

**Table 12-5**
**Memory Map for Data**

| Location | Contents |
|----------|----------|
| 1000 | 0A (constant) |
| 1001 | worker 1 |
| 1002 | worker 2 |
| 1003 | worker 3 |
| 1004 | worker 4 |
| 1005 | worker 5 |
| 1006 | worker 6 |
| 1007 | worker 7 |
| 1008 | worker 8 |
| 1009 | worker 9 |
| 100A | worker 10 |

register to 0A using a constant stored in memory as the operand. Then the accumulator is set to 1 by use of a literal operand. The address preceding the table ($1000_{16}$), indexed by the contents of the X register ($0A_{16}$), selects the memory cell with the tenth worker's hours to add to the number in the A register. After that worker's hours have been totaled, the A register is stored in the same indexed memory cell (Step 4).

Now the program comes to the decision point. After the index register is decremented, its contents are checked. If the X register does not equal zero, the next instruction is executed. That will certainly be the case the first pass through the program, so the jump instruction at Step 6 will be executed. A symbolic address called "LOOP" is used to indicate where the program will jump. After ten times through the loop, the X register will equal 1 prior to Step 5 and the last worker's hours will have been calculated. Then the index register will decrement to zero. At Step 5 the zero will be detected and the instruction at Step 6 will be skipped. The halt instruction will stop the processor after the program has been completed.

**Programming Review**

1. Define the terms: machine code, assembler, compiler, and loader.
2. Describe how the indexed skip instruction can be used for branching.
3. Distinguish between a directly addressed and an index addressed operand.
4. Define a literal operand. Give an example.
5. Why is no memory address required for the register-to-register operand format?

**CHAPTER SUMMARY**

1. A microprocessor provides the user with the ALU, registers, address and data buses, instruction set, and control which are the primary parts of a computer. A microcomputer needs to add only I/O, memory, and the clock to the processor.
2. The microprocessor registers include the accumulator, index register, memory address register, instruction register, program counter, and sometimes the stack.
3. The control section handles the sequences of instruction fetching the execution.
4. The ALU with its associated complement register, shift register, and status register forms the arithmetic and logic section.
5. Microprocessors are usually packaged as DIPs with from 28 to 40 pins.
6. Every instruction execution actually consists of a series of microprogrammed steps which route data or control signals to the appropriate location. Timing is maintained by using a multiphase clock.
7. The architecture of a microcomputer establishes the control paths between the processor and memory and the I/O ports.
8. Microprocessors most often use programmed I/O. More advanced applications may require the sophisticated interrupt or DMA features.

9. Programming a microprocessor requires detailed knowledge of the instruction set. The instruction repertoire is generally unique to each processor.

10. Operand addressing methods include direct, indexed, literal, and register-to-register.

**KEY TERMS AND CONCEPTS**

microprocessor
microcomputer
byte
accumulator
index register
memory address register
instruction register
program counter
stack
popping and pushing
stack pointer
stack overflow and under-flow
control section
instruction fetch and exe-cute
arithmetic section
internal bus
status register
complement register
shift register
parity

microprogramming
multiphase clock timing
microcomputer architec-ture
bit-sliced microprocessors
programmed I/O
synchronous and asynchronous I/O
universal synchro-nous/asynchronous re-ceiver transmitter (USART)
interrupts
direct memory access (DMA)
programming
operation (op) code
operand
direct addressing
literal
register-to-register
indexed addressing

## PROBLEMS

12-1. Which of the following numbers have odd parity?

a. $0111\ 1101_2$
b. $76_8$
c. $8C_{16}$

For the remaining problems in this section, the memory and register contents are shown before executing an instruction. Determine the contents of all memory cells and registers listed after the instruction is completed.

12-2. Instruction: LDA I, 5000

(A) = 0F
(X) = 02
(PC) = 177C
(M 5000) = 72
(M 5001) = 10
(M 5002) = 19

12-3. Instruction: STA X

(A) = 05
(X) = 42
(PC) = 0F93
(M 0519) = 92

12-4. Instruction: LDX 0121

(A) = 60
(X) = FF
(PC) = 7777
(M 0120) = 14
(M 0121) = 00

12-5. Instruction: ADD I, 1020

(A) = 80
(X) = 01
(PC) = FCBA
(Status register) = 00
(M 1020) = FC

(M 1021) = 17
(M 1022) = 02

12-6. Instruction: SUB 11AC

(A) = F2
(X) = 01
(PC) = FCBA
(Status register) = 00
(M 11AC) = 04
(M 11AD) = 0F

12-7. Instruction: AND 6324

(A) = F0
(X) = 00
(PC) = 2000
(M 6324) = 1F
(M 6325) = 0D
(M 6326) = A0

12-8. Instruction: OR FFFF

(A) = F0
(X) = 00
(PC) = 5532
(M FFFE) = 0F
(M FFFF) = F0

12-9. Instruction: JMP I, 2000

(A) = 01
(X) = 01
(PC) = 1000
(M 2000) = 33
(M 2001) = F2

12-10. Instruction: ISZ

(A) = 00
(X) = 14
(PC) = B0AC

# APPENDIX

**Powers of 2**

| $2^n$ | $n$ | $2^{-n}$ | | | | |
|---|---|---|---|---|---|---|
| 1 | 0 | 1.0 | | | | |
| 2 | 1 | 0.5 | | | | |
| 4 | 2 | 0.25 | | | | |
| 8 | 3 | 0.125 | | | | |
| 16 | 4 | 0.062 | 5 | | | |
| 32 | 5 | 0.031 | 25 | | | |
| 64 | 6 | 0.015 | 625 | | | |
| 128 | 7 | 0.007 | 812 | 5 | | |
| 256 | 8 | 0.003 | 906 | 25 | | |
| 512 | 9 | 0.001 | 953 | 125 | | |
| 1024 | 10 | 0.000 | 976 | 562 | 5 | |
| 2048 | 11 | 0.000 | 488 | 281 | 25 | |
| 4096 | 12 | 0.000 | 244 | 140 | 625 | |
| 8192 | 13 | 0.000 | 122 | 070 | 312 | 5 |
| 16,384 | 14 | 0.000 | 061 | 035 | 156 | 25 |
| 32,768 | 15 | 0.000 | 030 | 517 | 578 | 125 |
| 65,536 | 16 | 0.000 | 015 | 258 | 789 | 062 | 5 |

### Powers of 16

| $16^n$ | $n$ | $16^{-n}$ | | | | | |
|---|---|---|---|---|---|---|---|
| 1 | 0 | 1.0 | | | | | |
| 16 | 1 | 0.625 | | | | | |
| 256 | 2 | 0.003 | 906 | 25 | | | |
| 4096 | 3 | 0.000 | 244 | 140 | 625 | | |
| 65,576 | 4 | 0.000 | 015 | 258 | 789 | 062 | 5 |
| 1,048,576 | 5 | 0.000 | 000 | 953 | 674 | 316 | 406 | 25 |

### Boolean Algebra Summary

#### Identities

| | | |
|---|---|---|
| $x + 0 = x$ | $x \cdot 0 = 0$ | $\bar{\bar{x}} = x$ |
| $x + 1 = 1$ | $x \cdot 1 = x$ | |
| $x + x = x$ | $x \cdot x = x$ | |
| $x + \bar{x} = 0$ | $x \cdot \bar{x} = 0$ | |

#### Commutative law

$xy = yx$ $\qquad x + y = y + x$

#### Associative law

$(xy)z = x(yz) = xyz$ $\qquad (x + y) + z = x + (y + z) = x + y + z$

#### Distributive law

$xy + xz = x(y + z)$ $\qquad (x + y)(x + z) = x + yz$

#### De Morgan's theorem

$$\overline{u \cdot v \cdot w \cdot x \cdot y \cdot z \cdots} = \bar{u} + \bar{v} + \bar{w} + \bar{x} + \bar{y} + \bar{z} + \cdots$$

$$\overline{u + v + w + x + y + z + \cdots} = \bar{u} \cdot \bar{v} \cdot \bar{w} \cdot \bar{x} \cdot \bar{y} \cdot \bar{z} \cdots$$

## COMMON-EMITTER AMPLIFIER SUMMARY

We must be able to find the operational mode for transistors used in logic circuits to determine the output. The transistor may be in the cutoff, saturated, or transition (active) mode of operation. Our discussion will be limited to the common-emitter configuration because it is most commonly used in logic circuits.

Figure A-1 shows a common-emitter amplifier and the load line for the transistor. (A similar circuit for a PNP transistor would require reversing appropriate polarities.) The slope of the load line corresponds to the 1-kilohm load resistor. One end point of the line is determined by the +6-volt collector voltage, the other by simple use of Ohm's law:

$$I_{c,\max} = \frac{V_{CC}}{R_L} = \frac{6}{10^3} = 6 \text{ mA}$$

From inspection of the graph, the equivalent resistance provided by the transistor in either saturation or cutoff can be found.

$$R_{\text{sat}} = \frac{V_{CE,\text{sat}}}{I_{c,\text{sat}}} \approx \frac{0.5}{5 \times 10^{-3}} = 100 \text{ }\Omega$$

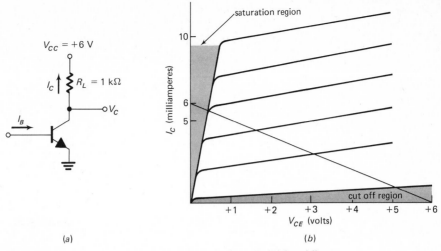

Figure A-1. Common-emitter amplifier. (a) Circuit, (b) load line.

$$R_{\text{cutoff}} = \frac{V_{CE,\,\text{cutoff}}}{I_{c,\,\text{cutoff}}} \approx \frac{5}{5 \times 10^{-6}}$$

$$= 1 \text{ M}\Omega$$

In summary a saturated transistor has a very small resistance while a transistor in cutoff has a large resistance. Table A-1 lists the characteristics of a common-emitter amplifier operating in each of its three modes.

## Table A-1
## Common Emitter Transistor Modes

| Parameter | Mode | | |
| --- | --- | --- | --- |
| | Cutoff | Active | Saturated |
| Resistance | high | medium | low |
| Base current | almost zero | small | equal to or greater than saturation base current |
| Output voltage | $V_{CC}$ | between 0.5 V and $V_{cc}$ | almost zero |

**THEVENIN'S THEOREM**  A useful technique for simplifying complicated linear networks is the theorem named for the French engineer, M. L. Thevenin. By use of this theorem several sources and impedances, regardless of how connected, can be represented by a single voltage source and series impedance. Because we are interested only in dc circuits, all impedances will be limited to resistors.

To use Thevenin's theorem, the equivalent resistance and voltage source are computed in a series of steps.

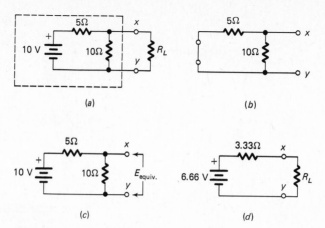

Figure A-2. Thevenin's theorem example.

1. Mark the terminals of the network for which you wish to find the equivalent circuit.
2. Calculate the equivalent resistance by first replacing all voltage sources with shorts and current sources with open circuits. Then find the resultant resistance.
3. Replace the voltage and current sources and then find the open-circuit voltage between the terminals marked in Step 1.
4. The equivalent series circuit is then drawn in place of the original network.

**Example**    Find the Thevenin equivalent circuit for the network enclosed by dotted lines in Fig. A-2a. The terminals $x-y$ designate the network. In Fig. A-2b the voltage source is replaced by a short circuit. The equivalent resistance looking into the network is

$$R_{\text{equiv}} = \frac{(5)(10)}{(5 + 10)} = 3.33 \ \Omega$$

In Fig. A-2c the voltage source is restored. We can calculate the open-circuit voltage between points $x$ and $y$ by using the voltage divider rule

$$E_{\text{equiv}} = \frac{10(10)}{(10 + 5)} = 6.66 \ \text{V}$$

The Thevenin equivalent to the original network is shown in Fig. A-2d.

# ANSWERS TO ODD
# NUMBERED QUESTIONS

## Chapter 2

**2-1a.**

| A | B | | Y | equality |
|---|---|---|---|---|
| 0 | 0 | | 1 | |
| 0 | 1 | | 0 | |
| 1 | 0 | | 0 | |
| 1 | 1 | | 1 | |

**2-1b.**

| A | B | | Y | exclusive OR |
|---|---|---|---|---|
| 0 | 0 | | 0 | |
| 0 | 1 | | 1 | |
| 1 | 0 | | 1 | |
| 1 | 1 | | 0 | |

**2-3.** AND

**2-5.** OR, AND

**2-7.** The output is at the one level when input $A$ is at zero for the second and third time. The output is zero at all other times.

**2-9a.**

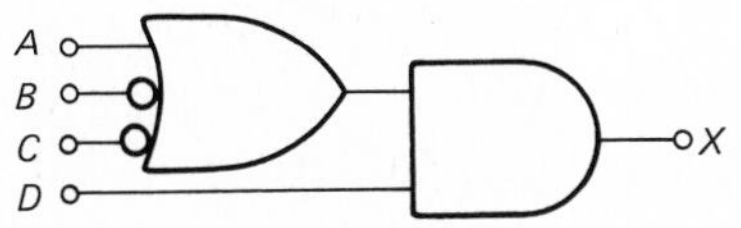

**2-9b.** $A + B + \overline{C}D + \overline{E}$

## Chapter 3

**3-1.** logic 0 = 0.2 volt, logic 1 = 4.7 volts

| A | B | | Output |
|---|---|---|---|
| 0.2 V | 0.2 V | | 4.7 V |
| 0.2 | 4.7 | | 4.7 |
| 4.7 | 0.2 | | 4.7 |
| 4.7 | 4.7 | | 0.2 |

**3-3.** An intermediate (not 0 or 1 level) voltage output results when the OR gate has a low out and the AND gate input is high.

**3-5.**

| A | B | | Output |
|---|---|---|---|
| 0 | 0 | | 5 |
| 0 | 5 | | 0.2 |
| 5 | 0 | | 0.2 |
| 5 | 5 | | 0.2 |

**3-7.** $x = -1.7, -1.7, -1.7, -0.7$
$y = -0.7, -0.7, -0.7, -1.7$
$v_K = -1.0$ V

$v_L = -0.9$ to $0$ V
$v_M = -1.4$ V
$I_R = 0$ mA
$i_S = i_T = 10$ mA

**3-9.** both high, $A = 2.1$ V, $B = 0.7$ V, both low $A = 0.9$ V, $B = 0$ V.

## Chapter 4

**4-1.** $\overline{A + B}$

**4-3.** 6.75 V

**4-5.** Use Fig. 4-5 for both gates.

**4-7.** $A$ is inverted and input with $B$ into a NOR gate to obtain output $C$.

**4-9.**

| $A$ | $B$ | Output |
|-----|-----|--------|
| 0 | 0 | 1 |
| 0 | 1 | 0 |
| 1 | 0 | 0 |
| 1 | 1 | 0 |

## Chapter 5

**5-1a.** $3 \times 8^3 + 4 \times 8^2 + 0 \times 8^1 + 1 \times 8^0 = 1793_{10}$

**5-1c.** $10 \times 16^2 + 6 \times 16^1 + 3 \times 16^0 = 2659_{10}$

**5-3a.** $17500_8$

**5-3c.** $0.11_8$

**5-5a.** $101\ 111\ 110_2$

**5-5c.** $110\ 101\ 101_2$

**5-7a.** $C1E_{16}$

**5-7c.** $8.FEE_{16}$

**5-9a.** $100\ 000\ 001\ 011_2$

**5-9c.** $001\ 000\ 101.100\ 010\ 110_2$

## Chapter 6

**6-1.**

**6-3.**

| $R$ | $S$ | $Q_n$ | $\bar{Q}_n$ | $R'$ | $S'$ | $Q_{n+1}$ | $\bar{Q}_{n+1}$ |
|-----|-----|-------|-------------|------|------|-----------|-----------------|
| 0 | 1 | 0 | 1 | 0 | 1 | 1 | 0 |
| 0 | 1 | 1 | 0 | 0 | 0 | $Q_n$ | $\bar{Q}_n$ |
| 1 | 0 | 0 | 1 | 0 | 0 | $Q_n$ | $\bar{Q}_n$ |
| 1 | 0 | 1 | 0 | 1 | 0 | 0 | 1 |
| 0 | 0 | 0 | 1 | 0 | 0 | $Q_n$ | $\bar{Q}_n$ |
| 0 | 0 | 1 | 0 | 0 | 0 | $Q_n$ | $\bar{Q}_n$ |
| 1 | 1 | 0 | 1 | 0 | 1 | 1 | 0 |
| 1 | 1 | 1 | 0 | 1 | 0 | 0 | 1 |

| $R$ | $S$ | $Q_{n+1}$ | $\bar{Q}_{n+1}$ |
|-----|-----|-----------|-----------------|
| 0 | 1 | 1 | 0 |
| 1 | 0 | 0 | 1 |
| 0 | 0 | $Q_n$ | $\bar{Q}_n$ |
| 1 | 1 | $\bar{Q}_n$ | $Q_n$ |

**6-5.**

| clock pulses | 1 | 2 | 3 | 4 |
|--------------|---|---|---|---|
| $Q$ | 1 | 0 | *unknown | *unknown |
| $\bar{Q}$ | 0 | 1 | *unknown | *unknown |

*race

**6-7.** Once set to one, it cannot reset to zero.

**6-9.**

| $P$ | $Q_{n+1}$ | $\bar{Q}_{n+1}$ |
|-----|-----------|-----------------|
| 0 | 0 | 1 |
| 1 | 1 | 0 |

## Chapter 7

**7-3.** 0001, 0010, 0011, 0101, 1001, 1110, 0000

**7-5.** 100, 001, 010, 011 (in order $Q_1$, $Q_2$, $Q_3$)

**7-7.** $T_0 = 1$, $T_1 = Q_0$, $T_2 = Q_0 Q_1$, $T_3 = Q_0 Q_1 Q_2$

**7-9.** counts from $000_2$ to $111_2$ and resets

## Chapter 8

**8-1.** sum = 0, carry = 1

**8-3.** $a, c$

**8-5.** $S_0 = H$, $S_1 = H$, $S_2 = H$, $S_3 = H$, $C_o = L$,

**8-7.**

| A | MPLR | MCAND | Operation |
|-------|------|-------|-----------|
| 00000 | 0111 | 1101 | clear A |
| 01101 | 0111 | 1101 | add |
| 00110 | 1011 | 1101 | shift |
| 10011 | 1011 | 1101 | add |
| 01001 | 1101 | 1101 | shift |
| 10110 | 1101 | 1101 | add |
| 01011 | 0110 | 1101 | shift |
| 01011 | 0110 | 1101 | do not add |
| 00101 | 1011 | 1101 | shift |
| | | | stop |

8-9. $F_0 = 1, F_1 = 1, F_2 = 1, F_3 = 1$

## Chapter 9

9-1. a zero is read

9-3. neither

9-5a. $x$ is $10_{10}$

9-5b. $y$ is $54_{10}$

9-5c. $2877_{10}$

9-7. 983,040

9-9. 8

## Chapter 10

10-1. The output is zero during the first half-cycle, inverted during second half. Peak voltage is 10 volts. $D_1$ is reverse biased and $D_2$ forward biased during the negative portion of input, the opposite on the positive portion.

10-3. Equation 10-9 can never equal $^1/_2$.

10-5. 100 $\mu$s, 0.0145 $\mu$F

10-7. $-2.5$

10-9. DCB

## Chapter 11

11-1a. 9.7 mA

11-1b. 0

11-3. 760 $\Omega$, 95 $\Omega$

11-5. Only pins $a$, $b$, and $c$ are connected through resistors to $+5$ volts.

11-7. 4

11-9. 33 min, 36 s

## Chapter 12

12-1. $b$

12-3. (A) = 05,  (X) = 42,  (PC) = 0F94,  and (M 0519) = 92

12-5. (A) = 97, (X) = 01, (PC) = FCBB, no memory change

12-7. (A) = 10, (X) = 00, (PC) = 2001, no memory change

12-9. (PC) = F2, no other changes

# INDEX